MILTON
and SCIENCE

MILTON
and SCIENCE

Kester Svendsen

Harvard University Press, Cambridge
1956

FOR MARGARET

ACKNOWLEDGMENTS

My obligations in this book are many. George Coffin Taylor suggested the subject to me years ago when he defined the encyclopedias and the hexamera as two streams of medieval culture culminating in DuBartas and Milton. The vigor with which he has supported a project not always in agreement with his own opinion testifies to his generosity and Miltonic integrity as well as to my debt. Marjorie Nicolson, who recommended publication of one of my first papers on this theme, Allan H. Gilbert, Francis R. Johnson, George Whiting, the late Grant McColley, and many another have instructed me to my great profit. The libraries of North Carolina, Duke, and Oklahoma have offered every courtesy. The final research and writing were done in the Folger Shakespeare Library, the University of Oklahoma DeGolyer Collection in the History of Science and Technology, and the Henry E. Huntington Library. I owe much to Dorothy E. Mason of the Folger, Mary Isabel Fry of the Huntington, and J. L. Rader, then Curator of the DeGolyer Collection. A good deal of the work was done on grants-in-aid from the University of Oklahoma Faculty Research Fund; it was finished under a Fellowship from the John Simon Guggenheim Memorial Foundation and a sabbatical leave from the University of Oklahoma. I am grateful to the Harvard University Press for the many courtesies of its staff and particularly for the labors of Mrs. Carl A. Pitha. My assistant, Laurie Bowman Zwicky, read the manuscript with me in its final stages and helped prepare the index.

Portions of this book have appeared in earlier form in *ELH: A Journal of Literary History, Studies in Philology, Bulletin of the History of Medicine, Modern Language Notes, Notes and Queries,* and *PMLA.* These articles have been revised and some of them distributed among several chapters, but I am no less indebted for permission to reprint.

The book is dedicated where my obligation is greatest.

April 1956

KESTER SVENDSEN

CONTENTS

NOTE ON THE ILLUSTRATIONS

Many sixteenth- and seventeenth-century books of popular science featured illustrations quite as wonderful as the properties of the creatures they described. Those included here are typical of the period and the genre. The plan of the universe at p. 49 is from the frontispiece of Robert Fage's *A Description of the Whole World* (London, 1658), and is reproduced through the courtesy of the Huntington Library, San Marino, California. The pictures of the four elements, of mining, and of the animal kingdom at pp. 51, 118, and 138, are from Bartholomew's *De Proprietatibus Rerum* (London, 1495); the strange fires at p. 89 are from Gregory Reisch's *Margarita Philosophica* (Strassburg, 1508). The basilisk on the title page is from Caxton's *Myrrour and Dyscrypcyon of the Worlde* (London, 1529), and is reproduced with permission of the Houghton Library, Cambridge, Mass.

MILTON
and SCIENCE

The Major Problems

WALTER RALEIGH would have been more nearly right had he called *Paradise Lost* a living monument, for ideas in theology and science that perished elsewhere in the great swing of seventeenth-century culture give life to the epic as well as gain it. Even the supposed flats and shallows are functional in the heroic scheme; rightly understood, Raphael's discourse on astronomy is, like the war in Heaven, part of a grand poetic strategy. The mode of critical inquiry is crucial here; the intentional fallacy has diverted many a Raleigh and many an Eliot from seeing what theology does in the poem. The same distraction awaits the student of science in Milton. He must work with what actually happened in *Paradise Lost*. The maker may indeed have moved from strategy to execution, from the governing idea to the supporting details; but the critic must proceed inductively as well, gaining insight into that poetic strategy from the examination of particulars. His concern is with a poem, not merely with a body of ideas; yet he must use everything which establishes the poetic vocabulary. It is a mistake, for example, to suppose *Paradise Lost* a systematic treatise on divinity; it is a greater one to neglect *Christian Doctrine* as a gloss. And it is folly to extract such ideas as relate Milton to one or another tradition in science, to fill in gaps from cultural history, and then to read the formal result back into his work as a fair picture of his knowledge, or worse, of his belief. The problem of belief is a hard one, as contemporary critical theory illustrates, and distinctions are difficult in treating an epic written with lyric intensity and inspired conviction. We know that Milton believed in the historicity of Adam and the providence of God; yet the fact of that belief really contributes little that is usable in, say, the study of his images.

The total problem of Milton and science is comparably difficult. The literary questions are: what is science in his work, how does science enter it, and what is its function there. Recent accomplishments in the history of ideas and the revived techniques of formalist literary analysis aid such inquiries. Studies in the past twenty-five years have advanced the knowledge of the seventeenth-century scientific background: the work of Gilbert, McColley, and Nicolson on Milton's astronomy, Johnson's *Astronomical Thought in Renaissance England*, Babb's *The Elizabethan Malady*, Kocher's *Science and Religion in Elizabethan England*. Bush's survey, *Science and Poetry 1590–1950*, confirms the attitudes being developed. That these scholars disagree in particulars promotes the study they have provided for; I am indebted to them and many more in this account of Milton's use of natural science in prose and poetry. Modern Milton criticism, like that of Brooks and Stein, has taught us to look for the movement beneath the surface of the lines; but it is modern Milton scholarship which makes perception of that movement possible.

The present combining of the two methods — scholarship and criticism — into a kind of critical perspectivism reveals four major problems: the descriptive and expository, the genetic, the philosophical, and the aesthetic. One must identify, describe, and explain the natural science in Milton; establish its origins and relation to seventeenth-century culture; define its place in the thought of his works; and show its function in his art. The first of these, the descriptive problem, splits at once into questions of category and limitation. "What is science" is a query more easily answered in our own day than in a time when a teleological universe and a closed moral system predicated a unity of knowledge in which natural philosophy was a contributory, not an independent, branch of learning; witness the tract *Of Education*. Even if one restricts his inquiry as I do to natural science and excludes mathematics, geography, and architecture, there remain such marginal subjects as angelology, where, as Robert West has shown, the digestive possibilities of angels became a matter of actual heresy. And it is the old science, rather than the new, which bulks the larger in Milton, despite his spectacular allusions to Galileo and his interest in some elements of the new cosmology. Donne made much of the "new philosophy" but Milton very little. Most of his science is traditional and conventional, a literary as well as scientific commonplace. It is also a now obsolete vocabulary of stereotypes.

The control for definition and explanation is the popular science of the Renaissance, from which most of that in Milton can be clarified. It can be glossed as to fact from Aristotle and Pliny, as to literary ancestry from Virgil, Ovid, and Spenser, which Milton knew from his youth, and as to moral implication from medieval, Renaissance, and even late seventeenth-century encyclopedias and vernacular handbooks of science. I have used a selection of these, not as Milton's sources, but as ours for seeing Milton's science as his century did. Taking them as Louis B. Wright and others have taught us to — the sort of learning accessible to every one — we must challenge again the impression encouraged from Addison on down that Milton showed vast or profound scientific learning; for what is recondite to the twentieth-century eye is almost always common knowledge to the sixteenth and seventeenth; and by the eighteenth century it is antiquarianism.

The effect of a knowledge of these repositories of neo-Plinyism on the second problem, the question of Milton's sources, is remarkable. I have quoted extensively from the encyclopedias to show the closeness of their very language to his. In view of the many recurrences of the theory of humours, the nature of the phoenix, or the cause of lightning, it would be the rash scholar who offered to establish the immediate origin of those ideas in *Paradise Lost* or *Eikonoklastes*. Literary genetics has come a long way since Raleigh disparaged the ledger school of criticism, and our extended knowledge of the seventeenth century weakens the persuasion of the parallel passage as a proof-text of indebtedness. Paradoxically, one may find Taylor's chapter on commonplaces in Renaissance thought more convincing than his case for DuBartas as a principal source for *Paradise Lost*. There can be no doubt that the influence existed, but that array of conventional elements blurs the lines of responsibility. We can confidently assign passages in Milton to a tradition of thought or of books or a genre of scientific literature, but seldom to specific authors. In his most striking effects, Milton uses widely known conventional material in its conventional associations.

In defining the function of science in the world view of the poems, the third of the problems indicated above, one begins with Milton's heritage as a Christian poet. The terms "Christian" and "poet" are critical. When in later demonstrations I speak of Milton's belief or Milton's knowledge, I would have it taken to mean Milton's belief and knowledge as poet, which must be kept separate from, even when identical with, his belief and knowledge as man. It is precisely this that Milton means, when in *First Defence* he warns that "we must not regard the poet's words as his own, but consider who it is that speaks in the play," for the characters "speak not always in the poet's own opinion." The prose is perhaps a safer index to Milton's personal belief, where even the chariest scholar, having worked so long in the subject, may be forgiven an uneasy conclusion or two. But the central reservation stands: all affirmed or denied here is for the world view of the work, not for the man.

Yet the man is the poet, and part of their common heritage is, as Mahood calls it, a theocentric humanism; in this, nature was the book of God's works and natural philosophy an approved method of knowing Him, as the encyclopedists never tire of asserting. Tillyard and Swedenberg have shown that epic theory demanded exactly the sort of learning Milton used as subject matter. The philosophical and theological implications of natural science were not lost on one whose Raphael bid Adam study that book of God's works but not inquire into His motives. The cosmic optimism early displayed in Milton's denial that nature was subject to decay is one with the conclusion of *Paradise Lost*. Nearly everything Milton read bore on the problem of the limits of knowledge, from the patristic writers and commentators on Genesis to Spenser. It is difficult to believe that Milton was especially concerned about conflicting cosmological theories; here Raphael would seem his spokesman, particularly since Milton did not attempt a system of natural philosophy like his system of divinity. As this problem of the impact of science on his thinking unfolds, it will be seen that the science in his works relates him closely to learning popular in his own youth and to medieval theories of knowledge surviving in his culture.

The final problem is the function of science in Milton's art. The prose assumes fresh importance in this connection. However one takes Theodore Banks's *Milton's Imagery*, it was right of him to include the prose. For there are anticipated or duplicated much of the scientific lore and many devices of the poetry; there in the rough are epic similes and metaphors and "precepts of beneficence," as Milton called them, "fetcht from the closet of Nature." Quite aside from science as subject-matter in the account of the Creation, the dialogue on astronomy, or Adam's explanation of Eve's dream, natural philosophy contributes extensively in *Paradise Lost* to structure, characterization, setting, and tone, not merely by formal figures but by hundreds of particulars. Satan, for example, with his shield like a moon and himself an eclipsing sun, and the metaphors of light and dark technically expressed and playing through the poem — these are the inevitable result of Milton's investment. There is no settled methodology for studying the impact of science on structure or form of poetry and prose. The principles of cluster and recurrence in imagery applied by Armstrong, Heilman, and Clemen to Shakespeare are no less fruitfully applied to Milton, as shown by Brooks, Hardy, Shumaker, and Stein. The figurative and symbolic structures created from this lore enforce the moral intent and literal meaning of the epic narrative. Milton often extends metaphorically the principles expressed in a scientific view or set of facts, as when he sustains a single cosmological figure through the fifth Italian sonnet or creates in rich detail a roughly Ptolemaic universe to emphasize fixed moral responsibility in a man-centered system of spheres. It is here that old and new in literary study meet, for in making this kind of reading one must exercise everything learned in the previous explaining, tracing, and evaluation of the natural science in Milton. To the critical perspectivist, this kind of synthesis is the preliminary to analysis. A clear gain from including the prose is that the rhetorical function of science in prose argument and its poetic function in the epic exemplify in one more direction the Renaissance fusion of rhetoric and poetic. If in his prose Milton had, as he said, the use of only his left hand, when he came to his poetry, his right hand knew perfectly well what his left had done.

What is proposed here, then, is a comprehensive study of natural science in Milton, based on the medieval and Renaissance encyclopedias of science in the vernacular but extending to popular learning in any form and occasionally including documents in new science as these are relevant.

Whiting has done some of this, and there are infrequent annotations elsewhere; but the encyclopedias of science have been by-passed in the work of most Miltonists, who have been led by Milton's extraordinarily extensive reading into sources unlikely to have reached most of his contemporaries. It must be said again that astronomy is not the only science in Milton; and that the classics, the patristic writings, the hexamera, the rabbinical commentaries are not the sole repositories of scientific lore. The Middle Ages and the Renaissance were full of lapidaries, herbals, bestiaries, and treatises on medicine and astronomy, all of which contribute to Milton's meaning, for his works are thick-sown in curious and half-forgotten lore. But all the divisions of scientific interest are represented in the encyclopedias. These compilations, many of which reached the vernacular, preserved in abundance the scientific lore of classical and medieval times, and are the lapidaries, herbals, natural histories, medical and astronomical works rolled into one, all characterized by ceaseless bookish inquiry (within due limits of religion, most of them) into the kinds, properties, and causes of all natural phenomena. I use those in the vernacular not because Milton needed them so — it will be remembered that I am not claiming direct indebtedness — but because in that form they are a common denominator of scientific information as it was disseminated to readers of every class in the sixteenth and seventeenth centuries. When Edward Topsell apologizes in the preface to his *Historie of Serpents* for failing to translate the many Latin verses in his earlier *Historie of Foure-Footed Beastes*, he is acknowledging the milieu in which he expects his writings to circulate. Here is a vast tradition of scientific literature intervening between Milton and the recondite sources attributed to him, important not as sources but as correctives to exorbitance. Out of these and Milton may be erected not a closed system of natural philosophy but a fairly complete gloss on his constant use of natural science.

Chapter I is introductory; it exhibits Milton's relation to the encyclopedic tradition and concerns chiefly the descriptive and genetic problems. The subsequent chapters, in which my four major objectives are pursued, follow the usual order of encyclopedia and hexameron alike: cosmology, mineralogy, botany, the animal kingdom, the body and the mind of man. The final chapters deal with science in the prose, especially *Doctrine and Discipline of Divorce*, and in *Paradise Lost*. Mindful of the instability of categories in defining image-clusters, I have attempted few inferences from statistics. In the chapter on physiology and psychology, for example, I take up particulars that a Spurgeon or a Banks might group elsewhere. My conclusions depend upon the imaginative activity of these allusions, not their formal construction or their number.

The Compendious Method of Natural Philosophy: Milton and the Encyclopedic Tradition

FROM THE ACADEMIC EXERCISES to the final prose tract, Milton's interest in natural science appears everywhere. One finds it in his school exercises, private reading, Italian travel. In the Sixth and Seventh Prolusions, young Milton urges his listeners to study clouds, snow, the sources of rain, hail and thunder, the natural laws of heavens and earth. The shiftings of the air, the secret powers of stones and metals, the nature of animals, the structure and surgery of the human body, and finally the mind, the center of the microcosm — these recommendations form a hierarchy of science no less than a course of study. The Vacation Exercise poem, linked to the Sixth Prolusion, versifies that encyclopedic interest and makes the promise, fulfilled in *Paradise Lost*, to "sing of secret things that came to pass / When Beldam Nature in her cradle was." In *Of Education,* Milton spoke for the natural questions of Seneca as well as for Aristotle, Pliny, Solinus, and "any compendious method of natural philosophy," the students to proceed from the "History of Meteors, Minerals, plants and living Creatures as far as Anatomy." This preoccupation with the scale of being, constant on the

title pages of the encyclopedias of science, emerges often in
the poetry, most notably perhaps in Adam's realization that
"In contemplation of created things / By steps we may ascend
to God." [1]

Editors and commentators have long recognized Milton's
knowledge of science, from his contemporaries Dato and
Francini, who praised his deciphering of the marvels of nature
through which God is portrayed, to the present generation of
Miltonists, who have investigated his concept of the power of
matter, his understanding of the firmament that divides the
waters, and his use of travel literature for the paradisaic zoo.
The vogue of which Milton was the last great exponent was
so old-fashioned in Addison's day as to draw his complaint of
ostentation and technical scientific terms. Newton and Todd
echo by their annotations Addison's remark that Milton
wished to show his acquaintance "with the whole Circle of
Arts and Sciences." Keightley, Masson, Verity, and Hughes
supply appendices and hundreds of notes on the cosmology
of *Paradise Lost*. Behind Hanford's remark that the poem is
"a kind of cyclopedia of the science of Milton's time" lies the
motivation for two centuries of investigation of the natural
science in Milton.[2]

But there were many formal cyclopedias of science in Milton's time and before, which were concerned with precisely
the sort of lore found in Milton, and with the same conviction of the unity of knowledge and its moral function. In examining his work against the background of popular learning
supplied by the encyclopedias of science, one not only explains the material from what were regarded by many as
authoritative sources but also establishes the milieu of a good
deal of Milton's information. The genre has been described
by Haskins, Thorndike, Wright, and others; but a brief history of it will suggest some attractive possibilities for the study
of Milton.[3]

To begin with, the science of medieval western Europe ran

in three main streams:[classical science surviving unassisted
or revived in the twelfth and thirteenth centuries;]Arabic
science as expressed in separate treatises and in expansions
and extensions of Greek and Roman science; and medieval
science proper, which arose largely from the stimulus of classical and Arabic thought. The forms in which medieval science is found are manifold: the hexameral and theological
writings of the Greek and Latin church fathers; the innumerable manuscripts, translations, and commentaries upon inherited knowledge; the many treatises of medieval scientists
and thinkers; and miscellaneous anonymous and pseudonymous pieces like the *Physiologus* and other bestiaries, the
Hermetic Books, and the *Secreta Secretorum*. All of these contribute, in one way or another, to the compendia of learning
that had survived as a tradition from earliest times and en-
joyed great popularity in the thirteenth-century Renaissance
as well as in the later one. Thus the intellectual revival of the
eleventh and twelfth centuries in Spain and Sicily recovered
much classical and Arabic science that later found its way into
the encyclopedias. In them, Albertus Magnus, with his pupil
Aquinas greatly responsible for that integration of classical
cosmology and Christian metaphysic characteristic of medieval thought, repeatedly appears to buttress a fact or solidify
an opinion. Whenever enough material was accumulated for
the collection and occasional comparison of authorities, the
scissors-and-paste scholarship of the encyclopedist followed.
The clerks of Vincent of Beauvais who copied excerpts for
his *Speculum Majus* are no isolated phenomenon. These an-
thologists gathered leaves for the extension of learning and
the greater glory of God and were only a little more secular
than the hexameral writers in their eagerness to load every
crevice of the sacred text with the learning that edifies even
when it does not clarify.

The encyclopedias of science which burgeoned in the
Middle Ages did so in continuance of a tradition that began

long before Pliny but has his *Natural History* (A.D. 77) as its first major example and the most popular single source of science of all kinds in the period. Marcus Terentius Varro's earlier *Antiquitatum Rerum Humanarum et Divinarum Libri XL* is preserved mainly through Isidore of Seville and Augustine, and Verrius Flaccus' *De Verborum Significatu*, now lost, was abridged by Pompeius Festus and used by Isidore. But the *Natural History* in form and content set the pattern for later encyclopedias and provided authority for thousands of chapters and subsections. Pliny properly described his work as an encyclopedia, for it is greater in scope than its title implies; and he claimed inclusion of twenty thousand topics gleaned from the study of about two thousand volumes by one hundred selected authors. Actually, this is a modest estimate; he appears to have used at first or second hand four hundred seventy-three writers, and of these chiefly Aristotle. These facts indicate the tremendous hoard passed on by Pliny to medieval and Renaissance writers and readers.[4]

After Pliny, Suetonius Tranquillus and Nonius Marcellus compiled encyclopedias, but it is Isidore of Seville's *Etymologies* (c. 623) that Thorndike describes as forming the connecting link between the *Natural History* and the encyclopedias of the thirteenth century. Certainly the book and chapter titles of this work were repeated hundreds of times in later centuries. Pliny's thirty-seven books are concerned with such matters as cosmology, earth science, and natural history (including the medicinal values of plants and animals), as well as human inventions and arts and crafts; Isidore's twenty were meant to cover the current learning of his time, doctrinal and secular, and include mineralogy, animal lore, medicine, and the seven liberal arts.[5]

Between the *Etymologies* and the encyclopedias of the thirteenth century come the works of Adelard of Bath, Alexander Neckam, and Thomas of Cantimpré, which are encyclopedic in kind if not in form or scope. The *Quaestiones Naturales*

(c. 1116) of Adelard surveys in seventy-six brief chapters botany, zoology, human physiology, astronomy, and the causes of earthquakes, tides, thunder, and rain. (One query that recurred in scientific treatises well into the seventeenth century and in Milton was whether the sun eats.) The first part of Neckam's *De Naturis Rerum Libri Duo* takes up the nature of light, the natural history of birds, fountains, fishes, metals, plants, trees, and animals, including man. The nineteen-book *De Natura Rerum* (c. 1244) of Thomas deals similarly with herbs, metals, animals, spheres and planets, and the parts of the human body. The sources of these books show how scientific authority accumulated. Adelard does not appear to have used much that is ultimately Arabic except in physiology, but Alexander draws upon Alfraganus and Isaac in addition to the hexameral tradition, Pliny, Isidore, and Adelard himself. Thomas brings together Basil and Ambrose with Albumasar and the *Physiologus*, Isidore, and again Adelard.[6]

These little books treat ideas and questions of interest to Milton, and with a moral purpose not unrelated to the justification of God's ways to men. The huge collections of Vincent of Beauvais' *Speculum Naturale* and Bartholomew of England's *De Proprietatibus Rerum* are thirteenth-century continuants of the encyclopedic tradition, which we may now follow from Bartholomew to Gossouin and Caxton's *Mirrour of the World*, John Maplet's *A Greene Forest*, Stephen Batman's *Batman uppon Bartholome*, Peter de la Primaudaye's *The French Academie*, and Swan's *Speculum Mundi*. These are typical of the outlines of knowledge. Although I draw on others (such as Camerarius' *The Living Librarie* [1595], Daniel Widdowes' *Naturall Philosophie* [1631], David Person's *Varieties* [1635], John Jonston's *An History of the Wonderful Things of Nature* [1657], and Wolfgang Frantze's *The History of Brutes* [1670]), these six, from Bartholomew to Swan, are surely representative of the scope and content of the encyclopedias and of the tradition as it entered the seven-

teenth century and died out in the eighteenth. They therefore deserve more detailed examination.

Perhaps Bartholomew of England is the best known of the
medieval encyclopedists. His *De Proprietatibus Rerum*, one
of largest of these scientific anthologies, was finished probably
in 1230 and was taken up by scribes and translators almost
immediately. European libraries in 1920 contained over one
hundred copies of the Latin text; in the fourteenth and fifteenth centuries it was turned into French, English, Spanish,
Dutch, Provençal, and Italian; extant at the time SeBoyar
wrote were sixteen editions of the Latin, twenty-four of the
French, three of the English, two of the Spanish, and one of
the Dutch translations. These figures, supplemented by
Steele's report of forty-eight separate editions, indicate the
widespread popularity of the book over Europe during the
Middle Ages and down into the Renaissance. It was readily
accessible to Shakespeare and his fellows in printings by
Wynkyn de Worde in 1495, Berthelet in 1535, and East in
1582, all based on the English translation by John de Trevisa
in 1397.[7]

Berthelet's text of Bartholomew is divided into nineteen
books, a summary of which suggests at once what a storehouse
of learning *De Proprietatibus Rerum* is. Book I treats God,
His Nature, and His attributes; Book II, the nature and
properties of angels and of demons; Book III, the human
mind and the soul; Books IV and V, the human body, its parts
and their properties; Book VI, medieval life and social intercourse; Book VII, medicine, with an exposition of seventy
diseases in as many chapters; Book VIII, the universe and
celestial bodies; Book IX, chronology, time and its parts; Book
X, form and matter; Book XI, the regions of air and their
properties; Book XII, birds and creatures of the air; Book
XIII, water and its inhabitants; Book XIV, the element earth
and the parts of the globe; Book XV, geography, classical and
medieval; Book XVI, gems, minerals, and metals; Book XVII,

trees and herbs; Book XVIII, animals; Book XIX, color, odor, savor, and liquors. The primary source for the material is Isidore's *Etymologies*, but Bartholomew also cites, quotes, and lists well over a hundred. Hexameral and theological literature appears in almost every chapter; Origen, Ambrose, Basil, Bernard, Gregory, and Augustine are only a few of the authors mentioned. From classical science come Aristotle, Pliny, Galen, Ptolemy, Theophrastus; from Arabic, Albumasar, Alfraganus, Isaac, and Rasi; from the scientific renaissance and after, Albertus Magnus, Michael Scot, and Alexander of Hales. The *Physiologus*, the bestiaries, the *Schola Salernitas* contribute extensively. Bartholomew relies heavily on previous encyclopedists, notably Pliny, Isidore, and Alexander Neckam.

Throughout the work the dominant purpose is to sustain a quality of moralized science. Bartholomew avers "righte lytel or nought have I sette of myne owne, but I have ensewed sothnesse and trouthe, and folowed the wordes, meanynge, and sawes and commentes of holye sayntes, and of Philosophers: That the symple that maye not for endelesse many bokes, seke and fynde alle the propritees of thynges, of whyche holy writte maketh mencion and mynde, maye here fynde somewhat that he desireth." This religious purpose and function distinguish the medieval and Renaissance encyclopedias from their classical predecessors. Certainly its moral quality helped establish *De Proprietatibus Rerum* as the most influential of all the medieval encyclopedias upon the English Renaissance, the one textbook which summed up the scientific heritage of the Middle Ages and was the "chief, not to say the only, authority on natural history until the end of the sixteenth century in England." Robert Steele even thought it the immediate source for most Elizabethan natural history in Shakespeare, Spenser, Lyly, and DuBartas; and though our present knowledge of the history of science would temper this claim, we cannot dispute his assertion of the usefulness of *De Proprietatibus Rerum* to the understanding of science in these authors. The persistence of Bartholomew's scientific lore into the second half of the seventeenth century will become apparent when hundreds of Milton's details are shown to be parallel in *De Proprietatibus Rerum*.[8]

Though *The Mirrour of the World* was not written by Caxton, his prose translation of the original poem gave it such popularity and influence that it now is known under his name. In its original form as *L'Image du Monde*, it is a rhymed poem of 6,594 French octosyllabic verses, in three parts, probably written by Gossouin in 1245. Oliver Prior, noting the fifty-three manuscripts of the first redaction in verse and the eight in French prose, concludes that Caxton's "choix de *L'Image* prouve l'importance de notre encyclopedie, même à cette epoque." It is the first work printed in England with illustrations and one of the earliest encyclopedias of science in English. Caxton's translation was made between January 2 and March 8, 1480; he printed it probably in 1481 and issued a second edition late in 1489 or early 1490. A third edition, by Lawrence Andrewe, came out in 1527.

Like its original, *The Mirrour of the World* is in three parts, of twenty, thirty-three, and twenty-four chapters respectively. In Part I, chapters I through III deal, appropriately enough, with the power and nature of God and with free will; chapters IV-XX, the reasons for and contents of the seven liberal arts; chapters XIII through XX, astronomy. In Part II, chapters I-IV describe the earth and its divisions; V-X, India; XI treats gems, beasts, fishes, and trees of India and Europe; XII, Africa and its countries; XIII, the islands of the sea, Abydos, Delos, Cyprus, and others; XIV, the wonders on these islands and elsewhere; XV, animals in Europe and Africa; XVI, birds; XVII, "dyvrsytes of somme comyne thinges" such as the properties of quicksilver, of the sun's rays, of lime, and of human breath; XVIII, theories of the location of Hell; XIX through XXIII consider the waters, rivers, oceans, fountains, and lakes of the earth; XXIV through XXX, the air and the causes of clouds, hail, tempests, lightning, frosts, snows, and the like; XXXI through XXXIII, planets, falling stars, the firmament. In Part III, chapters I-XXIV return to astronomy: the sun, moon, stars, eclipses, and other cosmological matters. The sources of Gossouin's and Caxton's information are chiefly Aristotle, Plato, Isidore, Solinus, Ptolemy, and Adelard of Bath, from the last of whom whole passages were taken word for word, as well as from Alexander Neckam's *De Naturis Rerum*.

Until G. C. Taylor drew attention to what he called "the Mirrour literature," little connection was made between this book and Renaissance poetry. It has only half a line in the *Cambridge History of English Literature*, despite Thomas Wright's testimony to its importance. Some indication of its usefulness to the study of the star-struck Renaissance appears from Francis R. Johnson's demonstration that it represents the best astronomical thought of the thirteenth century and that "Caxton's translation, therefore, became the best and most thorough presentation in English of the science of astronomy, and remained so until after 1543." Once again we have a book which can be used extensively to explain natural science in Milton, not so fully perhaps as *De Proprietatibus Rerum*, but sometimes with astonishing closeness. Witness, for example, Caxton's illustration of the "shaddowie Cone" in *Paradise Lost*.[9]

Between *L'Image du Monde* of 1245 and John Maplet's *A Greene Forest* of 1567 came many encyclopedias, but of those which reached the vernacular and became the common property of the English reader, Maplet's is chronologically next in importance. The title page proclaims its purpose and contents:

A Greene Forest, or a naturall Historie, Wherein may bee seene first the most sufferaigne Vertues in all the whole kinde of Stones

& Mettals: next of Plants, as of Herbes, Trees, & Shrubs, Lastly,
of Brute Beastes, Foules, Fishes, creeping Wormes, & Serpents,
and that Alphabetically; so that a Table shall not neede. Compiled by John Maplet, M. of Arts, and student in Cambridge:
entending hereby yt God might especially be glorified: and the
people furdered.

The first of its three books is devoted to stones and minerals,
and contains seventy-one items; the second contains one hundred and fifty-five "herbes, trees, and shrubs"; the third one
hundred and twelve animals.

The sources of this little encyclopedia are many more than
the list Maplet prefixed to Book I. Hexameral writings, always a popular medieval source with encyclopedists, are represented by quotations from Augustine and a familiarity
with Albertus Magnus. But aside from Isidore, cited in fifty-
five chapters, and Cardan, cited in eleven, Maplet's chief
sources are the classical authors. From Aristotle he draws material for thirty-two chapters, mostly in Book III, on animals;
from Theophrastus he uses plant lore in eighteen of Book
II; from Pliny, for fifty-six chapters that again are mostly
about animals. His greatest debt is to Dioscorides, upon whom
he depends directly or indirectly in seventy chapters, fifteen
in Book I and fifty-five in II. Scattered use of ten or a dozen
others reveals Maplet to be operating as most of the encyclopedists did, with a few major sources and diligent mention
of as many contributors as possible. His purpose is moral and
utilitarian; he writes for the ordinary man, "a Reader not
learned but unskilfull; yet rather learned than immoderate."

Thus *A Greene Forest* typifies the Renaissance digest of
natural history avowedly compiled for those who had no
Greek or Latin. It is narrower in scope than either *De Proprietatibus Rerum* or *Mirrour of the World*; but its concern
with the facts of nature and particularly with the unity of
nature establishes its place in the tradition. Its popularity in
its own day is attested by Andrew Maunsell, the first English

bibliographer, who listed it in his catalogue of 1595. Louis B. Wright and Hyder Rollins have recognized its significance in Renaissance literature, but its value in explaining Milton's science has pretty much been overlooked.[10]

The 1535 edition of *De Proprietatibus Rerum* was modernized and annotated in 1582 by Stephen Batman, sometime domestic chaplain to Archbishop Parker and to Henry Carey, Lord Hunsdon, recipient of the dedication of *Batman uppon Bartholome*. Batman notes on the title page the use of "the approved Authors, the like heretofore not translated in English" and in his preface announces that he has added "so much as hath been brought to light by the travaile of others," primarily Gesner, Fuchs, Paracelsus, Munster, Agrippa, and Ortelius. Robert Steele held that *Batman uppon Bartholome* shows numerous alterations from *De Proprietatibus Rerum*; but Louis B. Wright believes that Batman merely modernized the text and added a few observations from Renaissance writers. Most of the additions, carefully marked in text and margin with asterisks, are to Book XV, on geography; others of note are the whole chapter "De Morbo Gallico or the French Poxe" in Book VII and sixteen chapters on the elements from Agrippa's *De Occulta Philosophia*.

Batman's purposes are those of the previous encyclopedists. He retains with approval the prologue of the translator, which urges upon contemporaries the reading and using of natural as well as moral philosophy because doctors of theology and "poets in their fictions and fayned informations" employ it. With this edition the scientific lore of Bartholomew gained further control over the Elizabethan imagination, artistic or unlearned. Maunsell included it as one of three hundred important titles. Foster Watson advanced it as Shakespeare's source for natural history; and H. W. Seager admitted it as a possibility though he thought Shakespeare went to the 1535 Bartholomew. Anderson, Draper, Camden, Tuve, and

others have related it to Elizabethan literature; but although
Verity and Hughes have extracted a few passages in connection with Milton, the full resources of *Batman uppon Bartholome* have not been brought to bear upon the science in
his writings.[11]

Not until recently has the highly moral *French Academie*
been exploited very heavily for its contribution to Renaissance writers and thinkers. An English translation of the first
section in 1586 was followed by the addition of "A notable
description of the whole World" in 1594 and "Christian
Philosophie," theological and devotional, in the complete
edition of 1618. As La Primaudaye explains the origin and
organization of the work, the material was collected when
the fathers of four youths who were sent to an old knight
for their education visited their sons and heard them discourse. The author himself was one of the four and thought
the discourses so good that he put forth the results of eighteen
days' conversation and formal speeches as *The French Academie*. The frame and fiction of dialogue form, used also in
Antonio de Torquemada's *The Spanish Mandeville of Miracles* (1600) and other scientific works, do little to relieve or
impede the steady accumulation of facts and moralizing.

The contents of this omnibus bear notably upon questions
of interest to the student of Milton. Book I, "Institution of
Manners and Callings of all Estates," offers such examples as
Chapter 3, "Of the Diseases and passions of the Bodie and
Soule, and of the tranquillity thereof"; Chapter 47, "Of the
duties of a wife toward her husband"; and the chapters on the
office and duty of a king, the kinds of monarchy and tyranny,
the causes that breed the change and corruption of mon-
archies. Book II, "Concerning the Soule and Body of Man,"
contains one hundred chapters arranged by the days on
which the matters were discussed; they deal with the creation
of man and woman, bones, the elements of the body, flesh,
skin, hair, faculties of the mind like memory, understand-

ing, and will, and eventually the soul. Book III treats natural history proper, philosophically as well as scientifically, investigating the reasons for the newness and creation of the world and the errors of those philosophers who held that God did his outward work of necessity. The title page to this book is typical of the encyclopedists' coverage:

The Third Volume of the French Academie: containing a notable description of the whole World, and of all the principall parts and contents thereof; As namely, of Angels both good and evill; of the celestiall Spheeres, their order and number; of the fixed Stars and Planets; their light, motion, and influence: Of the foure Elements, and all things in them, or of them consisting: and first of firie, airie, and watrie Meteors or of impressions of Comets, Thunders, Lightnings, Raines, Snow, Haile, Rainbowes, Windes, Dewes, Frosts, Earthquakes, &c. ingendred above, in and under the middle or cloudy region of the Aire. And likewise, of Fowles, Fishes, Beasts, Serpents, Trees with their fruits and gumme; Shrubs, Herbes, Spices, Drugs, Minerals, precious Stones, and other particulars most worthy of all men to be known and considered.

Book IV, "The Christian Philosophie of the French Academie," expounds belief in God, duties of parents, children, and magistrates, true wisdom, and consolation of Christians.

The sources of *The French Academie* are like those of *Batman uppon Bartholome*: a heavy foundation of classical and medieval information overlaid with scatterings of Renaissance thought. The classical scientists and philosophers used are many: Aristotle, Plato, Homer, Pythagoras, Democritus, Empedocles, Macrobius, Strabo, Vitruvius, and others, not always at first-hand perhaps, but adduced wherever available as confirmation. On every page of Books I and II and almost as generally elsewhere occur such patristic writers as Augustine, Jerome, Basil, Chrysostom, Ambrose, and Gregory. Medieval translators and commentators are represented by Averroes, Avicenna, Sarrafin, and Alcinois. The Arabic scientist Algazel appears, as does Albertus Magnus. Anonymous and pseudonymous works like the *Physiologus* and the books attributed to Hermes Trismegistus are cited frequently. From the encyclopedic tradition, Pliny of course contributed heavily, and probably Batman. DuBartas, Munster, John Leo, and Cardan from the period of the Renaissance supplied excerpts and data, not to mention the travel literature as indicated in the citations from the voyages of Americus Vespucius and "Lewis de Barthoma in the discourses of his Indie voyages." La Primaudaye's scrupulously religious attitude toward his sources is typical of the genre. He culls from pagan authorities all that advances knowledge without challenging orthodoxy. In translator Richard Dolman's dedication of Book III to Sir William Mounson, the highest praise that he could apply extolled La Primaudaye's pious exercise of his sources:

> Considering the authors manner of handling this discourse, and the variety of choise writers both ancient and of our own times, which he alledgeth for confirmation of sundry truths, and for other purposes, purging by the fire of his exquisite judgement the drosse of their opinions from the pure mettal, and in all places adorning their gold and silver with the most orient and invaluable pearles of holy Scripture; I deemed it in all respects most worthy to shroud it selfe under your Worships patronage.

Only within the last few decades has this imposing volume been studied for its contribution to the understanding of English culture of the Renaissance. Bredvold, Anderson, Camden, Buckley, Craig, and others have testified to its significance. Francis R. Johnson ranks it second in importance in England only to DuBartas as an orthodox summary of man's knowledge of the divinely created universe. Contemporary evidence of its popularity derives from William London's *A Catalogue of the Most Vendible Books in England,* for London not only lists *The French Academie* as one of the best books of its kind but uses it several times in his introduction. It is surprising that so full a repository of classical, medieval, and Renaissance lore on every subject under the sun has not been studied in connection with Milton; for, like the other encyclopedias, it contains hundreds of parallels to Milton's facts, illuminates many passages based on ancient science, and relates his poetry and prose unmistakably to the Middle Ages as well as to the Renaissance. It is at once a touchstone and a dictionary of phrase and fable.[12]

Between *The French Academie* and *Speculum Mundi* of John Swan intervene such encyclopedias as *Naturall Philosophy* of Daniel Widdowes and *Varieties: or, a Surveigh of Rare and Excellent Matters* of David Person; however, I shall deal here more extensively with Swan as probably better known in his own day; certainly his work is more familiar to us. *Speculum Mundi, or a Glasse Representing the Face of the World*, published in 1635 and enlarged in 1643, is arranged according to the days of creation and in purpose is something of the "Hexaemeron" claimed by the title page. Chapter I considers the beginning of the world and its end; Chapter II, the popular patristic question, the time of the world's creation, even to the season; Chapter III, the work of the first day, the creation of light; Chapters IV and V include the firmament, the waters, the elements, rain, wind, snow, and like phenomena of the second day; Chapter VI continues with the work of the third day, the gathering of the waters, the originals of rivers and oceans, herbs, trees, metals, and stones; Chapter VII, matter, stars, astrology, astronomy, related to the fourth day; Chapter VIII, fish and fowl; Chapter IX, beasts and finally man.

The most important of the multiple sources of *Speculum Mundi* is DuBartas, but Swan culled information from many writers which he "garnished with a theological commentary delightful to Puritan readers." Much comes from the patristic writers Aquinas, Augustine, Lactantius, and Basil, much from Aristotle, Ptolemy, Galen, Seneca, Theophrastus, and Ælian. The encyclopedists Pliny, Varro, and Isidore orna-

ment many a margin. And in this book better than in any
other of those here studied is to be found the heavy overlay
of Renaissance scientific writing. Swan relies on Cardan's
De Subtilitate Rerum, Olaus Magnus' *Historia de Gentibus
Septentrionalibus*, Fulke's *Meteors*, Gesner's *Historia Animalium*, Topsell's translation of it as *The Historie of Foure-
Footed Beastes*, and the writings of Copernicus, Brahe, and
Kepler. A great deal of comment comes from histories like
Ralegh's, Stow's and Lanquet's. Travel literature, now a part
of the stream, supplies dozens of examples and bits of curiosa, particularly from Purchas. Luther, Calvin, and Hall are
to be found on almost every page. These various authorities,
cited and quoted, balanced against one another or marshalled
in unity, give the reader a digest of all relating to science that
Swan considered worthy. His stature as a purveyor of natural
knowledge has long been recognized and now recently re-
affirmed. Foster Watson showed *Speculum Mundi* to have
been widely used by orthodox religious schoolmasters. Louis
B. Wright calls it the culmination of the popular outline of
science in the period. Johnson and McColley recognize its
value, the latter citing it especially in connection with Milton's treatment of the temptation of Eve. As we shall see,
Speculum Mundi throws light on many passages in Milton's
prose and poetry and argues forcibly for the traditional nature
of much of Milton's science.[13]

These six typical books offer a handsome commentary on
neo-Plinyism in Milton. But the old science was everywhere,
in sermons, fiction, biblical commentary, travel literature,
broadside ballads, and sonnet sequences. In illustrating the
conventionality of much of Milton's science, I have drawn
not only upon these six but also from other encyclopedias
and writings, chiefly those not previously cited by Milton's
editors, who have already adduced evidence enough from
classical and Renaissance belles-lettres. In most of these ma-
trials, the attitude toward science, if not the accumulation of

it, parallels that of Bartholomew, Maplet, Swan, and the others. Some of the writers are directly in the encyclopedic tradition through their range and organization. Peter Boaystuau tells the readers of *Theatrum Mundi* (1574): "I have left no author sacred or prophane, Greeke, Latine, or in oure vulgar tongue, but that I have bereft him of a leg or a wing, for the more sounder decking and furniture of my worke." Danaeus makes the usual distinction in purpose between Christian and pagan natural knowledge in *The Wonderfull Woorkmanship of the World* (1578). Many items in the ten books of Thomas Lupton's *A Thousand Notable Things* (1595), especially medical secrets, are straight from the encyclopedias of science. Robert Allott, *Wits Theater of the Little World* (1599), defends natural philosophy as first professed by the poets, indeed invented by Prometheus, Linus, Orpheus, and Homer.[14]

At the turn of the century, Robert Cawdrey, *A Treasurie or Store-house of Similes* (1600), remarking how Christ and the prophets "use many Similitudes, and make so many comparisons of things, fetched off, and from the very secrets and bowels of nature," resolves to show "what store of excellent learning, profound wisdom, hidden knowledge, and exact skill of nature . . . there rested in those men." The six dialogues of Torquemada's *The Spanish Mandeville of Miracles* handle "sundry points of Humanity, Philosophy, Divinitie, and Geography." Edward Topsell regards his *Historie of Foure-Footed Beastes* as "Necessary for all Divines and Students, because the story of every Beast is amplified with Narrations out of Scripture, Fathers, Phylosophers, Physitians, and Poets: wherein are declared divers Hyerogliphicks, Emblems, Epigrams, and other good Histories." Thomas Lodge presents Simon Goulart's *A Learned Summary upon the Famous Poem of William Saluste Lord of Bartas* (1621) as a source "wherin the Map of Nature is discovered, the noblest Arts are illustrated, and the secrets of all Sciences are unfolded." Daniel Widdowes sets forth in his *Naturall Philosophy*

a Description of the World, and of the severall Creatures therein contained: Viz. of Angels, of Mankinde, of the Heavens, the Starres, the Planets, the foure Elements, with their order, nature and government: As also of Minerals, Mettals, Plants, and Precious stones; with their colours, formes, and vertues.[15]

The same motifs recur later in the seventeeth century. David Person, rebuking clergy and gown men for idle, unnecessary, and too curious questions in his *Varieties*, yet offers a survey in which "the principall Heads of diverse Sciences are illustrated [and] rare secrets of Naturall things unfoulded." The third edition of Thomas Taylor's *Meditations from the Creatures* (1632), a sermon on the eighth Psalm, is still quite traditional in its cosmology. Scipio Du Plesis, *The Resolver: or Curiosities of Nature* (1635), says his solutions are "for the most part drawne from the *Problems of Aristotle*, of Alexander Aphrodisea, and from the workes of the most excellent Physitians, Naturalists, and other grave Authours." J. A. Comenius cites Job 12:7 as justification for his *Naturall Philosophie Reformed by Divine Light* (1651). The frontispiece diagram of Robert Fage's *A Description of the Whole World* (1658) is so conventional a representation of the geocentric universe as to show the element of fire. Eusebius Renaudot's *A General Collection of Discourses of the Virtuosi of France, upon Questions of all Sorts of Philosophy, and other Natural Knowledg* (1664) reverts to such encyclopedia subjects as dreams, thunder, earthquake, *ignis fatuus*, sea salt, and comets. In 1670 publisher Francis Haley could still expect a market for a translation of Frantze's *The History of Brutes,* heavily indebted to the old lore. And as late as 1672 Thomas Sherley, though he abandons the theory of the four elements and rejects much sacred to the encyclopedists in his *Philosophical Essay,* follows their scissors-and-paste methods and defends being "frequent in quotations," which he recognizes as "a thing much out of fashion." Thomas Blount derives his *Natural History* of 1693 from "the best Modern Writers" but retains the old religious and moral purposes of the encyclopedias in asserting "Every Flower of the Field, every Fibre of a Plant, every Particle of an Insect, carries with it the Impress of its Maker, and can (if duly considered) read us Lectures of Ethicks or Divinity." On the upper levels, the Royal Society might laugh with Nehemiah Grew in *Musaeum Regalis Societatis* (1681) at the marshalling of authorities "as if Aristotle must be brought to prove a Man hath ten toes." But throughout the seventeenth century many a writer echoed by his material, his attitude, or his method Topsell's ingenuous aside on Aristotle "whom I so greatly reverence, and at whose name I doe even rise and make curtesie." [16]

When one turns from the history of this genre of scientific literature to examine Milton's natural science, the mass of parallels and even verbal echoes invites incredulity. It is advisable to repeat the ways in which these books illuminate Milton's meaning. They are not his sources, but they give evidence that the ideas and images for which others have sought specific sources are common property. To find Milton's particulars and sometimes his very words paralleled in not one but several of the popular encyclopedias of science is certainly to suggest that they and he are dealing with information current in the period. Possibly they all use the same source or sources; but the conventionality of most of the lore renders unlikely the positive establishment of single indebtedness. Of the hundreds of passages that relate Milton to the encyclopedias, the ten now to be considered in pairs concern mineralogy, botany, zoology, biology, and cosmology, as shown chiefly in the poetry. The quotations from Milton will perhaps be familiar; for they contain ideas which have been traced to dozens of classical, medieval, and Renaissance sources. The paralleled passages from the encyclopedias will enrich for the modern reader the meaning of lines that have never been adequately explained.

Probably the best-known mineralogical passages in Milton are those referring to the Dead Sea, "That bituminous Lake where *Sodom* flam'd." The apples which the demons in Book X of *Paradise Lost* ate were like the Dead Sea apples, for "instead of Fruit" the devils "Chewd bitter Ashes" and "thir Jaws / With soot and cinders fill'd." In *Eikonoklastes*, Milton had described the pious flourishes of Charles as "like the Apples of *Asphaltus*, appearing goodly to the sudden eye, but look well upon them, or at least touch them, and they turne into Cinders." For the *Paradise Lost* passage, Josephus' *Wars of the Jews*, Ralegh's *History of the World*, and *Genesis* have been cited as sources. But the bituminous Dead Sea and its asphaltic apples are everywhere in the encyclopedias. Batman describes "Bitumine" as a kind of gleaming earth found "beside the lake Asphalti in Judea." His predecessor Bartholomew offers a detailed description:

This place is . . . called Mare salinarum: And is . . . C. furlonges, or usque a vicina Sodomorum. . . In the brymme therof trees growen, the appeles wherof beene grene tylle they ben rype: and if ye kytte theym whan they ben rype, ye shall fynde ashes within them. . . And there growen most fayre apples, that maken men that seen them, have lykynge to ete of them: and if one take them, they fade and falle in asshes & smoke as though they were brenning.

Caxton describes the trees which "bere apples that ben right fair without forth. And within it is as it were asshes." Henry Howard's revised *Defensative against the Poyson of Supposed Prophecies* (1620) speaks of "the Pomgranats of that execrable Lake in *Palestine*, which entice a liquorish and wanton eye to plucke: but are no sooner touched with the finger, but they dissolve to ashes." The place was famous in travel literature; witness Mandeville's report in which the coals and ashes of the apples are "in token that through the ven-

geance of God those Cities were burnt with the fire of hell."
And Swan thus concludes his account of Asphaltus in *Speculum Mundi*:

> It is found throughout Babylon, and especially in the lake
> *Asphaltites,* near unto which stood those cities of Sodome and
> Gomorrah, that were consumed with fire and brimstone: and
> where also do as yet grow apples, which (according to *Solinus*)
> are fair and fresh without, but within are full of Sulphur; and
> being handled they fall all to ashes: In which they are Emblemes
> of the vanities of this world, always seeming more than they are.

These descriptions, which could be many times multiplied,
should be enough to modify any hasty expectation of isolating Milton's source.[17]

Another mineralogical passage shows how the encyclopedias reveal extra meaning in apparently single-level allusions. Milton describes the sun:

> If mettal, part seemd Gold, part Silver cleer;
> If stone, Carbuncle most or Chrysolite,
> Rubie or Topaz, to the Twelve that shon
> In *Aarons* Brest-plate, and a stone besides
> Imagined rather oft than elsewhere seen,
> That stone, or like to that which here below
> Philosophers in vain so long have sought,
> In vain, though by thir powerful Art they binde
> Volatil *Hermes,* and call up unbound
> In various shapes old *Proteus* from the Sea,
> Draind through a Limbec to his Native forme.
> What wonder then if fields and regions here
> Breathe forth Elixir pure, and Rivers run
> Potable Gold. . . ?   III, 595–608

These are not casual associations of brightness; the stones and
metals here were long accepted in special relations by the
encyclopedists. Milles' *Treasurie of Auncient and Moderne
Times* (1613) reports that the same sun that gives gold its
shine "also giveth vertue to the *Carbunckle,* to be so splendant
in the night and to bee powerfull against poyson." Caxton de-

scribes the carbuncle as a fiery substance, "the whiche, by nyght, or yf it be in a derke place and obscure, it shyneth as a cole brennyng." Maplet says that the carbuncle is so called "for that (like to a fierie cole) it giveth light." La Primaudaye holds that "golde representeth the Sunne" and quotes the traveler Lewis de Barthoma:

the king of *Pegum*, which is a citie in India, hath carbuncles called in Greek *Pyropi*, of such magnitude and splendor, that if any one should see the king in a darke place, with these stones upon him, he would seeme to shine like a cleere light, even as if he were fired by the beames of the sunne.

Milles says the chrysolite "shineth with a golden color quite thorow, and partaketh of the Suns vertue"; Swan's *Speculum Mundi* notes "the golden colour and shining" of the chrysolite and the ruby "shining in dark like a spark of fire," a phrase also in Widdowes' *Naturall Philosophie*. Person, conceding that gold is king of metals "as the Sun amongst the Planets," doubts that it can be made potable; but devotes a whole treatise to the philosopher's stone, with directions for making it. Bartholomew, citing Ambrose, Basil, Isidore, and Dioscorides, would have the topaz a stone "that foloweth the moone"; but Caxton, who compares its color to "fyn golde," and Swan, who describes it as "of gold colour, casting beams in the sun," incline to an association like Milton's. Nathaniel Wanley, *The Wonders of the Little World,* tells how long-burning lamps in Roman tombs were fed "by the oylyness of Gold, resolv'd by Art into a liquid substance." Agrippa, *Three Books of Occult Philosophy* (1651), lists these stones and Aaron's "Evanthum" in the chapter on "what things are under the Sun, which are called Solary." [18]

In botanical lore, the same situation prevails; on the one hand the encyclopedias modify the ascription of sources, and on the other, shed new light on a passage hitherto unrelated to the scientific background of Milton's day. The familiar passage is the famous description of the Indian fig tree, for which many sources have been suggested.

> there soon they chose
> The Figtree, not that kind for Fruit renown'd
> But such as at this day to *Indians* known
> In *Malabar* or *Decan* spreads her Armes
> Braunching so broad and long, that in the Ground
> The bended twigs take root, and Daughters grow
> About the Mother Tree, a Pillard shade
> High overarch't, and echoing Walks between;
> Ther oft the *Indian* Herdsman shunning heate
> Shelters in coole, and tends his pasturing Herds
> At Loopholes cut through thickest shade.
>
> IX, 1100–1110

Thomas Warton ascribed this passage to the description in Gerard's *Herball*. Henry Todd cited further parallels from Jonson's *Neptune's Triumph*, Terry's *Voyage to East India*, and Durst's *Histoire des Plantes et Herbes*. Firth believes Milton used Ralegh's *History of the World*. Whiting thinks he got the ideas about the tree directly or indirectly from Pliny, and more recently, Cawley assigns them to Gerard and *Historia Naturalis*. But the tree and its multiple rooting are treated by many authors, among them Maplet and Swan. Most of the traditional ideas in Milton's account may be found in Bartholomew:

there is a fygge tree of Inde, that beareth certayne smalle apples, and hath manye bowes & thycke that benden soo to the grounde by theyr owne weyght, that they sticke in the grounde, and of them spring new branches about the olde stocke, and maketh so greate shadow, that herdes come and abyde there under for socour ayenst heate wynde and wether. And the overest bowes of this tree stretchen upwarde fulle hyghe, and the syde bowes spreden wyde abowte the old tree, as it were growen, and maken a greate shadowe, and the leaves therof ben ful brode, and shape somewhat lyke to a shylde, and beareth many apples, but they ben smalle and passe unneth the greattenesse of a Beane.

Arthur Golding, in his translation of *The Excellent and Pleasant Worke of Julius Solinus Polyhistor* (1587), compares the leaf "to the shielde of the Amazons"; so does Jonston, *An History of the Wonderful Things of Nature*: "the broad leaves are like an *Amazonian* Target." Here again, the point is not that Bartholomew was Milton's source, but that each repetition of the account of the fig tree by the encyclopedists and others lessens the certainty with which one can identify the specific immediate source. Even Pliny is shadowed with doubt, although Milton certainly knew the *Natural History*, for he used it in his teaching.[19]

In a scurrilous passage in *Second Defence*, Milton plays with what would today be the most abstruse tree lore to rebuke More's immoralities:

> Then he might have shown the woman the manner of engrafting. He might now have praised the parterres; might even have wished for nothing more than shade; might have been allowed no other liberty than to engraft a mulberry in a fig, thence to raise, with the utmost dispatch, a line of sycamores — a most delectable walk.

As the editors of the Columbia Milton explain, the indecent but effective puns in the Latin original depend in part upon the meanings of *morus*, *ficus*, and *sycomori*. The whole passage has its basis in botanical lore. Bartholomew indicates that "Amonge all graffynge of trees, the beste is whan the graffe and the stock ben lyke . . . as if a fygge graffe be graffed on a fygge stocke." And the "sicomorus" or mulberry is "a nyce fygge tree, lyke in leaves to the tree that hyght Morus. . . . Or els as other men meane, it hath that name Sicomorus of sile, that is fig tree, and Morus, that is foly or nysetee, as hit were a fole or a nyce fygge tree, as the Glose sayth." Maplet's explanation is the same: "Sycomore or foolish Fig tree, in leafe is like the Mulberie tree: In other poynts, it is the selfe same with the Fig." One of the aphorisms from *Regimen Sanitatis Salerni* (1634) also supports the pun: "Both Lice and Lust by Figges engendred are."[20]

In animal lore, the familiar example is the whale, to which Milton referred several times. The two *Paradise Lost* passages in question have caused much disagreement among the editors.

> or that Sea-Beast
> *Leviathan*, which God of all his works
> Created hugest that swim th' Ocean stream:
> Him haply slumbring on the *Norway* foam
> The Pilot of some small night-founder'd Skiff,
> Deeming some Iland, oft, as Sea-men tell,
> With fixed Anchor in his skaly rind
> Moors by his side under the Lee, while Night
> Invests the Sea, and wished Morn delayes. . . .
>
> I, 200–208

> there Leviathan
> Hugest of living Creatures, on the Deep
> Stretcht like a Promontorie sleeps or swimmes,
> And seems a moving Land, and at his Gilles
> Draws in, and at his Trunck spouts out a Sea.
>
> VII, 412–416

Thomas Newton supposed that Milton got his information "from Olaus Magnus and other writers; and it is amply confirmed by Pontoppidan's description of the Kraken in his account of Norway." Todd quoted with approval Dunster's claim for Psalm 109:26 and DuBartas as sources for the second passage. Verity illustrates the first quotation with the story from Peter Heylyn's *Cosmographie* of a whale four acres big. Hughes adds the *Talmud*, the *Voyage of St. Brendan*, and medieval bestiaries, "which make the treacherous whale a type of Satan." Pittman holds that the source for both is the ubiquitous *Physiologus*. P. Ansell Robin finds some of the ideas in the voyage of Sinbad. Whiting points out that huge spouting whales were a common decoration of contemporary maps.[21]

The four major points in the two passages are the tremendous bulk of the whale, its similarity in appearance to an island, the mariner's mistake in anchoring to it, and its spouting water, or blowing. Bartholomew's section on the whale treats each of these:

> Also the whale and Balena is all one, & Balene ben anone great & huge, & ben called Belue ab emittendo, of outcastynge & shed-ynge of water. For they throwe water hyer than other greate fyshes of the see. . . And so in age for greatnesse of bodye, on his rydge powder and erth is gathered, and so dygged together, that herbes and smalle trees and bushes growe theron: soo that that greate fyshe semethe an Ilonde. And if shypmen comen unwarely therby, unneth they scape with out peryl. For he throweth so muche water oute of his mouthe uppon the shyppe, that he overtorneth it some tyme or drowneth it.

If Bartholomew's account were the only surviving treatment outside Milton, it would challenge acceptance as his original. But Caxton and La Primaudaye and Swan also survive; any one of these is as apropos as Bartholomew. Caxton treats the whale as one of the "ffysshes that be founden in Ynde":

> In this see of Inde is another fysshe so huge and grete that on his back groweth erth and grasse; and semeth properly that it is a grete Ile. Wherof it happeth somtyme that the maronners sayllyng by this see ben gretly deceyved and abused; ffor they wene cer-taynly that it be ferme londe, wherfor they goo out of their shippes theron, and lyghted fyre and made it to brenne after their nede, wenyng to be on a ferme londe, but incontynent as this merveyllous fysshe feleth the hete of the fyre, he mevyth hym sodenly and devaleth doun into the water as deep as he may.

La Primaudaye, arguing that God's power declares itself in the size of fish and their correspondence to land animals, says:

> The first is the hugenesse and power of the great fishes which hee hath created, as whales and such like, which rather seeme to be sea monsters then fishes, there being no beast in all the earth so great and strong: for there are some that seeme a farre off to bee islands or mountains, rather than fishes. . . They make an hor-rible crie, and spout out of two holes (of a cubite long, which they have nere to their nostrils) so much water, that oftentimes drowne ships therewith.

Swan devotes three and a half pages to whales and their kinds. He quotes Munster's statement "that near unto Iseland there be great whales whose bignesse equalizeth the hills and mightie mountains"; and from Olaus Magnus he draws the account of "Physeter or the Whirl-pool-whale [which] will sometimes lift up his head, above the sail yard, casting up so much water through certain pipes in his forehead . . . that great and strong ships are either compelled to sink, or else exposed to great and manifest danger." [22]

As a later chapter will show, Milton's data on the phoenix and the commonwealth of bees, to mention only two other commonplaces in natural history, may as easily be duplicated from the encyclopedias. But for an example of the way in which the animal lore of the encyclopedias indicates new significance in Milton's lines, one may look at the list of serpents in Book X of *Paradise Lost*:

> dreadful was the din
> Of hissing through the Hall, thick swarming now
> With complicated monsters, head and taile,
> Scorpion and Asp, and *Amphisbæna* dire
> *Cerastes* hornd, *Hydrus*, and *Ellops* drear
> And *Dipsas*.   521–526

In these lines are compressed pages of learning treasured by the encyclopedists. Swan says that out of the asp's forehead "grow two pieces of flesh like an hard skinne." The scorpion was commonly described as carrying its sting in its tail; the hydra was universally the many-headed serpent. Bartholomew, Batman, Torquemada, Topsell, Golding in his translation of Solinus, and Swan describe the amphisbaena as a two-headed serpent, Swan remarking that it "hath two heads and no tail, having a head at both ends." Caxton, Bartholomew, Swan, Maplet, Torquemada, and Topsell describe the cerastes as having on both sides of its head "as it were the hornes of a Ram, bending upward and wreathen all about." In several of these authors, amphisbaena, cerastes, and dipsas are de-

scribed within a page or two of one another. The encyclopedia accounts focus interest on the phrase "complicated
monsters," glossed by Verity as "twisted, twined together; Lat.
complicare, 'to tie up.'" The obvious intention of the passage is to suggest a confusion of serpents, coiled, twined, and
twisted together; and thus to indicate confusion in the minds
of the devils. The reptiles are appropriately chosen; their
physical peculiarities would make a group of them exceedingly complicated. The serpent dipsas, always associated with
thirst, found its way into the lines probably from some
such notion as Topsell's out of Nicander that the "Scytall"
and the dipsas were confused in some authorities, and that
the scytall's "outward forme or visible proportion . . . is
like that which wee have already called a Double-head, and
the Latines Amphisbena." [23]

To illustrate the bearing of medical lore in the encyclopedias on that in Milton, a well-known example is Adam's
discussion of reason and fancy and his explanation of Eve's
nightmare.

> But know that in the Soule
> Are many lesser Faculties that serve
> Reason as chief; among these Fansie next
> Her office holds; of all external things,
> Which the five watchful Senses represent,
> She forms Imaginations, Aerie shapes,
> Which Reason joyning or disjoyning, frames
> All what we affirm or what deny, and call
> Our knowledge or opinion; then retires
> Into her private Cell when Nature rests.
> Oft in her absence mimic Fansie wakes
> To imitate her; but misjoyning shapes,
> Wilde work produces oft, and most in dreams,
> Ill matching words and deeds long past or late.
> Some such resemblance methinks I find
> Of our last Eevnings talk, in this thy dream,
> But with addition strange.   V, 100–116

Todd cites Davies' *Nosce Teipsum* and Burton's *Anatomy of*

Melancholy; and Dunster thought the latter was Milton's source. Taylor quotes DuBartas as contributing to the dream lore; and Greenlaw offers Spenser's House of Alma as "the most convincing proof of Milton's indebtedness to Spenser's Platonism." But again the physiology and psychology here were set forth in dozens of medical treatises, schoolbooks, and popular literature. Bartholomew's description of the cells of the brain as three and his outline of their function summarize the common belief of his and later times:

For in the brayne ben thre small celles, that is to witte the formest in whiche the vertue Imaginativa worketh in. Therin thynges that the utter wytte apprehendeth without, ben ordeyned and put togyders within, as sayth Johannicus. There is also a myddell chaumbre hight Logistica: therin the reason sensible or vertue Estimativa is a mayster. Agayne there is the thyrde and the laste, which is memorativa, the vertue of mynde. That vertue holdith thynges that bene apprehended and known by the Imagination or reason.

Bartholomew uses *fantasie* as synonym for *imagination*; La Primaudaye similarly ignores the distinction later made by Coleridge: "there will be no danger if we use these two names *Fantasie* and *Imagination* indifferently. For Fantasie is derived from a Greeke word that signifieth as much as Imagination." The account of the brain in *The French Academie* compares with that in *De Proprietatibus Rerum*; two passages in special read like a prose version of Milton's lines:

Now besides this knowledge of things present, we see plainly that there is another knowledge within of things that are absent. For our own experience teacheth us that even when our externall sences are retired and withdrawne from doing their duties, the imagination, thought, consideration and remembrance of those things we have seene, heard, tasted, smelt, touched and perceived with corporall sences remaine still in us both waking and sleeping: as it appeareth by our dreames, in which the image & resemblance of those things which the bodily sences perceived waking are represented to our internall sences when we are asleepe. . . . This vertue is called *Imagination*, or the *Imagi-*

native vertue, which is in the soule as the eye in the body, by be-
holding to receive the images that are offered unto it by the
outward sences . . . . Now after that the *Imagination* hath
received the images . . . then doth it as it were prepare and
digest them, either by joyning them together, or by separating
them according as their natures require. They that distinguish
Imagination from *Fantasie*, attribute this office to *Fantasie*. . . .
Afterward it is requisite that all these things thus heaped together
should be distributed and compared with one another, to consider how they may be conjoyned or severed, how one followeth
another, or how farre asunder they are, that so a man may judge
what is to be retained and what to be refused. And this office
belongeth to *Reason*, after which *Judgment* followeth, whereby
men chuse or refuse that which reason alloweth or disalloweth.

The second passage from La Primaudaye reveals that fancy
was active in sleep, and we discover that Milton worked
within well-known psychological assumptions in having Eve
commit the sin she dreamed of:

Moreover this faculty of the fantasie is sudden, and so farre from
stayednes that even in the time of sleepe it hardly taketh any
rest, but is alwaies occupied in dreaming and doting, yea even
about those things which never have beene, shall be, or can be.
For it . . . taketh what pleaseth it, and addeth thereunto or
diminisheth, changeth and rechangeth, mingleth and unmin-
gleth so that it cutteth asunder and seweth up againe as it listeth.
. . . Neither is it altogether without reason which we commonly
use to say: that fancie breeds the fact which it imagineth. For we
see many fall into those mishaps and inconveniences, which they
imprint in their fantasie and imagination.[24]

In *Paradise Regained*, there occurs a physiological concept never adequately glossed or related to the medical lore
of the time. Satan explains away the storm he called up to
harass the Son:

> and these flaws, though mortals fear them
> As dangerous to the pillard frame of Heaven,
> Or to Earths dark basis underneath,
> Are to the main as inconsiderable,

> And harmless, if not wholsom, as a sneeze
> To mans less universe, and soon are gone.
>
> IV, 454–459

Editions of the poem and commentaries on Milton attribute no special significance to these lines. But from the encyclopedias one learns that the sneeze was seriously discussed as a purging of the brain and therefore a benefit to health. *De Proprietatibus Rerum* contains a whole chapter on the subject and advises: "snesynge is a vyolente mevynge of the brayne to put out superfluous fumosyties therof." *Batman uppon Bartholome* adds that "Sneesing is a good signe in an evill cause" and that "sneesing helpeth, and it bee excited." *The French Academie* emphasizes the usefulness of the nose in clearing evil humours from the head, for "the nose is given to man that it might serve the braine in stead of a pipe and spowt to purge it of flegmatike humours." As late as Sir Thomas Browne's time, the therapeutic effects of sneezing were commonly recognized and fully described in scientific treatises.[25]

Finally, there is cosmology. The encyclopedias contain almost every pre-Copernican concept to be found in Milton. One of the most commonplace of these is the idea that the earth is exceedingly small in contrast to the sun and the firmament. In *Paradise Lost*, Adam wonders, as Milton had in Prolusion VII, at Nature's disproportion in having the tremendous stars exist only for "this punctual spot," the earth:

> When I behold this goodly Frame, this World
> Of Heav'n and Earth consisting, and compute
> Thir magnitudes, this Earth a spot, a graine,
> An Atom, with the Firmament compar'd
> And all her numberd Stars, that seem to rowle
> Spaces incomprehensible (for such
> Thir distance argues and thir swift return
> Diurnal) merely to officiate light
> Round this opacous Earth, this punctual spot,
> One day and night; in all thir vast survey

Useless besides, reasoning I oft admire,
How Nature wise and frugal could commit
Such disproportions.   VIII, 15–27

Although Allan Gilbert pointed out thirty years ago that the
medieval *De Sphaera* of Sacrobosco contained the idea that
the earth was exceedingly small in contrast to the heavens,
Marjorie Nicolson in 1935 argued that the concept perhaps
resulted from Milton's experience with optics; and McColley
in 1937, though recognizing in a general way that the idea
was common, found its source in Wilkins' *Discourse that the
Earth May Be a Planet.* The encyclopedias of Caxton and La
Primaudaye support Johnson's claim that the idea was "constantly reiterated in all the astronomical works of the late
Middle Ages and Renaissance." The very words "punctual
spot" occur time and again in traditional cosmologies. Alexander Neckam writes: "Tanta est firmamenti quantitas ut
ipsi totalis terra collata quasi punctum esse videatur." Caxton's chapter "Of the mevynges of the heven and of the vii
planets, and of the lytilnes of therthe unto the Regarde of
heven" offers the opinion that "alle the erthe round a boute
hath nothyng of gretenes ayenst the heven, no more than hath
the poynt or pricke in the myddle of the most grete compass
that may be, ne to the grettest cercle that may be made on
therthe." Such diverse writers as Thomas Taylor, *Meditations from the Creatures,* and Nathanael Carpenter, *Geography Delineated forth in Two Books,* use the same language:
"pricke or point in comparison of heaven" and "no otherwise then a point." So Lodge in his summary of DuBartas,
quoting Pliny's "Terra universa nihil aliud est quam mundi
punctus." In a lyrical extolling of man's place in the universe (a paean not unlike Raphael's reply to Adam), La
Primaudaye writes what seems almost a prose recasting of
Milton's lines:

When I direct my flight now and then (my companions) even
unto the heavens, and with the wings of contemplation behold

their wonderfull greatnesse, their terrible motions, being contrary and without ceasing, the lively brightnesse, rare beauty, and incomparable force of the Sunne and Moone, their unchangeable course, one while cause of light and by and by after of darkenesse, the infinite number of goodly stars, and of so many other celestiall signes: and from this excellent and constant order of all these things, as one ravished and amazed, when I withdraw my spirit lower into the elementary region, to admire and wonder at the situation and spreading of the earth amidst the waters, both of them making one round masse or lumpe, whiche in the midst of this great firmament occupieth the roome but of a pricke or tittle in respect thereof . . . I cannot marvell ynough at the excellencie of Man, for whom all these things were created, and are maintained and preserved in their beeing and mooving, by one and the same divine providence alwaies like unto it selfe.[26]

A last illustration of how the encyclopedias of science extend our insight comes from Book IV of *Paradise Lost*, where Milton marks the time of night Ithuriel and Zephon began their search for Satan:

> Now had night measur'd with her shaddowie Cone
> Half way up Hill this vast Sublunar Vault.   776–777

The sense of these lines has been known for some time; for us, their depth is increased by that close relation to the material of the encyclopedias. Bartholomew's chapter "Of Shadowe" advances as lucid an explanation as Verity's:

And if the body of lyghte be more than the bodye, that letteth lyght, it maketh the shadow stretche forth shelde wyse, and the poynt forwarde. And suche a shadowe highte Conoydes. Hereof it followeth, that the sonne, for it is more than al the erth, maketh the shadowe Conoydes, that is shapen as a shelde. Than happenynge that the erthe beyng even sette afore the sonne in a certayne maner assygned, it maketh the shadowe stretche so hye, that it stretcheth to the moone.

La Primaudaye explains the phenomenon: "And the night also, is no other thing but the shadow of the earth, which shadow is in forme like a Pyramis, growing still lesse & lesse

taperwise towards a point, till at last it fadeth." Caxton is
more explicit; a diagram accompanies the following explanation:

And it [earth interposing between sun and heavens] maketh the
shadowe to goo alle alway tornyng after the sonne, which alle
way is ayenst it; ffor whan the sonne ariseth in the mornyng in
the est, the shadowe is in the weest; & whan it is right over &
above us at mydday, thenne is therthe shadowed under her. And
whan the sonne goth doun in the west, the shadowe of it is in the
eest; and thenne whan the sonne is under, we have thenne the
shadowe over us, which goth drawyng to the west, so longe til
the sonne ariseth and shyneth & rendridth to us the day.

What before may have seemed mere ingenuity in imagery is
now seen to have its basis in soberly related scientific fact.[27]

Having seen in these examples the characteristic relation
of the encyclopedias to Milton, we may now more knowl-
edgeably survey the major divisions of natural science as they
occur in his works, glossing Milton's lines from the vernacular literature of science and discovering if we can what
part science has in the philosophical assumptions and effec-
tiveness of pamphlet and poem. So far, the concern has been
only with the descriptive and the genetic problems mentioned in the introduction. Let us now deal with all four: descriptive, genetic, philosophical, and aesthetic. We must keep
in mind that Milton's science, like that of the encyclopedists,
is fundamentally classical and medieval. We cannot deter-
mine the immediate sources for his science, but we can define
the milieu out of which it comes, and can even find the tone
of it in the common purpose asserted by medieval and Renaissance compilers. The gulf between Milton's lore and the experimental science of middle and late seventeenth century
receives fresh emphasis from a notable coincidence: Sprat's
History of the Royal-Society, in part an attack on the kind of
lore woven in the fabric of *Paradise Lost*, was published in
1667.

CHAPTER II

The Harmony of the Spheres: Milton's World Picture

MILTON, IT IS TRUE, left no "compendious method of natural philosophy" to parallel his formal treatise on divinity and to serve a comparable purpose for modern readers, though not a few of these have reconstructed his cosmology, most recently Tillyard, Curry, Hunter, and Robins. Milton was a pamphleteer and a poet, not a scientist, — not even, for all his tampering with physic, an amateur of science. Hence, as we assemble a description of the universe from his prose and poetry, three of the resulting generalizations might have been predicted. First, there is little distinction between the universe of the prose and that of the poetry, though the latter is of course more systematically detailed. Second, a progressive scientist of his time, like Boyle, or a supporter of the Royal Society, like Bishop Sprat, would have regarded the world view in his works as quite old-fashioned, despite his references to the new astronomy. And third, the sum of Milton's allusions cannot be established or even regarded as his private belief; cosmology was a vocabulary for him, a quarry of images, not a formal statement of scientific theory the way *Christian Doctrine* is a formal statement of theology.

In delineating the principal features of the Miltonic universe, I have made use of some familiar scenes, though I have tried to avoid duplicating Gilbert, Nicolson, Curry, and McColley. But the light in which these scenes are exhibited warrants their repetition, because they come from all of Milton, not only *Paradise Lost*, hitherto the only argument heroic deemed. I do not include every astronomical allusion nor relate each to popular science nor suppose that each operates in some local or general scheme of images. The selection has been representative; but neglected features, like the cosmology of the sublunar vault, have been thoroughly explicated. Something has been reserved for later generalization on the aesthetic function of science in prose and poem; but something in that kind is also attempted here. The central harmony sought is the correlation between physical and moral order, the true and final harmony of the spheres.[1]

One must recognize that for Milton, as for the encyclopedists, problems in natural philosophy reached their last solution only in divine philosophy. His conviction of man's moral responsibility in a theocentric universe outweighed everything else. For him there could be no absolute issues between science and religion, though he knew the appeal of that quarrel for others. There is really small evidence for a genuine conflict of this kind in his work; he was not even seriously interested in a contest of cosmological theories. Raphael gives Adam a technically shallow sketch of the heliocentric system and the doctrine of the plurality of worlds and then dismisses the controversy as insignificant and impertinent to man's duty to God and to himself. McColley and Johnson have taught us that the wealth of astronomy in *Paradise Lost* is descriptive rather than technical. Only the general features of the Ptolemaic system are used, but they are used most cunningly for their focus upon man. In the express ambiguities of Satan's flight from the outside shell of the world to the sun, "by center, or eccentric, hard to tell," lies the clue to Milton's practice, which was in effect to get the best of both bargains. His persistent exploitation of science in poetry, justified by traditional acceptance of learning as epic subject-matter, led him to load every rift; his ignorance of up-to-date astronomy or his disinclination to shift emphasis away from man dissuaded him from committing his poem to controversy.[2]

In *Paradise Lost*, Milton repeatedly moves from circumference to center, retracing through stock images the arcs of focus upon earth and man. And it is a two-way passage. Satan and Adam are centers from which radiates the flow of imagination, as when Adam and Eve contemplate the heavens and pray or Satan apostrophizes the sun after he has flung himself from its sphere to the top of Mount Niphates. No other poem is more explicit as to place; in Heaven, Hell, earth or Chaos, the reader of *Paradise Lost* always sees things from a precise physical point of view and he always knows what it is. The same sweep from circumference to center occurs in the Seventh Prolusion and the Vacation Exercise poem, and from center to circumference in the Third Prolusion — evidence that this cosmic view was early a part of Milton's mode. In the Seventh Prolusion he asks if it is not a great accomplishment

to have comprehended every law of the heavens and of the stars? — all the motions and shiftings of the air, whether it brings terror to sluggish minds by the august sound of thunders or by fiery locks [comets], whether it becomes frozen in snow and hail, whether finally it falls soft and gentle in rain and dew; then to have learned perfectly the changing winds, all the vapors and gases which the earth and sea belch forth; next to become versed in the secret powers of plants and metals; also to have understood the nature and, if possible the feelings of each living creature; thence the most exact structure and surgery of the human body; and finally the godlike power and force of mind.

In the Vacation Exercise some of the same particulars occur:

Such where the deep transported mind may soare
Above the wheeling poles, and at Heav'ns dore

Look in, and see each blissful Deitie
How he before the thunderous throne doth lie,
Listening to what unshorn *Apollo* sings
To th' touch of golden wires, while *Hebe* brings
Immortal Nectar to her Kingly Sire:
Then passing through the Spherse of watchful fire,
And mistie Regions of wide air next under,
And hills of Snow and lofts of piled Thunder
May tell at length how green-ey'd *Neptune* raves,
In Heav'ns defiance mustering all his waves;
Then sing of secret things that came to pass
When Beldam Nature in her cradle was.   33–46

The Third Prolusion makes a comparably ambitious appeal to intellectual curiosity. It is among the first of many ethereal journeys that Milton wrote:

How much better would it be, fellow students, and how much more worthy of your name, to make at this time a tour as it were with your eyes about the whole earth as represented on the map and view the places trodden by ancient heroes, and to travel through the regions made famous by wars, by triumphs, and even by the tales of the illustrious poets: now to cross the raging Adriatic, now to approach unharmed flame-capped Aetna: then to observe the customs of men and the governments of nations, so admirably arranged; thence to investigate and to observe the natures of all living creatures; from thence to plunge the mind into the secret essences of stones and plants. Do not hesitate, my hearers, to fly up even to the skies, there to behold those multiform aspects of the clouds, the massy power of the snow, and the source of those tears of early morn; next to peer into the caskets of the hail and to survey the arsenals of the thunderbolts. Nor let what Jupiter or Nature veils from you be concealed when a baleful and enormous comet ofttimes threatens a conflagration from heaven; nor let the most minute little stars be hidden from you, however many there may be scattered and straying between the two poles. Yea, follow as companion the wandering sun, and subject time itself to a reckoning and demand the record of its everlasting journey. Nay, let not your mind suffer itself to be hemmed in and bounded by the same limits as the earth, but let it wander also outside the boundaries of the world.

Tillyard calls this sort of thing Baconian in its taking of all knowledge for its province; even so, it may be duplicated in content and scope from the title pages of dozens of medieval and Renaissance encyclopedias. A trip through space is one of the major motifs of Milton's Latin poems, and the nocturnal journey of *In Quintum Novembris* anticipates Satan's travels in *Paradise Lost*; scientific lore inheres in all of them. Though Milton never acquired all this learning, he never forgot its attraction. Nearly every page bespeaks his fascination with the secret powers of stones and metals, the lore of meteorology, the highly imaginative properties of natural history. Even at the end of *Paradise Lost* the ideal recurs, as Michael imposes a higher one: learning to obey and love with fear the only God:

> hope no higher, though all the Starrs
> Thou knewst by name, and all th' ethereal Powers,
> All secrets of the deep, all Natures works,
> Or works of God in Heav'n, Aire, Earth, or Sea.
>
> XII, 576–579

Satan's view of Chaos dark, illimitable, without bound; Adam's survey of the heavens; the Tempter's panorama of earth in *Paradise Regained* — these, like Michael's injunction, manifest a continued attraction to the cosmic. Later we shall see images of sweep and distance enlarge the canvas of *Paradise Lost*. The present exposition of the Miltonic universe works from circumference to center, following Prolusion VII in a movement from astronomy and cosmology to lapidary and herbal lore, to the natural history of animals, and last to man.[3]

I. THE FRAME OF THE UNIVERSE

No longer tenable are the clichés that only the Ptolemaic and Copernican systems stood as rivals before the world in Milton's time; that in *Paradise Lost* Milton compares and

evaluates them; that he favored the Copernican system but
for "poetic" reasons employed the Ptolemaic; or that he used
solid spheres (supposedly postulated by the Ptolemaic system) to explain celestial motions. McColley and Francis Johnson, chief among several, have shown how nineteenth-century
Miltonists depended upon each other to save appearances
rather than upon documents from the time of the poem.
McColley has proved that the age of Milton knew five important cosmological concepts, not merely two; and that in
Paradise Lost Milton mentions all except the geo-heliocentric. The Raphael-Adam dialogue has little to do with the
universe of the poem. It is not even a proper system, for although its static outline is Ptolemaic, the celestial motions
are not harmonized — indeed, the mode of the poem capitalizes upon their imprecision. Aside from Raphael's discourse,
nearly all astronomy in Milton refers to a geocentric universe: a world composed of a hard outside shell, a Primum
Mobile, a crystalline sphere to allow for "trepidation" or
retrogradation, a sphere of fixed stars, separate spheres for the
seven planets, a sphere of fire, a sphere of air divided into
three regions, and the earth. Below and to the left of this
world is Hell. Diagrams of such a system were plentiful in the
Renaissance; those in Caxton's *Mirrour of the World* and
Apian's *Cosmographie* (1539) are typical, though the location
of Hell is unspecified.[4]

But this is a prelapsarian cosmos, dominated by the circle
from the moment that God through the Son put forth his
virtue in Chaos, which before and after creation was a
tumbled anarchy of the four elements. Though Milton's
golden compasses have not excited the critics so much as
Donne's, still, as Mahood has shown, they symbolize the precision and perfection of the cosmic architect and convey ideas
of order and rhythm essential to the concept of the Deity. For
the original, innocent cosmos, Milton was not prepared to
break the circle, because that form was the very function of

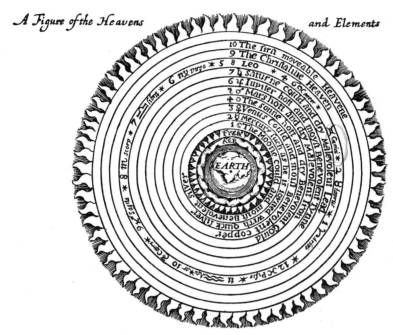

A Figure of the Heavens and Elements

Frontispiece from Robert Fage, Description of the Whole World, *1658.*

the compasses in the hand of God. To describe this cosmos from its fallen state, like creating an Adam and Eve only from experience with their descendants, could scarcely be accomplished save through contradiction and even paradox, into which Milton boldly ventured. As characters in a narrative, Adam and Eve must begin to fall long before Eve stretches her rash hand; the balance between majestic innocence and plausible human weakness seems maintained in a cosmic environment that is itself sufficiently ambiguous to emphasize moral truth instead of ultimately insignificant scientific fact. One means by which Milton unites the impression of a perfect prelapsarian cosmos with its grossly altered postlapsarian condition is through the juxtaposing of physical and spiritual disorder. The crystalline sphere was to protect from the inroads of darkness and anarchy the orderly arrangement of the elements inside the world, even as the angels were to repulse Satan. But with his success came the introduction of chaos into physical and spiritual worlds, a disturbance from which neither the mind of man nor the materials of the universe ever return to their original state.[5]

The nature and origins of Milton's idea of matter have long exercised the scholars, who rely chiefly upon patristic commentary. William Hunter's latest researches seem to have settled upon Augustinian as well as Aristotelian matter, though the implications of creation from pre-existent matter still offer scope for discussion. Certainly in the system abstractable from his works, Milton employed the generally accepted notion of a world made of the four elements — earth, water, air, fire — and a fifth or quintessence, though he knew something of atoms and the Paracelsan triad of salt, sulphur, and mercury. When Satan looks "in sudden view" upon Chaos, he sees

> a dark
> Illimitable Ocean, without bound,
> Without dimension, where length, breadth, & highth,
> And time and place are lost; where eldest Night
> And *Chaos*, ancestors of Nature, hold
> Eternal *Anarchie*, amidst the noise
> Of endless Warrs, and by confusion stand.
> For hot, cold, moist, and dry, four Champions fierce
> Strive here for Maistrie, and to Battel bring
> Thir embryon Atoms.   II, 891–900

Inside the world and below the sphere of the moon the same elements "in quaternion run / Perpetual circle," nourish all things, and change ceaselessly but without the wild disorder outside. Reversals and dislocations of nature, like distemperature of the humours in man, introduce the external anarchy; but there is always some measure of control. The "ethereall and fift essence," of which the stars are made, does not change, though stars and planets, like "whatever was created" need

To be sustaind and fed; of Elements
The grosser feeds the purer, Earth the Sea
Earth and the Sea feed Air, the Air those Fires
Ethereal.[6]

The four elements, from Bartholomew, De Proprietatibus Rerum,
English ed., 1495.

Habitation of the spheres by spirits, an old belief, appears in
Milton with the later neo-Platonic idea that separate orders
of them controlled the four elements. *Il Penseroso* mentions
"those Daemons" of "fire, air, flood, or under ground" whose
power has "a true consent / With Planet, or with Element."

Satan in *Paradise Regained* addresses his "demonian Spirits" as "Powers of Fire, Air, Water, and Earth beneath" and alludes to them as tetrarchs.[7]

All of this is cosmological commonplace before and during Milton's time. Bartholomew, in telling "What is the Worlde," repeats an old story:

the vertue of god made and ordeined primordyall matter, in the whiche as it were in a massye thynge, the foure elementes were potentially, and not distyngued in tale and nombre, as they arne nowe: but they were medled. . . . And therof the wisdome of god made and broughte forthe all the elementes, and all that is made of elementes, and ordeyned theym in theyr owne qualitees and place. For that whiche was hotte and drye, in that maner passed in to kynde of fyre. And by cause of lyghtnesse therof the wysdome of god sette it above other. And such as was mooste colde and drie, passed into kynde of erth: and for hevynes and sadnesse therof, he sette it beneth that was hote. And moyst he put into kynde of ayre, and such as was colde and moyste passed into kynde of water. And as these two elementes ben more lyghte clere and subtill, he set them betwene fyre and erthe.

Swan describes Chaos as "a confused heap . . . lump, without form, and void; a darkened depth and waters; a matter of no matter . . . a rude and undigested Chaos or confusion of matters." Caxton tells "How the four Elements ben sette"; Bartholomew, Batman, La Primaudaye — indeed every ambitious cosmologist — devote long chapters to each element, its nature, position, and function.

The substance of the stars is likewise a cliché, together with that of angels and spirits. Milton's references to ethereal substance, fiery essence, purer essence, purer fire, and "Intelligential substances" indicate his acquaintance with the kind of lore Caxton recounts in treating an ethereal "hester" of which "thangels taken their bodyes & their winges." Bartholomew, Swan, and La Primaudaye testify to the quarrel over the Aristotelian concept of a fifth essence for the stars. As to sustenance of the stars, many a writer willing to concede the transmutation of elements balked at the equally wide-spread opinion that the stars and planets fed upon sea and air. Where Swan is sure that the stars "are of such a nature that they be rather fed and nourished by vapours, then compelled to suffer an unwilling wasting caused by an exhaling virtue," Thomas Vaughan, *A Brief Natural History* (1669), remarks "that therefore they should be fed with vapours, *Aristotle* deservedly laughs at it" because all vapors are distilled again upon sea and earth when they reach the middle region of air.8

The whole scheme of the elementary world restates the concept of "one first matter," altering in degree, according to Raphael's description, as the forms of being approach Deity. The intercourse of elements manifests the dynamism of existence — a dual process by which natural objects stem from God, and instinctively move back toward God. Man wills his own refinement until "body up to spirit work." Much of the imagery and analogy in Milton's references to the elements and their processes derives from encyclopedic science; and behind even the most casual allusion rest long traditions of debate and discussion. This conclusion applies to the system of spheres occurring in *Paradise Lost*, and particularly to the controversial structure of the firmament and "waters above the firmament."9

As Satan approaches "this pendent world," he sees it "hanging in a golden chain." He lands on the hard outer shell, "a firm opacous Globe" distinct from the Primum Mobile just inside it, for the latter was constantly in motion and the former was a "Wall / Immoveable." The original function of "the outside bare / Of this round World" was to divide "luminous inferior Orbs" from Chaos and the inroad of darkness. Satan's entrance through the aperture near the chain and stair to Heaven symbolizes a fracture of this protective sheath; and in time the outside shell became a limbo for "all the unaccomplisht works of Natures hand." Inside this shell revolve concentric spheres, "the ten-fold ranks of heaven" which include the Primum Mobile as well as the crystalline sphere (often omitted in the diagrams). Both occur in another of those arcs with whose extension Milton deepens the space of his universe. Superstitious men, dying, disguise themselves in Franciscan robes, and

> pass the Planets seven, and pass the fixt,
> And that Crystalline Sphear whose ballance weighs
> The Trepidation talkt, and that first mov'd.
>
> III, 481–483

The spheres are separate and distinguishable, though obviously not solid. The "first mov'd" is the Primum Mobile, the action of which affects the spheres within. The "fixt" are the constellations, moving as a group in a single orb. The crystalline sphere, added by the Arabian commentators upon Ptolemy to account for the apparent retrogradation of the fixed stars, appears elsewhere in Milton as "the cleer Hyaline, the Glassie Sea." The pole of the sphere of fixed stars was thought to describe a small circle upon the circumference of the crystalline sphere, so that their "trepidation" might be accounted for, but lack of unanimity about it is reflected in qualification "talkt." Some older authorities argued that the crystalline was solid; others considered it as Milton did, liquid; new scientists did not care to think about it at all, The traditional argument often involved the "firmament," or sphere of fixed stars, which now requires some explanation.[10]

The Primum Mobile, "that high first-moving Spheare" of *On the Death of a Fair Infant*, that "First Wheel of the Universe" later called the "Wheele / Of Day and Night," was in some accounts imagined to sweep along all the spheres that it enclosed. In others it was counteracted by the opposite motion of the sphere of fixed stars, which tended to slow down the planets nearest it as they moved with the Primum Mobile.

The sphere of fixed stars was called "the firmament" and "the heavens"; its incorruptibility was a cosmological byword, put to humorous use in Milton's allusion to Hobson as "Made of sphear-metal, never to decay." But "firmament" was also used to mean the atmosphere or air between earth and the utmost sphere. Similarly "heaven" or "heavens" meant variously the blue sky, the sublunar air, the planetary atmosphere, and the dwelling place of God and angels. Bartholomew's chapter "Of the distinction of heven," like Swan's "How to understand the word Heavens," was an attempt to clear up the confusion.[1]

The "pillar'd firmament" of *Comus* and the firmament glowing "with living Saphirs" of *Paradise Lost* clearly refer to the sphere of fixed stars. But the "calm Firmament" through which the sun bends his course, the "Firmament . . . and all her numbered Starrs," and the firmament of Prolusion VII are the air or space extending from the region of fire to and including the sphere of the stars. Finally, in "yon Western Cloud that draws / O're the blew Firmament a radiant white," the firmament is the blue sky. In *Christian Doctrine*, Milton set down as one of the things invisible to us "the highest heaven, which is the throne and habitation of God"; *Paradise Lost* is of course full of allusions to heaven in this sense. But that it can also be identified with "firmament," as the space between earth and God's abode, is shown in the moon's pursuing her course "through mid Heav'n." It means the separate spheres above the earth in the line "Terrestrial Heav'n, danc'd round by other Heav'ns." And it means the sphere of fixed stars in the "heavenly Wain" of *Elegy V*, as it does in

> another Heav'n
> From Heaven Gate not farr, founded in view
> On the cleer *Hyaline*, the Glassie Sea;
> Of amplitude almost immense, with Starrs
> Numerous, and every Starr perhaps a World
> Of destind habitation.   VII, 617–622

The "Glassie Sea," it will be recalled, is the "Crystalline
Sphear" and "Crystalline Ocean," i.e., the sphere next above
the fixed stars. A seventeenth-century reader got the meaning
of each term from context; a twentieth-century reader finds
that context described in the scientific handbooks, where if
there was not agreement there was at least explanation.[12]

Ordinarily the encyclopedists took firmament to mean the
sphere of fixed stars. Caxton and Apian label it *coelum firma-
mentum,* and Caxton devotes a chapter to the "mevyng and
gooyng aboute of the ffyrmament and of the sterres that ben
therin" adding that the "heven that is so sterred is the firmament." Bartholomew lists seven "heavens"; and Batman's
addition to the chapter "Of the Christalline or watry heaven"
shows the variance of opinion:

> The Schoole men omit the seate of God, and in the place of it
> they put three moe, as appeareth in this resitall. The ninth
> Coelum Aqueum, or Christallinum, or Adamantium, the water-
> ish, or ycie, or harde heaven, as harde as an Adamant stone. The
> tenth Primum mobile. The eleventh Coelum Emperium, the
> burning Heaven.

La Primaudaye believed the "true firmament" to be the
sphere of fixed stars but recognized that the word could refer
to the atmosphere or interstellar space. Swan conceived of it
as a solid body stretched thin and containing the fixed stars;
but the planets had no solid orbs, and "the whole concave of
the heavens is filled with no firmer matter then soft and
penetrable air." The crystalline sphere is an early problem
in the controversy over the firmament and its function, and
discussion of it occupies a good deal of space in the encyclopedias. Bartholomew describes it as "made by the myght of
god of waters, whiche ben sette above in the firmament"; he
quotes Bede's saying "that those hevenly waters ben hanged
above the fyrmament" to temper its swiftness or to assuage
the heat that arises from its motion. La Primaudaye's discussion, like so many in *The French Academie,* glosses the whole

question as it occurs in *Paradise Lost,* including the "Trepidation talkt":

some modern Philosophers doe place betweene the firmament and the first moover a ninth sphere, which they call the Christalline heaven, for that some starres are not seene therein. And this is because that they cannot perceive, how there might be made in the eight sphere, the motion called Trepidation or tottering of the fixed stars if there were not a ninth heaven enclosed within the first moover. . . . For this eight sphere hath one daily motion from the west to the east upon the poles of the Zodiacke, which is the circle of the signes, upon which (according to Ptolemy) in each hundred yeares it runneth one degree, or else in sixty yeeres, as others hold, then hath it the foresaid motion of Trepidation. . . . But . . . many therefore reject the opinion of those which make tenne: because that nothing maketh for them but onely the motion of Trepidation.[13]

The vexing problem of what Milton and the seventeenth-century reader understood by the firmament that separates the waters above it from the waters below it actually originated in the Genesis account, labored over by theologian and scientist. It reappears in Milton's outline of creation:

> Again, God said, let ther be Firmament
> Amid the Waters, and let it divide
> The Waters from the Waters: and God made
> The Firmament, expanse of liquid, pure,
> Transparent, Elemental Air, diffus'd
> In circuit to the uttermost convex
> Of this great Round: partition firm and sure,
> The waters underneath from those above
> Dividing: for as Earth, so hee the World
> Built on circumfluous Waters calme, in wide
> Crystallin Ocean, and the loud misrule
> Of Chaos farr remov'd, least fierce extreames
> Contiguous might distemper the whole frame.
>
> VII, 261–273

This controversy is to cosmology what the dispute over reason in animals is to Renaissance natural history. Only recently

has the sense of these lines been clarified; and the disagreement among Milton's modern commentators parallels the
indecision of the encyclopedists. Here the crystalline sphere
is a liquid upon which the world floats and by which it is
buffered against Chaos. The firmament is an expanse of liquid
(yielding) elemental air, which is nonetheless a "partition
firm and sure." "Waters" is a key word over which many an.
exegete worried. Thomas Lodge, who thought the truth about
the crystalline sphere "is not yet concluded betwixt those
that have pleaded *pro & contra*," followed his author Du-
Bartas in maintaining that there are waters in it "suspended
by the same power which holdeth the whole Universe suspended, and retained only by his will." Sir Walter Ralegh
collected the problems into one section of his first chapter,
"Of the Firmament, and of the waters above the Firmament:
and whether there bee any cristalline Heaven, or any Primum
mobile." He denied the existence of these last and explained
the waters above the firmament as "cloudes and waters engendered in the uppermost Aire." Petavius, in his *History
of the World* (1659), concurs, as does William Pemble the
minister, whose *Vindiciae Gratiae* (4th ed., 1659), like his
other works, shows wide acquaintance with traditional scientific lore. So thought Thomas Vaughan in his *Brief Natural
History*, perhaps expressing himself more feelingly because
the interstellar waters had been an issue between him and
Henry More in *Man-Mouse* (1650). That redoubtable Cambridge man, Thomas Burnet, was sure in 1691 that none
"would seriously assert these Supercelestial waters" or at
least make use of them so extravagantly as to account for
the Deluge. By 1697, one "T. C." could say in his notes to
the first of *The Five Books of M. Manilius*: "The Waters
above the Firmament are exploded." Here and there a die-
hard might still find support in Comenius, *Natural Philosophie Reformed*, who clung to the idea that the waters existed not as clouds and rain but as waters. "The *waters in*

heaven are one thing," he says, "and the *waters above heaven* another"; they "are placed there for ends known to God." [14]

As the dispute broadened from biblical commentary into general scientific interest, the implications of another key word, *expansum*, proliferated. Vaughan had already indicated the importance of the word. La Primaudaye, Swan, and others explained to their readers that the difficulties arose from mistranslation of the Hebrew, and labored to save appearances. In discoursing "Of the Expansum, or stretching out of the Heavens," Swan begins with the Hebrew "*Rakiah* translated *Firmament*, [which] signifieth Expansum, or expansionem, which is a stretching out, not onely from the earth [vertically], but about the earth [horizontally]." He rejects the notion that the waters are clouds because that would put them above the stars, and clouds are limited to the middle region of air in the sublunar vault, many spheres below the fixed stars. Citing Pareus on the cloud theory, he concedes that some learned men do believe that the expansum was vertical from the sphere of the fixed stars to the earth and therefore was a kind of air. He believes in the horizontal stretching out, that under this stretched shell was "soft and penetrable air", and that above it were special waters. La Primaudaye follows the Aristotelian line that material waters would be corruptible; if they are stabilized beyond corruptibility, "hardened and converted into chrystal," then one may reasonably think of this heaven as crystalline "because the christall is made of ice, and ice of water." But he concludes upon the cloud alternative.[15]

Thus it appears that Milton selected out of a contemporary, pseudo-scientific controversy the elements he liked and yoked them together, using neither side consistently. "Crystalline ocean" and "Glassie sea" are nowhere in Milton synonymous for clouds; the liquidity of the crystalline sphere is not the liquidity of a cloud. His firmament, instead of being merely a husk or shell, as Swan called it, floating upon the circumfluous waters and containing the other spheres, is (like the firmament of the cloud theory) a vertical expanse of soft and penetrable liquid air, extending from the earth to the "uttermost convex" of the world. Certainly he used *firmament* for a single though not solid sphere, and just as certainly he used it to mean air space. In the disputed passage, it is obviously not the sphere of fixed stars but an air space; yet it supports an expanse of water upon which floats the world inside that air space. Milton is here conventional, old-fashioned, and ambiguous; but it is not necessary to defend the eclecticism. It is consistent with his practice of leaving alternatives, letting the scientific question remain unsolved. But the whole matter was such a familiar, well-worn cosmological controversy that Donne had made a joke about it, and Milton belongs in his poem to that group — Swan, DuBartas, and Comenius — who thought that if God could create waters on the earth he could surely create them above the firmament and keep them there, whether the firmament was solid, spherically perceptible, or simply thin air.[16]

This dispute does function symbolically, as an imagery of ideas, and it is one of the modes by which Milton kept *Paradise Lost* alive, as it were, on several levels. But it is a local and occasional thing. Far more pervasive is the concept of the music of the spheres, a metaphor recurring from the earliest poems. Dato praised the young poet as one "who with Astronomy to guide him hears the harmonies of the heavenly spheres"; and the whole Second Prolusion "On the Music of the Spheres" expresses Milton's preference for that which symbolized divine order to that which was scientifically verifiable. No single idea was more current than this, from Pythagoras forward, and Milton might have first met it nearly anywhere: Plato, Pliny, Martianus Capella, Isidore, Ambrose, Boethius, or Bartholomew. Casual allusions to the "nine-fold harmony" in *Nativity Ode* and "nine-enfolded Sphears" in *Arcades* culminate in the choiring of *Paradise Lost*, where angelic motion and song are united to those of the spheres, which were thought inhabited by spirits:

> That day, as other solemn dayes, they spent
> In song and dance about the sacred Hill,
> Mystical dance, which yonder starry Sphaere
> Of Planets and of fixt in all her Wheeles
> Resembles nearest, mazes intricate,
> Eccentric, intervolv'd, yet regular
> Then most, when most irregular they seem:
> And in thir motions harmonie Divine
> So smooths her charming tones, that Gods own ear
> Listens delighted.   V, 618–627

The image contains several implications central to the poem: the music is divine, mortal ears are too feeble to hear it; the music is also movement and there is an order to the sound like the ordered movement of the spheres which produce it; order is heaven's first law. Milton's universe is static only in its outlines; as many have remarked, there is movement everywhere, in the smallest detail of Paradise as in the great wheel of the universe and the inexpressive nuptial song.[17]

II. THE FIXED STARS AND THE PLANETS

Milton's early desire to comprehend "every law of the heavens and of the stars," like his exhortation not "to let the most minute little stars be hidden," reappears in the description of Mopsus in *Damon's Epitaph* as expert in the lore of the stars; in his wish to "sit and rightly spell / Of every Star that Heav'n doth shew"; and in the hundreds of references to planets, constellations, and other heavenly bodies in the major poems. [Traditional cosmology offered three classes: planets, fixed stars, and comets or meteors, and an epic laid in three worlds would invoke them all.] Most commonly used, perhaps, was the zodiac, for along it could be traced the heavenly journeys, the passage of time, and the immensity of

the universe. To speak of Phoebus speeding on through the
zodiac is conventional enough an image. Yet one finds Milton
adapting this commonplace into original tropes even in his
prose. The *Apology for Smectymnuus* equates zeal with the
sun and alludes to its chariot as "drawn with two blazing
Meteors, figur'd like beasts, but of a higher breed then any
the Zodiac yields." The metaphoric issues are more com-
plexly drawn in *Tetrachordon*:

For Nature hath her Zodiac also, keeps her annual circuit over
human beings, as truly as the Sun and Planets in the firmament;
hath her anomalies, hath her obliquities in ascensions and declinations, accesses and recesses, as blamelessly as they in heaven.
And sitting in her planetary Orb with two rains in each hand,
one strait, the other loos, tempers the cours of minds as well as
bodies to several conjunctions and oppositions, freindly or un-
freindly aspects, consenting oftest with reason, but never contrary.

The dominant metaphor here denies the ridicule Milton later
bestowed upon astronomers who build and unbuild to save
appearances. Not that Milton learned better in the interval;
he simply took what came to hand, so to speak, quarrying out
of common knowledge the kind of science that made his
points. On the other hand, he kept natural science pretty much
out of *Christian Doctrine*, even though Polanus' *Syntagma*,
probably one of his sources for the treatise, was full of it;
which is to say that he did not regard exact science as proper
or necessary to the expounding of a formal system of divinity. But he did consider it useful in controversy and essential
to his poem, an imaginative "system" of divinity.[18]

The zodiac frequently appears throughout Milton, as indeed it did in most Renaissance poets, together with other
stars and constellations hallowed by mythology. The best-
known fixed star was of course the Pole star, around which
the rest seemed to revolve. It should be noted that the "twin
poles" of *To My Father* and the "wheeling poles" of the

Vacation Exercise refer to the imaginary axle of the universe, which was thought to coincide with the Pole or North star. Hence the heroic vagueness of "from the Center [of the Universe] thrice to the utmost Pole" as an indication of the distance of Hell from Heaven; for time and space, height and breadth are lost in cosmos as in Chaos. Milton fell in with a traditional metaphor when in *Eikonoklastes* he compared Charles to an unskilful pilot misled "by any wandring Starr mistak'n for the Pole." This common knowledge had a bookish equivalent in the Milky Way as a collection of stars,

> A broad and ample rode, whose dust is Gold
> And pavement Starrs, as Starrs to thee appeer,
> Seen in the Galaxie, that Milkie Way
> Which nightly as a circling Zone thou seest
> Pouderd with Starrs.   VII, 577–581

Marjorie Nicolson once held that the conception of the Milky Way as a group of separate stars and not simply an expanse of whiteness arose after the publication of Galileo's *Sidereus Nuncius* in 1610. But the idea flourished much earlier. Bartholomew and Batman call the "mylky cercle" as Milton does, "Galaxias," and conclude: "in the place where Galaxias is sene ben many smal sterres and bright, and in those sterres shyneth that brightnes." [19]

The fixed stars and planets were the very instruments of astrological theorizing; and a survey of Milton's chief allusions to them will facilitate discussion of that fateful subject. The sun dominates his world picture as it did everyone else's, and accounts from his works and from contemporary science of its creation, maintenance, and functions are preliminary to seeing how it pervades *Paradise Lost* as a symbol. The encyclopedists usually began with the Bible; and we will do well to begin there in Milton. The sun was not created until the fourth day. Before that time

> Light
> Ethereal, first of things, quintessence pure

Sprung from the Deep, and from her Native East
To journie through the airie gloom began,
Sphear'd in a radiant Cloud, for yet the Sun
Was not; shee in a cloudie Tabernacle
Sojourn'd the while.   VII, 243–249

Patristic theory had by Milton's time pretty much accounted
for the difficulty implicit in the delayed creation of the
heavenly bodies by calling the first light "informed," though
real, and by assigning its perfection in form to the fourth day.
Not that the question was dead. Swan reflects a whole controversy in his section "The creation of the light":

And therefore that Light which at the first made his works appear, is no spirituall Light; but such and the same that now is in
the Sunne. And yet perhaps, as *Aquinas* thinketh, it was but.
. . . *An informed light, which on the fourth day had its perfect
form* . . . others think that the element of fire was moveable, by
the presence of it making day, and by its absence making night.
. . . Thirdly, if (as some have done) we should think that this
was the very light of the sunne, and then in the sunne, or in such a
cloude or subject as was the matter of the sunne, the text would
be objected against it; which affirmeth that the sunne was not
until the fourth day . . . by which it appeareth that this first
Light was made in motion, and was created in the Eastern part
of that Hemisphere in which Man was made.

Milton repeats the idea that light was in a sort of cloud when
the Creator disposed of most of the original light thus:

Transplanted from her cloudie Shrine, and plac'd
In the Suns Orb.   VII, 360–361

The history of light or of Milton's use of it would make a
book in itself. *Paradise Lost*, as Allen has said in the best discussion of this subject, is suffused with light up to the fall,
when real darkness descends on Adam. The characteristic associations of light with reason and goodness and dark with
passion and evil are so managed as to deepen the central conflict of the poem. For as in *Comus* the magician is portrayed

in images of light and dark like Thyrsis his humanly imperfect antagonist, in *Paradise Lost* Satan and God alternately embody the double metaphor. God's skirts dark with excessive bright appear, and Satan shines not less than arch-angel ruined. God dwells in light incorruptible, but the throne can darken in his anger; Satan moves through darkness visible and brings the palpable obscure with him to the world of light. His apostrophe to the sun is a climactic positing of growing darkness with a physical yet insupportable brightness. The sun is god of the new world to one whose eyes so recently had looked upon an ocean dark, wasteful, wild. The light of the universe opposes the darkness of Chaos; but Satan introduces the dark into a world where night became not uniform alternation with day but a condition of Adam's soul, dimming his eye with carnal fear so that he could neither recognize Michael nor without heavenly grace see the visions. This is one great pause in the changes rung on the three-fold imagery of essential light, material light, and the enlightening shed by Divine inspiration. The infinite variations Milton works on the materials of such imagery commit him now to the expected equation, now to an inversion in which the transferred values in a sense proclaim man's ambivalence between good and evil. We will see more of this later.[20]

In Chapter I, we observed how Milton illustrated the substance of the sun through comparison with stones and metals constantly assigned to it by the encyclopedists and others. The emphasis on brightness, light, and fire in its composition repeats La Primaudaye's ascription of those attributes to the "one selfe same substance & matter of heaven, and of all the spheres." The standard question of the sun's sustenance, glanced at in the discussion of the elementary world, forms an important part of Raphael's demonstration of the unity of matter:

> The Sun that light imparts to all receives
> From all his alimental recompence

In humid exhalations, and at Even
Sups with the Ocean.   V, 423–426

Here is a "textbook case" of Milton's method. The passage
occurs in Raphael's justification of angelic appetite; yet it
expresses also the concept of dynamic order, of a moving pattern in teleological nature; Milton alludes to it several times.
Everything fits into the scheme; the whole universe insists
upon unity in variety, interdependence of parts, and purposiveness. Adam's environment is a metaphor for his own
nature; and the final meaning of the relentless parallels between macrocosm and microcosm develops as almost infinite
affirmation of man's place in the universe. The decay of Aristotelian cosmology led to nonsupport of the notion of the
sun's sustenance. Vaughan, we have noted, will admit no
vapors above the sphere of fire, but the older opinion did.
Pliny, Adelard of Bath, Bartholomew, his reviser Batman,
Swan, and even that learned lady, the Duchess of Newcastle,
form a part of this tradition. Swan, who prefers to believe
that the sustenance derives from the waters above the firmament, dutifully reports majority opinion in *Speculum
Mundi*:

Cleanthes, who allowed the matter of the sunne to be fierie, and
that it was nourished by humours attracted from the ocean. Also
Anaximander and Diogenes, after whom Epicurus, and the Stoics
. . . . amongst others, it was *Cicero's* opinion in his second book
De natura deorum; making the sea, and waters of the earth, their
daily storehouse.

The Duchess, elaborating her conviction that long, square,
flat, and sharp atoms are the originals of everything, calls the
sunbeams chains drawing vapors for nourishment; each ray
is a conveyor "which brings down *Food* and draws *Food* back
again." [21]
    The sun as life-giver is a stock image of creativity; adapta-
tions of it range from invective in *Animadversions* to glorifi-

cation in *Paradise Lost*. Grasping prelates who unite teaching the word of God with seeking preferment engender "a baseborn issue of Divinity like that of those unperfect and putrid creatures that receive a crawling life from two most unlike procreants, the Sun and mudde." In the epic, Milton wonders not that

> Th' Arch-chimic Sun so farr from us remote
> Produces with Terrestrial Humor mixt
> Here in the dark so many precious things
> Of colour glorious and effect so rare.   III, 608–612

This is "the mounted Sun" that

> Shot down direct his fervid Raies to warme
> Earths inmost womb.   V, 301–303

Batman, repeating Bartholomew, shows how close Milton's lines are to the traditional lore. For "though the chinkes, holes, and dens of the earth, bee not lighted: yet the vèrtue of light worketh in them, as it is seene in oares of mettall, and in other things that be gendred and bred deepe within ye earth." [22]

The related question of star and planet light links the poem with the older lore in yet another direction; and as Milton treats it, this cosmological metaphor amplifies the basic hierarchical assumption. Some writers supposed the heavenly bodies derived all light from the sun; others attributed a small measure to their own nature. In the First Prolusion, Milton shares the more popular view that the sun supplies all light to the moon and other stars "for these do not possess the light which they transmit, except that which they mutually receive from him." But in *Paradise Lost*, he affirms the second attitude:

> Of Light by farr the greater part he took,
> Transplanted from her cloudie Shrine, and plac'd
> In the Suns Orb, made porous to receive
> And drink the liquid Light, firm to retaine

Her gather'd beams, great Palace now of Light.
Hither as to thir Fountain other Starrs
Repairing, in thir gold'n Urns draw Light,
And hence the Morning Planet guilds her horns;
By tincture or reflection they augment
Thir small peculiar, though from human sight
So farr remote, with diminution seen.   VII, 359–369

La Primaudaye, using "fountain" like Milton, points to the metaphorical directly, instead of obliquely:

Moreover as this visible sunne is a fountain of light, which is never exhausted nor yet diminisheth in communicating himselfe with all creatures, but is perpetuall, so is it of God, concerning whom it is written, that he hath garnished the excellent works of his wisedom.

De Proprietatibus Rerum repeated the truism that "sterres and the mone receive lyght of the son as a glasse set byfore a candel receiveth lyght of a candel"; *Speculum Mundi*, in a section on this very problem, offered both opinions:

And as touching the brightnesse of the sterres, the sunne may well be called *Oculus mundi, The eye of the world.* For he is indeed the chief fountain from whence the whole world receiveth lustre. . . . From whence some Philosophers and Astronomers have been of opinion that the fixed starres shine not but with borrowed light from the sunne. . . . But according to the minds of the best Authours, and nearest equipage to truth, the starres are called lights, as well as the sunne and moone. . . . For if they had not their proper and peculiar light (being so farre distant from inferiour bodies) it is thought they could not alter them in such sort as they sometimes do.

The verbal parallels here, like "fountain" and "peculiar" exemplify the diffusion of cosmological terminology. The opposed views of prolusion and poem represent not necessarily a change of attitude but, despite the years between them, a possible preservation of alternatives, like those multiplied in the epic. We are not expected to make a choice between these alternatives, nor to accept them as impartial rendering of both sides. Most probably we are to perceive in them the constant metaphor of ambiguity, the play of alternates that in more complex construction becomes an end in itself — the reflection of man's dual nature, the pull of extremes, the conflict of reason and passion, body and spirit, Adam and Eve, Satan and mankind. Before proceeding to the two most striking of these options concerned with the sun, one may observe how the phenomenon of eclipse enlarges the characterization of Satan into the structure of ideas informing the whole of *Paradise Lost*.[23]

In *Eikonoklastes* Milton picks up Charles I's image of doom for his opponents and for England:

He bodes much horror and bad influence after his ecclips. He speaks his wishes: But they who by weighing prudently things past, foresees things to come, the best Divination, may hope rather all good success and happiness by removing that darkness which the mistie cloud of this prerogative made between us and a peaceful Reformation, which is our true Sunlight, and not he, though he would be taken for our sun itself.

This equation is pretty much the mode of metaphor in the prose, although we will see later, in such a piece as *Doctrine of Divorce*, how the levels multiply beyond simple comparisons into a structure of their own. The eclipse in *Lycidas* is comparably conventional. Elizabethan scientific and religious literature abounds in discussion of the evil that attends eclipses, among which Howard's *Defensative against the Poyson of supposed Prophecies* is a notable demurrer. Milton drew on the superstition for the dramatic picture of Satan towering above his fellows:

As when the Sun new ris'n
Looks through the Horizontal misty Air
Shorn of his Beams, or from behind the Moon
In dim Eclips disastrous twilight sheds
On half the Nations, and with fear of change
Perplexes Monarchs. Darkn'd so, yet shon
Above them all th' Arch Angel.   I, 594–600

Where in *Eikonoklastes* Milton followed the usual symbolism of light and dark, and chose the light of truth over the King, here he links Satan with the greatest single natural symbol of truth, which occupied in the hierarchy of planets the position corresponding to that of the lion, the eagle, and God himself. Natural light, as we have seen, was the visible symbol of both essential light, coeternal with God, and inner light, God-given understanding or perception. Here Satan's progressive deterioration from his original lustre, his retention of some of his pristine appearance, his superiority to the other demons, and his ominous import for mankind are all involved in the simile. The enforced association with Deity, like the parallel between the infernal trinity (Satan, Sin, and Death) and the Holy Trinity, creates an undertone of apparent comparison which in reality strengthens the contrast. The honorific implications of sun-like majesty do not survive the fact of Satan's evil; but they last long enough to indicate its complex nature. The potent word "dark'n'd" epitomizes image and idea. Satan, like the sun, is new risen, from the burning lake into the career of evil. For a moment the qualities which made him great in heaven obscure his evil, an evil communicated by the very association with the eclipse, presage of disaster. His double identity suddenly emerges; he is the early sun, about to "scatter the mists," as Milton says elsewhere, and the ominous sun in eclipse, a thing of good made evil. The perversion of creative force, in many ways a major theme of the poem, balances between the two.[24]

References to the sun are frequent in the prose as well as in the brilliantly lighted epic. In *Doctrine of Divorce*, the simile "Truth is as impossible to be soil'd by any outward touch, as the Sun beam" repeats an idea like Bartholomew's "thoughe it passe by vylenes and fylthe, it is not defoylled." In *Paradise Lost* Adam speculates on fire-making by the sun's "gather'd beams reflected"; and, as we have seen, Milton marks time in a system of perfect prelapsarian spheres with the conical shadow of night. It is not surprising then to find him extending the effects of the fall into dislocation of the sun's axis, another of the great alternatives, like Raphael's cosmological monologue. The direct incidence of the sun in Book V contrasts with the options given in Book X to account for seasonal change, for an immediate cosmic effect of original sin was that the sun would now so move and shine as to affect earth with extremity of heat and cold. At Creation, the sun's rays were direct because the poles of earth and sun coincided. Now

> Some say he bid his Angels turne ascanse
> The Poles of Earth twice ten degrees and more
> From the Suns Axle; they with labor push'd
> Oblique the Centric Globe: Som say the Sun
> Was bid turn Reines from th' Equinoctial Rode
> Like distant breadth to *Taurus* with the Seav'n
> *Atlantick* Sisters and the *Spartan* Twins
> Up to the *Tropic* Crab; thence down amaine
> By *Leo* and the *Virgin* and the *Scales*,
> As deep as *Capricorne*, to bring in change
> Of Seasons to each Clime.   668–678

Before the fall, the path of the sun was presumably on a plane perpendicular to the axis of the earth; hence the road was equinoctial, for in its diurnal progress the sun was at all times equidistant and at equal angles from earth. The equator of the earth extended as a plane would produce the ecliptic. Upon the fall, however, the plane of the ecliptic was put at an angle to the plane of the earth's equator, a dislocation accomplished by turning "ascanse" the axle of the earth from the sun's axle, or by shifting the center of the sun's orbit so that the ecliptic would slide forward on the globe until, instead of coinciding with the extended plane of the equator, one arc of the ecliptic would touch the Tropic of Cancer and its opposite arc that of Capricorn. Once more Milton declines to choose and even points up the insignificance of decision by the parallel of the indefinite "some say." This is not

evasion but focus; Adam's sin had spread its effects into the
cosmos, and the fact, not the mechanics, of dislocation was
important. This is the real origin of the decay of nature so
confidently denied in the Latin poem and so clearly attractive
to Milton later. Yet how admirably the style manages cosmic
effects. The first result was earth's wound; the next man's
passion; then into the cosmos for the stupendous distortion
(it was labor even for angels); and last back to earth and
within Adam, now like Satan "inly racked." These tremendous arcs bind the universe and the poem together and contribute to the sense of visual image and cosmic rhythm.[25]

Next in interest in the Miltonic world is the moon, about
which a good deal more appears than the conventional mythology dutifully thrust into the Latin poems. "The triform
goddess," "Endymion's goddess," and "the Delian goddess"
show chiefly that Milton had read his Ovid and was minded
to use him. The prose and especially the major poems reveal
that Milton was familiar with theories of the moon's luminos-
ity, its sustenance, its spots, and its influence over nature. As
early as the First Prolusion, for example, he was tinkering
with ideas of the origin of its light; and in the Seventh he
describes the will, illuminated by the intellect, as "otherwise blind and dark, that like the moon shines with another's
light." Later he has Raphael suggest to Adam that perhaps
other suns with their attendant moons were even then "communicating Male and Female Light," though in the account
of creation he had said:

> less bright the Moon,
> But opposite in leveld West was set
> His mirror, with full face borrowing her Light
> From him   VII, 375–378

A little about the moon's light has been mentioned earlier
in the discussion of the light of the sun; it is interesting to
note that the debate recurs in popular science even as in Mil-

ton. Bartholomew, in the chapter on the moon in *De Proprietatibus Rerum*, agrees, so to speak, with the Milton of the prolusions: the moon "hath no light of her selfe, but borroweth and taketh of the plente of the sonne." So Caxton in *Mirrour of the World*; the "clernes & lyght" which the moon renders "she taketh alway of the sonne"; like nearly everyone, he compares the moon to a polished mirror. In *The French Academie* La Primaudaye is equally positive: "alwaies, except when she is eclipsed, she receiveth light from the sun into one halfe of her globe." Swan demurs, but sets out both views in *Speculum Mundi*, following Goclenius in asserting a double light of the moon, proper and strange. "The Proper is that which is Homogeneall to it self [Milton's "small peculiar"] . . . a light begotten together with the moon, and essential to it, although it be but weak." The other is that "which it borroweth from the sunne." [26]

Milton's recognition of the seventeenth-century controversy over a world in the moon develops in several ways, especially through the related ideas of the moon's nourishment and its spots. Raphael tells Adam the moon sustained itself like other heavenly bodies from the elements:

> Earth and Sea feed Air, the Air those Fires
> Ethereal, and as lowest first the Moon.
> Whence in her visage round those spots, unpurg'd
> Vapours not yet into her substance turnd.
>
> V, 417–420

An earlier passage in the same book had offered a different possibility in Galileo's observing "Imagind Lands and Regions in the Moon"; but the qualification is clear, the lands are not real any more than in the still earlier reference to the Tuscan artist who views the moon through his optic glass "to descry new lands, / Rivers, or mountains, in her spotty globe." The locution "views . . . to descry" implies purpose, not accomplishment. In Book VIII both options occur when Raphael says

> if Land be there,
> Feilds and Inhabitants: Her spots thou seest
> As Clouds, and Clouds may rain, and Rain produce
> Fruits in her soft'nd Soile, for some to eate
> Allotted there.   144–148

Certainly Milton was interested in telescopes and in the more dramatic speculations of the new astronomy, but it is a mistake to suppose the glazed optic tube entirely responsible for his curiosity. The moon's cavities and depressions were always part of the encyclopedic tradition. Alexander Neckam viewed their shadowy outlines with unaided eyes and concluded in *De Naturis Rerum* that they were irregularities and blemishes in the moon's surface. Caxton, who had compared the moon to a mirror conventionally enough, reported the opinion that the spots were the earth "that appereth within" and added a possibility, strangely omitted by Milton:

Other thinke otherwyse and saye that it happed and byfelle whan Adam was deceyved by thapple that he ete, which greved alle humayne lignage, and that thenne the mone was empesshed and his clerenesse lassed and mynuysshid.

Swan too compared the moon to a mirror, and likens the spots to scratches or unsilvered places. Milton's mirror figure owes something to this tradition, though he did not offer that explanation; and his references to moonspots relate him further to medieval and Renaissance moon-lore as available in the compendia.[27]

To conclude upon the moon's offices and functions, one may observe its eclipse and its influence on nature. The "labouring moon" of the fourth Italian poem shows up again in an epic simile:

> Nor uglier follow the Night-Hag, when call'd
> In secret, riding through the Air she comes
> Lur'd with the smell of infant blood, to dance
> With *Lapland* Witches, while the labouring Moon
> Eclipses at thir charms.   II, 662–666

The encyclopedists limited themselves pretty much to explaining eclipses by natural means; but demonologists and writers on witchcraft considered Satanic intervention long and heavily, from medieval times forward. Milton states the power of witches here as if it were fact, despite the "exiling of Satan," as Kocher calls it, by emergent Renaissance rationalism. Institor and Sprenger, *Malleus Maleficarum* (1487), held that witches could raise storms and tempests but not govern the stars. Guazzo, *Compendium Maleficarum* (1608), believed they could produce these and darkness too. Scot, *Discoverie of Witchcraft* (1584), denied any influence at all over the heavens. Yet Jonston's *An History of the Wonderful Things of Nature* (1657), shows the encyclopedic cultural lag in faithfully reporting that the ancients thought the moon might "be drawn from Heaven by Charms, and being thrust down, she might be compelled." Whether this passage or the tempest raised by Satan in *Paradise Regained* puts Milton himself outside the main direction of contemporary thought as to Satan's powers, both tend to affirm his unflagging iteration of physical and moral disorder. Witches are the spiritual offspring of Satan, even as the hellhounds to which they are compared for ugliness; the complex of evil and the impression of horror ("smell of infant blood") amplify beneath the lines.[28]

Consideration of the moon's gravitational pull and its influence over nature leads to the final cosmological question in this chapter, the movements of the other planets and the elements of astrology in Milton. In the second Hobson poem he puns on the power of the moon over tides, with the carrier's fate "Linkt to the mutual flowing of the Seas"; and in *Comus* the waters with all their finny drove "Now to the Moon in wavering Morrice move." Despite the efforts of advanced scientists in the generation before Milton to cast out belief in lunar influence upon man's health, enough of a relation survived for Milton to speak of moon-blasting and moon-struck madness as facts and for Jonston in his *History of the Wonderful Things of Nature* to assert: "If you would run over all the field of Nature, Plants, Animals and mens bodyes are subject to the Moons Government."

Something of this is suggested in the *Paradise Lost* passages on the creation of the stars and their functions. In the first of these, the Creator called for lights

> High in th' expanse of Heaven to divide
> The Day from Night; and let them be for Signes,
> For Seasons, and for Days, and circling Years,
> And let them be for Lights as I ordaine
> Thir Office in the Firmament of Heav'n
> To give Light on the Earth; and it was so.
> And God . . . made the Starrs
> And set them in the Firmament of Heav'n
> To illuminate the Earth, and rule the Day
> In thir vicissitude, and rule the Night,
> And Light from Darkness to divide.   VII, 340–352

The stars' triple function, then, is to illuminate the earth, be time-signs, and separate day and night. Two of these duties occur in Adam's answer to Eve's query, an inquiry he was later to pursue with Raphael. He tells her

> Those have thir course to finish, round the Earth,
> By morrow Eevning, and from Land to Land
> In order, though to Nations yet unborn,
> Ministring light prepar'd, they set and rise;
> Least total darkness should by Night regaine
> Her old possession, and extinguish life
> In Nature and all things, which these soft fires
> Not only enlighten, but with kindly heate
> Of various influence foment and warme,
> Temper or nourish, or in part shed down
> Thir stellar vertue on all kinds that grow
> On Earth, made hereby apter to receive
> Perfection from the Suns more potent Ray.
>   IV, 661–673

The *De Proprietatibus Rerum* passage apropos here must be

given in full because the verbal parallels indicate how thoroughly the language of the encyclopedias had permeated poetic vocabulary. Stars, says Bartholomew, are

berers of lyghte: for that they ben bryghte bodyes and yeve to man and beastes by nyghte, whan it is derke, the comforte of lyght, and ornate and lyght the overparty of this world, and as ferforth as they may, they ben in stede of the sonne, of whome they receyve lyght, and by contynualle sendynge oute of beames, they clense and pourge thayre: by vertue of theym, corruption of pestilence is take away from the nether worlde. Also by vertue of sterres, elementes, that ben contrary eche to other, ben concyled and acorded, and beshyned with everlastying shynyng of sterres. By heate of them all thynges ben norysshed and saved . . . In myght and werkynge the sterres ben moste vertuous amonge bodyes. For the sterres gendre, and chaunge, and save the nether thynges.

Caxton stresses similar points in his claim that "the hevenes and the sterres ben the very instruments of nature to the world, by whiche she werkethe alle, as God wille." The tempering of the sun's rays and of the earth to receive them appears from Caxton's statement that although the sun is more powerful than the other stars yet "somtyme they restrayne his heetes and after they enlarge them, after that they be fer or nygh, as he otherwhile hath nede." [29]

Milton's condemnation of astronomers who attempt to chart the orbits of the planets and speculate beyond due limits is a *locus criticus* in his presumed anti-intellectualism, like Christ's supposed rejection of classical culture in *Paradise Regained*. It is anticipated in the encyclopedias, notably by David Person's characteristic praise, in *Varieties*, for the research and discovery of Nature's secrets "in those things which are obvious to our outward senses, leaving those contemplative mysteries afore spoken of, to the omniscious Author of them"; with the warning that when man has "dived into the depths of the secrets of the heavenly bodies and their changes, then the Creator, to check (as it were) their curiositie and presumption, altereth that orderly course that they presumed to have gathered thereby." Raphael tells Adam that the heavens are "as the Book of God" wherein to read his wondrous works, but that whether Heaven move or earth imports not:

> the rest
> From Man or Angel the great Architect
> Did wisely to conceal, and not divulge
> His secrets to be scann'd by them who ought
> Rather admire; or if they list to try
> Conjecture, he his Fabric of the Heav'ns
> Hath left to thir disputes, perhaps to move
> His laughter at thir quaint Opinions wide
> Hereafter, when they come to model Heav'n
> And calculate the Starrs, how they will weild
> The mightie frame, how build, unbuild, contrive
> To save appeerances, how gird the Sphear
> With Centric and Eccentric scribl'd o're,
> Cycle and Epicycle, Orb in Orb.   VIII, 71–84

This contradicts the enthusiasm of the Prolusions, to be sure, but to call it anti-intellectualism is hasty. In *Doctrine of Divorce*, *Eikonoklastes*, and *First Defence*, Milton dealt with the astronomers sympathetically, accepting their honest effort to reconcile theory and experience. He rebuked exegetes who offered "too foule *Hypotheses* to save the *Phaenomenon* of our Saviours answer to the Pharises" and hoped to "perfect such *Prutenick* tables as shall mend the *Astronomy* of our wide expositors." He reproved Salmasius for attacking "astronomers and physicians who should be trusted to their own faculties." The metaphors are more involved in *Eikonoklastes*, where in picking at Charles's words, he condoned the irregular motions of the heavens and by implication the effort to chart them:

He saith of his surprisal that it was a *motion eccentric and irregular*. What then? his own allusion, from the Celestial bodies, puts us in minde, that irregular motions may be necessary on earth sometimes as well as constantly in Heav'n. . . . Great Worthies heertofore by disobeying Law, ofttimes have sav'd the Commonwealth: and the Law afterward by firme Decree hath approv'd that planetary motion, that unblamable exorbitancy in them.[30]

In *Paradise Lost*, Milton certainly girded the sphere with most of the commonly accepted circles: the ecliptic, the equinoctial, the colure; not "to save appearances" but to keep plausible a story born in paradox and occurring in a prelapsarian cosmos. The accumulation of such images and allusions promotes the sense of breadth and depth and motion, all primary characteristics of the poem. They balance the tightness of the cosmos, the security of a world shut off from Chaos. The frame of Milton's universe is never rigid; there is too much motion in it for that. Only the earth is a still center, and it only until Eve's sin.

In such a purposive universe, where the human drama is repeated, anticipated, and underscored by the stage on which it unfolds, astrology is inevitable. The true answer to the question "Did Milton believe in astrology?" rests here, that in *Paradise Lost* the commitment to a teleological universe was a commitment to astral influence. Not the vulgar casting of horoscopes — though careful records in the Milton family Bible and survival of his own horoscope might imply belief — but rather, the kind of astrology in which the stars and planets are instruments in the Divine plan, in which they influence but do not compel. Like many another Renaissance man, Milton found no incompatibility between this kind of astrology and free will with its attendant moral responsibility. His early writings show at least a literary acceptance, and this in truth is all we need to know. "The star of Saturn has often been baleful to shepherds," he warns in *Damon's Epitaph*; in *Elegy V*, "the sailor propitiates his stars by night"; in *Arcades*, "the cross dire-looking planet smites." But not all planetary force is hostile. In *To Manso*, "kindly Jupiter

and Phoebus and the graudson of Atlas shed a gentle light
upon you at your birth"; and the stars in *Nativity Ode* are
"bending one way their pretious influence." [31]

The prose also manifests considerable acquaintance with
the jargon of almanacs, prognostications, and horoscopes. It
is usually satirical in purpose. In *Reason of Church Government* the metaphor is dignified: "a Lordly ascendant in the
horoscope of the church, from Primate to Patriarch, and so to
Pope." In *Animadversions* it is common:

Remonst. As if Arguments were Almanacks.
Answ. You will find some such as will prognosticate your date,
    and tell you that, after your long *Summer Solstice,* the *Æquator*
    calls for you, to reduce you to the ancient, and equall house of
    Libra.
Remonst. Truely, brethern, you have not well taken the height
    of the *Pole.*
Answ. No marvell, there be many more that doe not take well
    the height of your pole; but will take better the declination of
    your altitude.

In *Apology for Smectymnuus* Milton ridicules as "our Chal-
dean" one who had imputed fortune-hunting to him, who
"will needs erect figures, and tell fortunes"; he will learn
from Milton "how his Astrology is wide all the houses of
heav'n in spelling marriages." Tenor and vehicle tend to
become absorbed in satiric discourse, and some of the contempt rubs off on the subject. Prophetically, Milton says
here that he "would choose a virgin of mean fortunes,
honestly bred, before the wealthiest widow." Ironically, after
he had got her, he wrote feelingly of the possible influence
of the stars on incompatibility, declining to appear so much
a philosopher as to conjecture whether "each one's allotted
genius or proper star, or whether the supernal influence of
schemes and angular aspects, or this elemental *crasis* here
below" is responsible. Finally, his comparison of human
nature to the sun and planets in *Tetrachordon* seems to take

seriously the anomalies, obliquities, ascensions, and declinations which temper "the course of minds as well as bodies to several conjunctions and oppositions, friendly or unfriendly aspects, consenting oftest with reason but never contrary." [32] *Paradise Lost* abounds in astrological lore. The most forceful example of its integration into the world view of the poem is the passage relating cosmic effects of the fall, where both the meteorological and the judicial are accounted for:

> To the blanc Moone
> Her office they prescrib'd, to th' other five
> Thir planetarie motions and aspects
> In *Sextile, Square,* and *Trine,* and *Opposite,*
> Of noxious efficacie, and when to joyne
> In Synod unbenigne, and taught the fixt
> Thir influence malignant when to showre,
> Which of them rising with the Sun, or falling,
> Should prove tempestuous.   X, 656–664

Dozens of other passages employ astrological imagery, in which Milton's belief as a poet or his poem's belief is inescapable. The fight in Heaven is a good example:

> two broad Suns thir Shields
> Blaz'd opposite, while expectation stood
> In horror; from each hand with speed retir'd
> Where erst was thickest fight, th' Angelic throng,
> And left large field, unsafe within the wind
> Of such commotion, such as to set forth
> Great things by small, If Natures concord broke,
> Among the Constellations warr were sprung,
> Two Planets rushing from aspect maligne
> Of fiercest opposition in mid Skie,
> Should combat, and thir jarring Sphears confound.
> VI, 305–315

Adam discoursing of love to Raphael is sure all Heaven and "happie Constellations on that houre / Shed thir selectest influence." It is part of Satan's anguished realization of God for him to say that the earth, central in the cosmos as God in

Heaven is central, receives "all the precious beams / Of sacred influence." Mainly it is a matter of degree to move from this meteorological astrology, necessary in an ordered universe, to the kind Adam extols, and to the kind forming the first quotation. In *Paradise Regained*, Satan is the complete judicial astrologer, with the ironical addition of ignorance:

> if I read aught in Heaven,
> Or Heav'n write aught of Fate, by what the Stars
> Voluminous, or single characters,
> In thir conjunction met, give me to spell,
> Sorrows, and labours, opposition, hate,
> Attends thee, scorns, reproaches, injuries,
> Violence and stripes, and lastly cruel death.
> A kingdom they portent thee, but what Kingdom,
> Real or Allegoric I discern not,
> Nor when, eternal sure, as without end,
> Without beginning: for no date prefixt
> Directs me in the Starry Rubric set.   IV, 382–393

The encyclopedias and popular handbooks of science hold forth extensively on astrology. Few subjects were so widely debated in sixteenth- and seventeenth-century England, and few books attained the popularity of *The Kalender of Shepherdes*. Every year saw publication of almanacs and prognostications by the dozen. For what appears in his works, Milton needed no sources; astrology was in the air. But the fact that his astrological allusions can be explained from popular science shows both the cultural lag and the general availability of much of his material. Even such a trifle as Saturn's malignance assumes interest when we find *The Kalender of Shepherdes* dolefully listing the evils that beset a child born under Saturn and *The French Academie* singling it out as a point of attack on absolute judicial astrology in the chapter "Of the Planet Saturn, and how it is not evill, nor any other starre." The "houses of heav'n" in *Apology for Smectymnuus*, another astrological commonplace, may be understood as readily from *De Proprietatibus Rerum* as from any textbook; they are a constant upon which the movements of zodiac and planets are traced, a chart of the heavens, as it were, composed of twelve thirty-degree segments. From Bartholomew one gleans the fact that the sun rising in the sign Aries exerts its greatest power; and this was its situation when Satan in the likeness of a comet-angel was returning triumphant to Hell, steering his way between the Centaur and the Scorpion. A single page of *De Proprietatibus Rerum* or *Batman uppon Bartholome* explains "sextile," "trine," "opposite," and the other terms in the passage from Book X. Even the quarrel over the whole subject finds place in *Speculum Mundi* as well as in *The French Academie*. Both conclude upon the kind of influence acceptable to a believer in free will: La Primaudaye cautiously concedes that the heavenly bodies work in man "not in constraining, but disposing"; Swan admits only "an inclination; for there can be no compulsion where the cause is so remote." [33]

Historians of culture have so often recounted the Renaissance conflict over judicial astrology, and so frequently written it off, that its survival in Milton's later work may seem unusual, even incompatible with the idea of free will. But as Allen and others have pointed out, extraordinary shadings of belief and attitude were common. Whatever Milton's private opinion may have been, he saw in astrology the perfectly logical corollary to the order and symmetry of the world made by God for man. On this note we may review the implications of the world-picture of his works, especially *Paradise Lost*, for it is only there that enough facts are given. In the cosmos of most of the other poems and the prose, the allusions form a kind of metonomy: the eclipse in *Lycidas* must be referred to something external, to an assumed cosmos for which the eclipse is a representative part. The schoolboy learning in the Prolusions and Latin poems gives way to the unbelievably integrated cosmos of the epic. Where decay and corruption operate in the universe after the fall, all is order and direction in the prelapsarian universe, for it is the immediate personal manifestation of God. Raphael suggests other worlds and Adam may believe in them if he likes, but the world of this poem is the center of God's interest, and everything in it tends toward Him. As Milton translated the perfect cosmos through postlapsarian language, he perceived the thousands of interrelations, comparisons, identities, of which the microcosm-macrocosm equation was only one. Within the world are the symbols for everything; the extension of meaning capitalizes no less upon the sun's representation of God as brightest in the universe than upon its suggestion of Satan when in eclipse. The sun creates within the womb of earth, and so is godlike; but Satan creates too: Pandemonium, Sin and Death, the Hell-hounds. God with his golden compasses is the author and architect of the world; but Sin calls Satan author and architect, as indeed he is, of the causeway from Hell to that world. Nowhere is the contrast between his negative creativity and God's positive so sharply set as in Satan's apostrophe to the sun, which reminds him of God, of his own former brightness, and of the kind of creation he is engaged upon. Light, the essence of God himself, is a disappearing property of Satan; but it is there. The cosmological symbols work three ways: for God and the good, for Satan and the fallen angels; and for the contrast between good and evil. The harmony of this universe asserts Satan as it asserts God; and Satan depends upon a stable order to introduce disorder. The scale of being is not a ladder but an endless moving chain in which those things instinct with life tend ever upward. The dance of life, proclaimed everywhere in the poem, excites the stars themselves.[34]

It is not strange then that Milton cast his story into this cosmos, not merely because it had been hallowed by centuries of poets nor because he believed in it, but because its multiple correspondences had been absorbed into a teleological world-view. Only an earth-centered world provided ready-made the thousand concretions to illustrate the central significance of man. In the world at its birth, the circle had not yet been broken; and however dislocated Milton himself may have believed it in his time, the geocentric universe was one massive metaphor for its Maker and his ways to the first man. But Milton never forgot that it was a metaphor, though earth might be more like Heaven than was thought. Hence his discovery that he could use the metaphor many ways in posing alternatives and options that reflected the ambiguity and ambivalence of good and evil as they exist in the world. He never lost sight of man's immediate moral responsibility and his duty to his Creator as the prime wisdom. The dark splendor of Satan, the serene light of God, the freedom to stand or fall are all implicit in this cosmos. The materials he worked in were old-fashioned, like much found in the encyclopedias; yet they were expressive. The new cosmology had not yet built its myth nor its symbols nor even its language. The poem is, in Douglas Bush's words, the last great presentation of the traditional concept of a single divine and natural order. Aquinas, Augustine, and Albertus Magnus had done their work too well for Milton to use anything else. Theirs was the Christian world-view. For Milton this was the true harmony of the spheres.[35]

CHAPTER III

This Vast Sublunar Vault

IN TRADITIONAL COSMOLOGY everything above the moon is predictable, unchangeable, incorruptible. But within the tremendous frame sketched in the preceding chapter exists another universe, contained by the spheres of fire, air, water, earth, alive with comets, hail, wind, rain, snow, lightning, and earthquake. It is to this postlapsarian sublunar vault, this "elementary world," that all of Milton's meteorological imagery refers, whatever Raphael's alternatives and wherever occasion arises, before or after the fall, though the change from an undisturbed atmosphere is sharply marked in the narrative itself. By Milton's time many astronomers and some poets had become skeptical about such matters as sublunar origin of comets and the sphere of fire. The encyclopedic writers generally had not, and Milton's prose and later poems rely upon assumptions in science parallel to theirs and already seen in the ambitious programs of the Prolusions and the Vacation Exercise poem. What is more, Milton integrates those assumptions with the major impulses of his epic narrative, creating from the comet alone a paradoxical metaphor to support and extend the paradox of the fortunate fall. The present chapter offers a composite of this inner universe from Milton and popular science and some demonstration of its function in the structure and texture of his poetry. As the passages from poet and encyclopedists accumulate, it will be seen how he and they speak a common language inherited from classical and medieval culture.[1]

The region of fire, "next under the moon," had only logical existence in the old cosmology; when the new philosophy called all in doubt, as Donne says, it was one of the first features to go. Yet the element of fire was not put out for Caxton, William Cuningham in his *Cosmographical Glasse* (1559), Person, Swan, or Milton. The young poet had urged his academic audience to fly up into the skies, to study clouds, snow, and rain, to "peer into the caskets of the hail and to survey the arsenals of the thunderbolts"; a little later he had acclaimed the opportunities for learning "all the motions and shiftings of the air," thunder and comets, snow and hail and dew, changing winds, "all the vapors and gases which the earth and sea belch forth." In the vacation poem, he mentioned "mistie Regions of wide Air" and "hills of Snow and lofts of piled Thunder" and the "Spherse of watchful fire" — watchful in protecting the supralunar vault from contamination by a "corruptible," an exhalation drawn or driven upward. Comets, for example, were thought to be earthy exhalations risen to the upper region of air and then ignited by proximity to the element of fire. Nearly everything that happened in the sublunar vault was portentous, even sometimes the rainbow, sign of God's convenant. The term exhalation itself conveyed a sense of potential evil, for it could turn into meteor, comet, or lightning. Satan's high capitol, built like a temple, rose with the sound of dulcet symphonies; but Milton's double irony is evident in the phrase "like an Exhalation," which carries the ominous meaning for man as well as the sense of the easy construction of this evil edifice. Now Milton speaks of "ambient Aire wide interfus'd" as "imbracing round this florid Earth" like an envelope. Though most of his allusions are to the "middle empire" of the "Airy region," he knew something of the properties of the upper region, and understood what was thought to occur in the lower. The three layers of atmosphere were of course well known to meteorologists and encyclopedists. *Speculum Mundi* defines the upper region as hot and dry because of its contiguity with the region of fire. *Mirrour of the World* describes such a region above the air; *Varieties* casts some doubt, especially in Volateran and Cardan, on the existence of this region, but seems to favor it. Cuningham's *Cosmographical Glasse* is typical in assessing the middle region as cold because the upper protects it from the region of fire and the lower blankets it from the beams of the sun, which rebound from earth and warm the lower region itself. Above these three and the element of fire was the "pure marble Air" of the "worlds first Region" into which Satan projects himself. It was not for human beings to breathe — *Mirrour of the World* shows it in chart and text as a place where nothing mortal may survive. Hence Milton's remarks on the "tempring" necessary for him to have "drawn Empyreal Aire." [2]

But in the upper layer of the sublunar vault are "generated Comets or Blazing Starres, and such like fiery Meteors of divers sorts," says Swan. Caxton's chapter "Of the fyre and of the sterres that seme to falle" anticipates in "sparkles of fyre" Milton's *Comus* simile "Swift as the Sparkle of a glancing Star" or the autumnal star of *Paradise Regained,* an inescapable simile for Satan. The image "dropt from the Zenith like a falling Star" suddenly and effectively concludes one of the most remarkable passages in *Paradise Lost,* the expulsion of Mulciber. And the comparison of Uriel to an autumnal meteor illustrates both a common belief and Milton's subtle interplay of symbolic values. Uriel came to Gabriel

> swift as a shooting Starr
> In *Autumn* thwarts the night, when vapors fir'd
> Impress the Air, and shews the Mariner
> From what point of his Compass to beware
> Impetuous winds.   IV, 556–560

"Vapors fir'd" and "Impress the Air" were cosmological clichés from the time of *De Proprietatibus Rerum*; and the meteorology here originated even before the time of Seneca, whose *Natural Questions* (1620) Lodge translated to say: "The Mariners thinke it to bee a signe of a tempest, when as many Stars shoot." *Speculum Mundi* recounts "Stellae cadentes, Shooting or Falling starres" as caused by an exhalation from the earth not thoroughly compacted, nor so apt to ascend; as it hovers aloft, by an "Antiperistasis, or repulsion by the contrary to it on every part" it ignites and slides away. Scipio DuPlesis, *The Resolver: or Curiosities of Nature*, answers the query, why "falling starres . . . are a certain index, or signe of great windes comming," by saying that such fires as resemble stars in falling are thrust downward by the "winde which beginnes sooner to blow aloft then below." No one in Milton's generation could fail to know this superstition; nor would he find anything strange in the comparison to Uriel, for that angel is here a sign of tempest between Gabriel and Satan and an omen of disaster for the latter as well as for Adam and Eve. In the

Various fires, from Gregory Reisch, Margarita Philosophica *(Strassburg, 1508, 3rd ed.).*

same relation are the two blazing meteors mentioned in *Apology for Smectymnuus* and the figure for Satan's imperial ensign, which "Shon like a Meteor streaming to the Wind";

here are not merely brightness and movement, but a prolepsis of disaster.[3]

The great book of the Renaissance on meteors was of course William Fulke's, seldom called by even this much of its title, *A Most Pleasant Prospect into the Garden of naturall Contemplation, to behold the natural causes of all kinds of Meteors* (1563, 1602). Swan drew copiously upon Fulke's collections; and nearly everyone followed his acceptance of the distinction between "vapor," which was drawn from or consisted chiefly of water and reached only middle air, and "exhalation," drawn from earth and attaining the upper layer. Modern use has narrowed the meaning of the word "meteor"; at this time, as *The French Academie* carefully indicates, it was applied to anything engendered in the air. In his five books, Fulke includes thunder, lightning, earthquakes, rain, hail, dew, clouds, springs, and stones, metals, and earths. *Speculum Mundi* lists thirteen kinds of meteors generated in the upper and middle regions of air alone. One of these is the comet, long a cosmological stereotype devotedly considered by astronomers, encyclopedists, poets, and preachers. Milton's allusions are traditional enough, but the use to which he puts symbolic associations of the comet with evil and disaster in the conclusion of *Paradise Lost* is remarkable. One may first notice a comparison in *Of Reformation*:

Let the Astrologer be dismay'd at the portentous blaze of comets, and impressions in the aire as foretelling troubles and changes in states: I shall beleeve there cannot be a more ill-boding signe to a Nation (*God* turn the omen from us) then when the Inhabitants to avoid insufferable grievances at home, are inforc'd by heaps to forsake their native Country.

This sentence nicely exemplifies the qualification that the encyclopedias introduce into source study. Gilbert has suggested that Galileo may have supplied "impressions in the aire" as well as the "Aereal vapours" like which things transitory and vain rose to the Limbo of Vanities. Whiting has claimed that the allusion is due "not to Galileo but to a paragraph in *The Third Speech of Lord Digby.*" The terms are certainly in Galileo, and no less certainly in Digby's speech, unquestionably Milton's starting point. But for these terms Milton needed no source at all; they were as common to his age as Oedipus complex and nuclear fission are to ours. Witness the title of Book XI of *De Proprietatibus Rerum*: "De Aere et eius Impressionibus." [4]

The famous "error" in locating the constellation Ophiucus in the north occurs in the equally renowned comet simile as Satan parleys with Sin and Death:

> on th' other side
> Incenc't with indignation Satan stood
> Unterrifi'd, and like a Comet burn'd,
> That fires the length of *Ophiucus* huge
> In th' Arctick Sky, and from his horrid hair
> Shakes Pestilence and Warr.   II, 706–711

This, we shall discover, should be taken with the simile in the conclusion to the poem:

> High in front advanc't,
> The brandisht Sword of God before them blaz'd
> Fierce as a Comet; which with torrid heat,
> And vapour as the *Libyan* Air adust,
> Began to parch that temperate Clime.
>   XII, 633–636

The adjective "huge" was perhaps Milton's effort to enlarge as hyperbole the area covered by Ophiucus from south to north. Location of comets in the north was traditional. Thomas Hill's *A Contemplation of Mysteries: Contayning the Rare Effectes and Significations of Certayne Comets* (1571) cites Cardan's note that a comet "is oftner engendred in the North"; Lodge's *A Learned Summary upon DuBartas* says they "appeare by night in the Northern parts"; and F. Nausea's *A Treatise of Blazing Starres in Generall* (1618)

adds marginally "All mischiefe commeth from the North."
Milton may have made a mistake in placing Ophiucus, the
serpent-bearer; but more probably, he simply manipulated
details to strengthen the relationship between Satan and the
comet and the serpent.

Most of the other ideas and even terms in these passages
are likewise to be found in many places. Bartholomew describes the structure and functions of "impressions, that ben
gendred in the ayre," of which "sterre cometa . . . is a
sterre byclypped with brennynge gleymes, as Beda doth saye,
and is sodainlye bredde, and tokeneth chaungynge of kynges,
and is a token of pestylence, or of warre, or of wyndes, or of
grete heete." No words occur more frequently in accounts
of the "hairy star" than "pestilence and war." Howard in
A Defensative against the poyson of supposed Prophecies
and John Bainbridge in *An Astronomicall Description of the
Late Comet* (1619) might evince skepticism; but Thomas
Day interprets the meteorological disturbances of September
1583 as God's warning to men for their sins in *Wonderfull
straunge sightes seene in the Element over the Citie of
London* (1583). Nausea gives the fortieth chapter of his
Treatise to a history of the mischiefs which have followed
blazing stars, and Person a whole book of *Varieties* to miracles and prodigies, many dealing with comets. Jonston
approves the popular belief that the comet is a forerunner
of calamities; Gadbury piously asserts that comets are "the
certain signes, (*but not* causes) of Mundane Catastrophes";
and his fellow astrologer William Lilly, in *Strange News
from the East, or a Sober Account of the Comet or Blazing-
Star* (1677), sides with the Paracelsans in thinking comets
formed by angels at God's direction for a presage of great
events but not a cause. As late as 1685, the *Orbis Sensualium
Pictus* of Comenius agrees; and the definition in the fourth
edition of Edward Phillips' *New World of Words* concurs.
Swan and Gadbury, among others, report that a comet

shaped like a sword "signifieth warres and destruction of cities." [5]

The rational explanations of *The French Academie* and *Speculum Mundi* are so closely related to Milton's concentrated allusions that they demand attention. La Primaudaye sets out a logical chain of natural causes and effects:

Then through this drines of the aire it commonly happeneth, that the seas are much turmoiled with tempests, and that great blustering windes doe follow thereupon, and that Monarches and great Princes, who are most dry through cold and watchings, or else through abundance of hot and delicate meates and of strong wine, doe thereupon die: So likewise the dry and attenuated aire causeth the waters to diminish, fishes to die, and scarcity of victuals, which oftentimes stirreth up seditions, and the change of lawes, and finally the subversion of states.

Swan's account of wars, deaths, famines, and pestilence as natural results of comets follows this line of argument. Since the comet is made of "hot and drie Exhalations" which "stirre up heate, drie and parch the aire" and cause drought, the bodies of living creatures are hurt by the "distemper of the aire" and suffer "detriment in the consumption of their radical moisture," from which "there cannot but be sicknesses, plagues, and much mortalitie." Besides which, "that they should usher in warres, seditions, changes of kingdomes, and the like, may also proceed from the same cause"; and great personages, living more delicately and feeding more daintily than other men, "die sooner in such a calamitie then other people." Milton's ideas, indeed his very words, on comets were the common property of his age. Even the skepticism in *Of Reformation* has some basis in the encyclopedias of science, not to mention the array of treatises Kocher, Wiley, and Allen produce in their accounts of Renaissance and seventeenth-century rationalism.[6]

So much, then, for the hot upper region of air. In the cold middle layer, variously spoken of by Milton as "middle

empire of the freezing aire" and "middle Region of thick
Air," arose clouds, winds, rain, hail, snow, ice, thunder, and
lightning. It is thick, Bartholomew explains, for "thre maner
cause": vapors mingle earthy parts with air, cold freezes it,
or new air thickens it in generation. The clouds there, as
we know from the Prolusions, produced almost every other
activity, an idea glanced at in the "labouring clouds" of
L'Allegro, in "got a race of mourners on som pregnant cloud"
of *The Passion*, and in the cloud "Instinct with Fire and
Nitre" that unluckily saved Satan in Chaos. Swan supports
the term with the distinction that a cloud is "two-fold; either
fertill or barren." The evil potential of the black clouds in
Satan's stand-off with Death might have been available from
observation; but it was also in books.

> and such a frown
> Each cast at th' other, as when two black Clouds
> With Heav'ns artillery fraught, come rattling on
> Over the *Caspian*, then stand front to front
> Hov'ring a space, till Winds the signal blow
> To joyn thir dark Encounter in mid air.   II, 713–718

Bartholomew's chapter "Of Cloudes," like the statements
of other encyclopedists, establishes the milieu in which Milton's references operate:

A Clowde is impression made in the ayre in the midle of many
vapours gaderyd and bredde in to one bodye, in the mydle region
of the ayre thicked togyders by coldnesse of place. And so a
clowde is comonly mater to snowe reyne and heyle. And a clowde
is gendryed in this maner: The heete of heven, by his owne
vertue, drawyth to it ryght subtyl vaporable parties of water and
of erth, and wastyth the mooste subtyll parties therof, and make-
the the other deale thycke, and tournyth it in to a clowde of ayre.

He too speaks of the cloud "as it were mother of all thynges
that ben gendred in the ayre." Caxton's *Mirrour of the World*
points out that storm clouds are "black & moyste." La Primaudaye explains much as Bartholomew does; Swan adds

a note applicable to the signal for the encounter in saying their "motion is caused by the wind most commonly." [7]

This sort of information lies behind Milton's remark in *Pro Se Defensio*: "It seems, then, that instead of being a blind man I am metamorphosed into a rain-wind, and have myself collected those clouds of worthless fellows I was determined to drive before me." The early poems are full of conventional allusions like "perfume laden Zephyrus" and "chill Aquilo"; by the time of the great poems the eager student had "learned perfectly the changing winds." When he remarks the "cold Septentrion blast" as "a keen North-winde, that blowing drie" had "Wrinkl'd the face of Deluge" and driven the clouds away, he is referring to a coldness and dryness endlessly repeated by the encyclopedists. The culmination of this interest is the description of the winds as macrocosmic effects of the overthrow of reason in the microcosm:

> These changes in the Heav'ns, though slow, produc'd
> Like change on Sea and Land, sideral blast,
> Vapour and Mist, and Exhalation hot,
> Corrupt and Pestilent: Now from the North
> Of *Norumbega* and the *Samoed* shoar
> Bursting thir brazen Dungeon, armd with ice
> And snow and haile and stormie gust and flaw,
> *Boreas* and *Caecias* and *Argestes* loud
> And *Thrascias* rend the Woods and Seas upturn;
> With adverse blast up-turns them from the South
> *Notus* and *Afer* black with thundrous clouds
> From *Serraliona*; thwart of these as fierce
> Forth rush the *Levant* and the *Ponent* Windes
> *Eurus* and *Zephir* with thir lateral noise,
> *Sirocco* and *Libecchio*.   X, 692–706

Whiting finds in the ninth volume of Jansson's *Novus Atlas* "the only chart giving all the names that Milton used"; he adds that Milton inquired about the book in a letter to Peter Heimbach. There are some objections to his proposal

that Milton used this map, one of them being Milton's statement in the same letter that pictures were, on account of his
blindness, of little use to him; but the main point, that the
chart throws light on Milton's meaning, is well made. The
encyclopedic lore also enlightens the passage. Bartholomew's
"Of wynde orientall and subsolane" lists many in Milton's
accounts and discourses on their properties:

And the fyrste of Cardinall wyndes hyghte Subsolanus, as some
men meane. But amonge other men it is callyd Eurus, the easte
wynde that arysethe in the Eeste under the cercle, that hight
Parallelus equinoctorialis. . . . And towarde the Southe a
wynde, that hyghte Eurus: that is the South Eeste wynde. . . .
The seconde Cardinal and cheyf wynde is Favonius, the west
wynde. . . . And this wynde hath bysyde hym two wyndes:
. . . . [one] hyght Zephirus, the weste Southweste wynde. . . .
The thyrde . . . is Auster, the Southerne wynde . . . And this
wynde hath two wyndes bysyde hym. . . . Nothus, the Southeest wynde: and. . . . Affricus, The Southe southeest wynde.
. . . And other whyle he blowyth, that the ayre is full of the
forsayde vapour and so fallyth in to reyne. And for he putteth
and showyth the ayre out of large countree into streyght countree, therfor he makith the ayre thycke, and therof comen clowdes.
. . . The fourth . . . Borias, the Northerne wynde . . . Sep-
tentrionalis. . . . by great strengthe of his coldnesse, the North-
en winde constreynyth and byndyth the over partye of the erth,
and of water, and chaungyth theim, and tornyth theim now into
kind of yse, and now into kynde of crystalle, as the hardnesse is
more or lesse.

Like Milton, La Primaudaye includes Italian names with
Latin; they that frequent the Mediterranean sea "do call the
north Transmontano: the south Austro: east Levante; west,
Ponate; northeast, Greco; northwest Maestro, southeast Si-
rocho." Swan's enumeration of winds, which includes Caecias
and Thrascias, follows his account of their being "secondarily
effected." Milton had offered both "Exhalation hot" as the
cause and "brazen Dungeon" as the repository, elsewhere the
"hollow Rocks" which retain "blustering winds." Swan claims

that God willed the winds and they resulted from "an hot and
drie Exhalation" drawn from the bowels of the earth by the
sun, and relates the ancient opinion that winds "do actually
reside somewhere, and are shut up as in a prison." [8]

Interaction of wind and cloud in the middle region pre-
cipitated rain, snow, and hail. The "dusky clouds" of the
"lowring Element" that "Scowls ore the dark'nd lantskip
Snow, or showre" in the extraordinary meteorological metaphor for the debate in Pandaemonium appear "when the
North wind sleeps." Milton's bookish familiarity with the
operation of the south wind and exhalation shows again in
the story of the Flood:

> Meanwhile the Southwind rose, & with black wings
> Wide hovering, all the Clouds together drove
> From under Heav'n; the Hills to their supplie
> Vapour and Exhalation dusk and moist,
> Sent up amain; and now the thick'nd Skie
> Like a dark Ceeling stood; down rush'd the Rain
> Impetuous, and continu'd till the Earth
> No more was seen.   XI, 738–745

"Rayne," says *De Proprietatibus Rerum*, "is impression that
cometh of moche colde vapour and moyst, ther gathered in
a cloude." The "fumosyties" drawn from water and earth
reach the "nethermest party of the mydle space of the ayre"
and resolve into rain; and "wyndes that blowe uppon the
see, gatheren moche humour." According to *The French
Academie*, the thinner of the two sorts of vapors that rise
makes rain; and *Batman uppon Bartholome* adds to a parallel
account the operation of the south wind. Everyone who said
anything at all about the formation of rain said these things;
Person, Jonston, and the compiler of *The Knowledge of
Things Unknowne* (1619, 1668) are typical.[9]

Even the common rainbow had its lore, biblical and secular. Milton refers to it casually in *Nativity Ode*, fancifully in
Comus as the residence of some creatures of the element,

and with his persistent attention to natural causes in *Paradise Lost*:

> A dewie Cloud, and in the Cloud a Bow
> Conspicuous with three listed colours gay,
> Betok'ning peace from God.   XI, 865–867

Adam sees it as God's forehead and asks Michael its import, carefully supplying the meteorological data:

> But say, what mean those colourd streaks
>   in Heaven,
> Distended as the Brow of God appeas'd,
> Or serve they as a flourie verge to binde
> The fluid skirts of that same watrie Cloud
> Least it again dissolve and showr the Earth?
>   879–883

Bartholomew discusses it as an impression in "an holowe cloude and dewy"; La Primaudaye emphasizes a thick, watery cloud full of drops in the middle region; Swan repeats "hollow, watery, distilling, or dropping cloud directly opposit to the Sunne." So Lodge in his *A Learned Summary of DuBartas* and his translation of Seneca. Jonston observes the usual belief about the covenant, God's promise touching the conservation of the world, as Lodge put it; he appends a detail Milton would have regretted missing: "The blew colour is said to shew that the Flood is past, but the fiery colour shows that which is yet to come." For occasionally the rainbow was ominous, as in the *Account of the Late Terrible Earthquake in Sicily* (1693), which describes three rainbows as a presage, two after the usual manner, "a third ranvers'd," with no clouds in the sky.[10]

Differing influences in middle air upon clouds fertile for rain produced snow or hail. The symbolical value of tempests came as easily to Milton as to Elizabethan dramatists. The landscape darkened with snow and shower in the doubly ironical metaphor of demonic concord points to this, as does

> Thunder mixt with Haile,
> Haile mixt with fire, must rend th' *Egyptian* Skie,
> And wheel on th' Earth, devouring where it rouls.
> XII, 181–183

Caxton, Bartholomew, La Primaudaye, and Swan particularize the effect of the great cold in this region, converting clouds into snow and hail instead of water; *The French Academie* and *Speculum Mundi* distinguish hail as rain frozen by sudden cold in the lowest of the three regions of air. Milton in *Pro Se Defensio* refuses to "mount so high: for in the instant I . . . among the clouds, should be frozen to death." Michael compares Pharaoh's stubborn heart to ice "more hard'nd after thaw." Fulke's *Meteors* and Swan's section "Of Snow" affirm that snow "melting on the high hilles, and after frozen againe, becommeth so hard, that it is a stone, and is called Christall." The anonymous propagandistic *Mirabilis Annus* (1661) reports "a dreadful Storm of Fire and Hail mingled together." Satan's control over tempests, denied by some Renaissance rationalists, was accepted by the young poet who related the *In Quintum Novembris* disasters with which Satan, "wrapped in a smoking whirlwind of blue flame," assailed people and cities as he stirred "furious tempests in mid-air." And it was similarly worked into *Paradise Regained* by the old poet:

> and either Tropic now
> 'Gan thunder, and both ends of Heav'n, the Clouds
> From many a horrid rift abortive pour'd
> Fierce rain with lightning mixt, water with fire
> In ruine reconcil'd: nor slept the winds
> Within thir stony caves, but rush'd abroad
> From the four hinges of the world, and fell
> On the vext Wilderness.   IV, 409–416

These lines suggest Milton's manner in *Paradise Lost*, not only for their energy but for the inclusion of meteorological

motifs. They also indicate adoption for the poem of such a
view as La Primaudaye's in the chapter "Of the true Meteors
of Christians, and of the supernaturall causes of thunder and
lightning": evil spirits "doe sometimes raise up tempests,
thunder and lightning, because that the principall power
of them is in the aire. And therefore when it pleaseth God
to slacke their bridle, they raise up terrible and wondrous
storms." [11]

Thunder and lightning, the final effects of the middle
region considered here, had by Milton's time acquired a
great deal of lore. Behind the "cloudless thunder" alluded to
in *Samson Agonistes* lay the association of the eagle with the
sun, with Jupiter, or, as Milles says in his *Treasurie*, the
theory that the eagle cannot "bee smitten with lightning or
thunder." The "thwarting thunder blew" of *Arcades* bears
some relation to Hill's discourse in *A Contemplation of
Mysteries*, how "the diversitie of colours in the lightning
proceedeth of the diversitie of matter." So in the comparison
in *Reason of Church Government*, a sentence of excommunication has "such a penetrating force, that swifter than any
chimical sulphur, or that lightning which harms not the
skin, and rifles the entrals, it scorches the inmost soul." Or
Adam, learned in natural causes, giving his technical exposition of firemaking:

>   bids us seek
> Som better shroud, some better warmth to cherish
> Our Limbs benumm'd ere this diurnal Starr
> Leave cold the Night, how we his gather'd beams
> Reflected, may with matter sere foment,
> Or by collision of two bodies grinde
> The Air attrite to Fire, as late the Clouds
> Justling or pusht with Winds rude in thir shock
> Tine the slant Lightning, whose thwart flame
>   driv'n down
> Kindles the gummie bark of Firr or Pine,
> And sends a comfortable heat from farr,
> Which might supplie the Sun.   X, 1067–1078

Milton was so confident of his knowledge of traditional cosmology that he ridiculed an error of Salmasius, famous annotator of Pliny, because he had said the news of Charles' death struck hearers like a lightning flash and lifted their hair on end. This to Milton was something "unheard of for natural philosophers to learn, that to be struck by lightning makes hair stand on end." [12]

These topics had occupied scientists since Aristotle and were to continue, for real advancement in meteorological science awaited the eighteenth-century discoveries in electricity. The encyclopedias endlessly repeat that lightning is bred of a great vapor, ignited when it "is shufte and put by beatynge and shovynge and puttynge of clowdes." Caxton, La Primaudaye, Swan, Hill, Jonston, Lodge, and others explain the phenomenon much as Milton and Bartholomew do. Simon Harward's *A Discourse of the Severall kinds and causes of Lightnings* (1607) describes judicial, instructive, and fatidical causes of harm from lightning, though his account of its generation is conventional; God uses it to punish sinners, to teach them fear of Himself, and to give warning of greater calamities. And surely the most popular examples in the literature of the subject were those gathered about Harward's "lightening callled *penetrans, a pearcing lightening*," the type that passes through "outward pores of the body and slayeth the vitall parts within." From Aristotle, Pliny, and Seneca came the stories of gold melted in purses, swords in scabbards, wine solidified in tuns, children killed in the womb. Fulke, Widdowes, Lodge, DuPlesis, Bartholomew, Renaudot, La Primaudaye, and Swan purvey these anecdotes; and so interestingly enough for literary genetics, does Olaus Magnus in *Historia de Gentibus Septentrionalibus* (1555), which Milton probably owned and the information in which could be found in a hundred other sources.[13]

Besides these phenomena, Milton often alludes to vapors, dews, exhalations, and mists that arise from earth and sea but not far enough to develop into clouds, snow, or rain. They stop and inform or precipitate in the primary atmospheric layer. There, says Swan, "In the lowest Region, we have Dews, Mists, Hoarfrost, Ice and Frost. As also here is your *Ignis fatuus*, or *foolish fire*." Milton mentions three kinds of dew: the "fresh dew" of everyday experience, the dangerous "chill dew" or "mildew blast," and the heavenly "dew manna." The obvious metaphor in "Dew-drops, which the Sun / Impearls on every leaf and every flouer" embodies a submerged scientific theory: Batman and Maplet in *A Greene Forest* mention, like La Primaudaye, the ancient opinion that "the pearle was engendred in shels of fishes" which at one time of the year "doe open and gape in the night time, by that meanes filling themselves with dewe, whereby they conceive pearles." Swan discourses on "bitter blasting dew" which the Germans call "Mildaw" but he prefers to name "Ros Noxius" because "it hurteth and killeth such herbs and plants as it falleth on, and sticketh or cleaveth to." This contingency is avoided by the Son in *Paradise Regained*, when on each of the forty nights he sought some cave "to defend him from the dew." Biblical manna passed easily into a symbol of grace, the "Evangelick Manna" in *Of Prelatical Episcopacy*, and a symbol of sweet persuasion — Belial's tongue "dropt Manna." Both meanings underlie a comparison in *Eikonoklastes*:

But suppose them savoury words and unmix'd, suppose them manna itself, yet if they shall be hoarded up and enjoynd us, while God every morning raines down new expressions into our hearts, in stead of being fit to use, they will be found like reserv'd manna, rather to breed wormes and stink.

Medicinal manna, a common honey-and-herb concoction of the time, was theoretically *"coeli sudor,"* a fat and pure vapor untainted by putrid or corrupt exhalations, or *roris melliti genus, sed concreti,* "a kind of hony-sweet dew, but concrete

or compact more close together," according to La Primaudaye. He adds that manna is a singular medicine for the eyes,
a fact which may account for Milton's sometimes "taking
manna," as Aubrey reported.[14]

Before discussing the way in which Milton used the symbolism of mists and wandering fires, also generated in this
lowest atmospheric layer, let us examine the earthquake,
considered a "meteor" by encyclopedists and other early
scientists. When in *Nativity Ode* Milton says the "aged Earth
. . . shall from the surface to the center shake," the hyper-
bolic level is made more apparent if we know, as did La
Primaudaye, that terrestrial earthquakes were local phenomena, not movements of the earth as a whole. The "brute
Earth" in *Comus*, that in emergency might "lend her nerves
and shake" suggests the sort of identity with human anatomy familiar to seventeenth-century readers of Spenser and
Phineas Fletcher. *Animadversions* is more explicit: whoso-
ever "earnestly labors to keep such an incumbring surcharge
of earthly things, cannot but have an earthquake still in his
bones." However else they might differ about earth tremors,
"the professors of this science" agreed upon this analogy.
Swan cites those "who have taught, that the same reason is in
earthquakes, as there is in the shaking of mens bodies: and
that they are like fevers and maladies of the earth." Person
constantly sought such parallels: earthquakes are like agues,
and vapors like moist or flatulent humours sent up by the
stomach. Jonston's explanation of the cause includes a word
(bowels) not really metaphorical for his time: exhalation
"bred from fire under the Earth, and shut up in the bowels
of the Earth." All this came ultimately from Aristotle, as
Lodge's *Learned Summary of DuBartas* mentions, and later
from the *Natural Questions,* wherein Seneca claimed author-
ship of a treatise on earthquakes.[15]

In Book I of *Paradise Lost,* Milton attributes the cause of
earthquakes to wind, as do Widdowes in his translation of

Scribonius' *Naturall Philosophie* and Person in *Varieties*. The burning marle over which Satan walked appeared in hue like the crater of a volcano erupting after earthquake:

> as when the force
> Of subterranean wind transports a Hill
> Torn from *Pelorus*, or the shatter'd side
> Of thundring *Ætna*, whose combustible
> And fewel'd entrals thence conceiving Fire,
> Sublim'd with Mineral fury, aid the Winds,
> And leave a singed bottom all involv'd
> With stench and smoak.　　　　　I, 230–237

In Book VI and in *Samson Agonistes*, he includes water with wind as cause, like Bartholomew, Caxton, Batman, La Primaudaye, and others:

> as if on Earth
> Winds underground or waters forcing way
> Sidelong, had push't a Mountain from his seat
> Half sunk with all his Pines.　　　VI, 195–198

Samson strains at the pillars until they shake "As with the force of winds and waters pent, / When Mountains tremble." The disagreement among natural philosophers over the cause did not impede classification as to kinds. *The French Academie* asserts no point in all natural philosophy wherein the teachers are so entangled; and Agrippa illustrates one aspect of *The Vanity of All the Arts and Sciences* in this dissension:

Let us discourse of any thing which they say proceeds from a Natural Cause; as for Example, let it be an Earthquake, yet are they at no certainty therein, but wander in Extravagancies; while *Anaxagoras* makes the Cause thereof to be the Air; *Empedocles*, Fire; *Thales Milesius*, water; *Aristotle, Theophrastus,* and *Albertus*, Subterraneal Wind or Vapour; *Asclepiades*, great Mischances or Devastations; *Possidonius, Calisthenes,* and *Metrodorus,* the Destinies. *Seneca* and others variously dissenting, seem to have labour'd in vain in the search thereof.

Speculum Mundi admits the confusion about cause but catalogs five kinds, one of which, "a laterall, or sidelong shaking,"
pinpoints Milton's mention of that detail as scientific, not
merely vigorous, in connotation. When we recall from Donne
that moving of the earth brings harms and fears or see with
Thomas Twynne's *A Shorte and pithie Discourse, concerning
the engendring, tokens, and effects of all Earthquakes in Generall* (1580) that it is evidence of God's displeasure, we understand more particularly how Milton adds dimension to God's
punishment of Satan, the evil angels, and the Philistines.[16]

These earthquakes in Heaven or Hell, even by association,
remind us that although Milton occasionally distinguishes
between terrestrial natural features and celestial-infernal,
more often than not his imagery depends upon processes at
work in the elementary world. We have seen the elevation of
Pandaemonium "like an Exhalation" out of the nether soil.
So in the garden, before the fall with its resulting black night
and damp, Satan is compared to a "black mist low creeping,"
and followed as gliding obscure he moves "wrapt in a mist
of midnight vapour." He enters the second time involved in
a rising mist; the distinctions between that and a low creeping mist were encyclopedic fact. In the same way, the *ignis
fatuus* was separated from the *ignis lambens*, both used in
the poem for characterization and idea.

The extraordinary importance of detailed knowledge
about activity in the sublunar vault appears nowhere so
strongly as in the conclusion to *Paradise Lost*. A close reading of the final twenty-five lines may be allowed as a test case
of Milton's manner throughout, for around them is an atmosphere of ambivalence and paradox penetrable only
through an understanding of medieval and Renaissance
pseudo-science. To begin with, the debate of our elders over
the ending has been settled at least in one direction by Lovejoy's exposition of the fortunate fall. We need not choose
between Addison's notion that the epic was stylistically in-

consistent because it did not end happily and Erskine's contention that it was theologically contradictory because it did. Now we recognize the balance between the cosmic optimism of a providential Deity and the immediate human tragedy of the fall and expulsion from the garden. Seen through Lovejoy's glasses, the narrative satisfies both classical epic tradition and Christian dogma. But out of that conflict of ideas that is the *felix culpa*, ambiguity and ambivalence emerge, somewhat like the good and evil springing forth from the rind of one apple tasted. Working with the symbols associated with Satan earlier in the poem and now with the Cherubim and the sword of God, one can see a paradoxical transfer of values, a metaphoric resolution of the apparent contradiction raised by the final image of Adam and Eve hand in hand, and a reassertion of the central theme correspondent to the paradox of the fortunate fall. This theme is the conflict of good and evil and the suspension of final decision between them. The problem of evil is always in solution in Milton, never absolutely resolved. Adam and his posterity must repeat the temptation of the tree and the fall until the final trumpet.[17]

> So spake our Mother *Eve,* and *Adam* heard
> Well pleas'd, but answer'd not; for now too nigh
> Th' Archangel stood, and from the other Hill
> To thir fixt Station, all in bright array
> The Cherubim descended; on the ground
> Gliding meteorous, as Ev'ning Mist
> Ris'n from a River o're the marish glides,
> And gathers ground fast at the Labourers heel
> Homeward returning. High in Front advanc't,
> The brandisht Sword of God before them blaz'd
> Fierce as a Comet; which with torrid heat,
> And vapour as the *Libyan* Air adust,
> Began to parch that temperate Clime; whereat
> In either hand the hastning Angel caught
> Our lingring Parents, and to th' Eastern Gate
> Led them direct, and down the Cliff as fast

To the subjected Plaine; then disappeer'd.
They looking back, all th' Eastern side beheld
Of Paradise, so late thir happie seat,
Wav'd over by that flaming Brand, the Gate
With dreadful Faces throng'd and fierie Armes:
Som natural tears they drop'd, but wip'd them soon;
The World was all before them, where to choose
Thir place of rest, and Providence thir guide:
They hand in hand with wandring steps and slow,
Through *Eden* took thir solitarie way.   XII, 624–649

We began the epic in Hell, with Satan and his legions, the enemies of mankind, on the burning lake. We end in a corrupted, converted Paradise, all the eastern side scourged by a comet-like sword, Michael and the Cherubim thronging the gate with dreadful faces, strangely like Satan and his cohorts. They are Adam's enemies should he attempt to remain in the garden. Indeed, one version of the story identifies them as an order of evil angels. This is not merely an end to the poem but a return, as it were, to the beginning; Adam and Eve are fallen angels, suffering a like expulsion except for grace and the promised Redeemer. The ambiguous problem of evil is ubiquitous in time and space; the drama of the fall repeats itself in double plot. The very organization of the poem repeats the theme, as may be seen at once in the comparison of the Cherubim with evening mist. The surface effect is to amplify the impression of brightness and smooth soundless movement of the angels "gliding meteorous." But Whaler and others have taught us that Milton's similes seldom operate upon a limited resemblance or conclude in a single comparison. The figure of the laborer homeward bound is a curious touch; it might seem too homely, for the angels are military. Indeed, its overtones of rest and peace after a day's work conflict with the image of Adam and Eve banished from their home after the worst day of the world's history, unless we suppose it an unassimilated ornament reinforcing the contrast between the faithful angels and

fallen man. In this context, the laborer is undisturbed by the
mist; yet we remark something ominous in the phrase
"gathers ground fast," as though the mist were hurrying the
laborer, or taking up the ground behind him. Adam and Eve
have talked too long; Michael hastens to escort them from
the garden. There is not only the speed with which the
Cherubim move to their station for the banishment, but a
suggestion of control or possession. Adam and Eve no longer
hold Paradise; it is gathered in by these guardians. All of this
is at one with the narrative. On the surface, Adam and Eve
are being expelled by God's agents; beneath it, the implications of their sin show in the Satanic image of the cherubim
and the sword of God.[18]

We have seen how Milton identifies Satan with the comet,
universally feared in popular superstition as a punishment
or warning. Now we may observe how the Tempter's delight
at Eve's curiosity is disclosed in an image of brightness not
unlike that for the Cherubim:

> Hope elevates, and joy
> Bright'ns his Crest, as when a wandring Fire
> Compact of unctuous vapor, which the Night
> Condenses and the cold environs round,
> Kindl'd through agitation to a Flame,
> Which oft, they say, some evil Spirit attends,
> Hovering and blazing with delusive Light,
> Misleads th' amaz'd Night-wanderer from his way
> To Boggs and Mires, oft through Pond or Poole
> There swallow'd up and lost, from succour farr.
>
> IX, 633–641

These are the "fals and dazling fires" held out "to stumble
men" in *Doctrine of Divorce.* Writers on meteorology regu-
larly treated *ignis fatuus* and *ignis lambens* together, and
nearly always as emblems of self-deception. Person's *Varieties*
reports them at sea before a storm or "to flutter about Horse-
meines and feet, or amongst people gone astray in darke
nights. And these our Meteorologians call *Ignes Fatui* &

ignes lambentes, wilde fires." Renaudot's *Discourses* explains by displacement of air why "they pursue those that fly them, and on the contrary fly before those that pursue them"; whereupon "the ignorant vulgar takes them for evil spirits because they drive and lead them to precipices and bogs." Jonston's *An History of the Wonderful Things of Nature* offers the same information and conclusion: "they thinking that it is Light from Towns, fall into bogs." Swan's *Speculum Mundi* reads here so much like a paraphrase of Milton that it must be quoted in full to indicate that *unctuous, vapor, agitation,* and *meteorous* are scientific vocabulary, like *kindl'd, condenses,* and *compact.*

a fat and oily Exhalation hot and drie (as are all Exhalations which are apt to be fir'd) and also heavie in regard of the glutinous matter whereof it consisteth: in which regard the cold of the night beats it back again when it striveth to ascend, through which strife and tossing it is fired . . . and being fired it goeth to and fro according to the motions of the Aire in the silent night by gentle gales. . . . These kinds of lights are often seen in Fennes and Moores, because there is always great store of unctuous matter fit for such purposes. . . . Wherefore the much terrified, ignorant, and superstitious people may see their own errours in that they have deemed these lights to be walking spirits. . . . They are no spirits, and yet lead out of the way, because those who see them are amazed, and look so earnestly after them that they forget their way . . . sometimes to waters, pits, and other dangerous places; whereupon the next day they will undoubtedly tell you strange tales (as one saith) how they were led up and down by a light, which (in their judgment) was nothing else but some devil or spirit in the likenesse of fire which fain would have hurt them. . . . *Ignis lambens* is a cleaving and licking fire or light. . . . These flames may be caused two wayes, as the learned write. First, when clammie Exhalations are scattered abroad in the aire in small parts, and in the night are set on fire by an *Antiperistasis;* so that when any shall either ride or walk in such places as are apt to breed them, it is no wonder that they stick either on their horses, or on themselves.[19]

The parallels between Satan and this meteor are obvious

beyond the basic comparison of brightness. He is deluding
Eve and leading her to disaster, even a physical fall from the
hill of Paradise to the plain. His light of reason is a false
light. The whole figure expresses confident evil, glittering
deception, and catastrophe. To link mist with Satan and then
with the Cherubim is to attach some of his quality to them;
to play upon both with *ignis fatuus* and *ignis lambens* is to
confirm the transfer.

So it is with the sword, which expresses more directly the
ambiguity introduced into the concluding lines of the epic.
Comets presage disaster, but here not only the immediate
catastrophe of banishment. Swan and Gadbury, it will be
recalled, found a portent of war in the comet shaped like a
sword. The comet over Paradise prophesies not only the
threat of war between the Cherubim and Adam and Eve, if
they resist, but the war of Adam and Eve against the world,
the flesh, and the devil. It is an omen not only of what
happens now, their banishment, but of what will happen.
The scientific writers compared the comet to a sword, symbol
of war; Milton compared the sword to a comet prophesying
war. Satan against his son Death burned like a comet "that
from his horrid Hair / Shakes Pestilence and Warr"; and
the ensign of his troops shone like a meteor streaming to the
wind. Returning triumphant to Hell, he was like a comet
between Centaur and Scorpio while the sun rose in Aries.
These metaphors carry over into the concluding image — the
comet is not only a sign of God's displeasure, it is an attribute
of Satan. Thus, images communicating evil, amplified by
quite conventional seventeenth-century connotations, here
reveal and heighten God's justice and its execution.

Yet Milton is not equating good and evil or failing to
maintain final absolute distinction between them. There is
no real conflict of symbol and idea, but a paradox remarkably like that of the fortunate fall itself. The Cherubim and
sword of God are evil only in the sense that Adam and Eve

have made them so, and so the chaos let into the cosmos by their sin is reflected. For the moment they have converted good into evil, yet still paradoxically — since except for Adam's fall, Christ had not become savior. The transfer of evil in comet and in mist from Satan to the agents of God asserts the ambivalence of Adam's action, one of the multiple ambiguities in the poem; even he, excited over the Atonement, cannot say whether it was better to have fallen or not. The metaphoric paradox conforms to the theological. The dreadful faces and fiery arms at the gate of Paradise suggest demons at the gate of Hell precisely because Adam's sin has made the Cherubim so, has altered their relation to him.

But we are not left thus. The balance between sorrow and comfort is preserved in the narrative and in the poetic texture. The final picture of Adam and Eve hand in hand completes the variations played on this hallowed image of unity. Camerarius, for example, in *The Living Librarie* collects numerous examples of such symbolism from Alexander of Alexandria, Numa Pompilius, and others to show the joining of hands as a consecration of faith. In Book IV at our first view, the lovers pass before Satan's gaze, hand in hand. They are mankind — reason and emotion, as it were, united here, to divide later. As Eve recalls Adam's courtship, the touch of his hand was the final persuasion. After their conversation they move hand in hand to their bower, and after prayers are still so joined. They are separate when Eve dreams, but the singleness is restored when Adam wakes her, touching her hand. Raphael describes the perfect unity of seasons by saying that Spring and Autumn in the garden "danc'd hand in hand." During their last talk and even during the argument before the fall, they have been holding hands; for as Eve departs, "from her Husbands hand her hand / Soft she withdrew." Mankind has been split apart; reason and emotion, as far as they may be identified with Adam and Eve, are no longer unified in man; both are ripe for the fall. The "rash hand" with which Eve plucked the fruit emphasizes it as an instrument of falling humanity. So with the garland Adam wreathed: when he saw her, it dropped "from his slack hand." She gave him the fruit "with liberal hand." As it aroused his lust, "her hand he seis'd"; and in that violence may be seen the failure of a union of mere flesh. With all these images behind it, there is a special poignancy in Adam's excuse that from her hand he could suspect no ill.[20]

And now in this scene, even as they are expelled from Paradise, even as Michael hurries them along, he grasps their hands to insure their departure. But such has been the accumulation of images that for a moment, in that dreadful light and under banishment, there is unity among them, Michael, Eve, and Adam. Reason and emotion and grace are united, as mankind, to this extent whole again, faces a new world. It is all before them where to choose their place of rest. Their passage through Eden is solitary, wandering, and slow — but it is hand in hand. The enemies of Book X are reconciled. The harmony is stressed by this final image of joined hands, which symbolizes affection, friendship, and singleness, which resolves the paradox of friends and enemies created by mist and sword. And how exquisitely we are returned to the homely image of the laborer, how apropos to the hope and comfort accompanying Adam and Eve. The peaceful image is a counterpoise to the foreboding tone of the mist. The portent of war to come is modified by the gesture of unity between the agent of God and the creature man; Michael has been and is an embodiment of God's grace. The dreadful faces and fiery arms of a parched Paradise are set against the prospect of a new world, a new home full of promise as well as of constant war against evil, where Adam like the laborer must earn his bread by the sweat of his brow.

There is too much Milton, of course, for similar close analysis of many other passages, but the several examples certainly establish Milton's method — a succession of balances wherein the apparent contradictions and conflicts create depth and variety in dramatization of the profoundly complex nature of good and evil. In this metaphoric density, the effects produced by scientific lore have begun to clarify. Milton manipulates abstract and concrete so skilfully that science gets into his works naturally and operatively, never mechanically. The levels of air in the sublunar vault have each an ordered place and function; phenomena there are specified in scientific terms and as processes closely related to man and his problems. From the farthest reaches of his universe to the smallest detail of the sublunar region, order and correspondence are dominant motives. Rain, snow, winds, lightning, hail, comets, and earthquakes result from orderly relationships in the natures and properties of things. Classification, analysis, and category multiply correlations within the structure of this smaller universe. As we advance from it to the first links in the chain of being, we observe the same principles in Milton's strategy as poet: classical, medieval, and Renaissance science informs and particularizes meaning in the constant interplay of image and idea.

CHAPTER IV

The Secret Powers of Stones and Plants

W_{E HAVE MOVED WITH MILTON} from
the circumference of his universe to the center; now we shift
with him from geometry, as it were, to hierarchy, and follow
his sequence, repeated in the Prolusions, *Of Education*, and
Paradise Lost, from stones and plants to living creatures and
at last to man. Yet the spatial quality is not lost, for a sense of
movement pervades the epic structure of hierarchies. Satan's
apostrophe to the sun expresses a physical point of view as
well as a sense of order. So, in Raphael's analogy for the scale
of being, spiritual gradations are conveyed in images of movement. All things *proceed* from God and up to him *return;*
they are more *spiritous* as "neerer to him *plac't* or neerer
tending." The plant, a visual epitome for the whole scale,
grows before our very eyes:

> So from the root
> Springs lighter the green stalk, from thence the leaves
> More aerie, last the bright consummate floure
> Spirits odorous breathes.   V, 479–482

In selecting the simplest form of life to illustrate the complete chain, Milton is not only implying that ontogeny recapitulates phylogeny; he is using a figure already well-known from
Mercator's version in *Historia Mundi*:

In summe, if any man will search more diligently the order of things, and consider the communion and difference of Species, he will perceive that the Creation of things (beginning from the more base and ignoble Species) so almost ascended upward, as a tree hath at first but onely a truncke, wherein all things which are from the roote to the very top, are but one and the same thing by the Communion of Species, every of the parts in the meane time having their veines therein: but when they beginne to have any difference among themselves, the first division of the truncke is made into branches, after (every branch remayning a certaine time untill their veines divide themselves one from another) is made the second division, and so consequently untill we come to the last branches and fruits. So the Chaos is the onely truncke of all the Species to be created, having his roote and beginning in the Universall Idea Creatrix, which is in the mind, and divine will.

When Mercator continues that the universal idea "doth by little and little goe by the lesse noble, and more noble species, to the production of the highest," his ideas and language, like Milton's, are common stock. He concludes upon the "sequent, and more noble ranck, as we see in the creation of plants, living Creatures, and of man," finding, again like Milton, "that even the spirit of man is extracted out of the first matter." Recapitulation of stages and powers of lower forms by the higher orders, also a commonplace, forms part of the theory in books so widely separated in time as Maplet's *A Greene Forest* of 1567 and Matthew Hale's *The Primitive Origination of Mankind, considered and examined according to the Light of Nature* of 1677. Maplet declares that in plants nature comes "somewhat more neare" than in stones to the principal creature man. In the plant, he adds, "it is spoken on that wise properly and after such sort, as mankind first next after his conception is saide to quicken and continue withall in reaching" by natural order to his final form. When Maplet apologizes for omitting man from his third book, he says that the animal "steppeth up a Stayer higher, layeth holde and apprehendeth another kinde of life in degree more Princely" than plants. Hale affirms that a knowledge of man gives a full account of the vegetable and animal kingdoms because he "comprehends all the excellencies that are in the inferior ranks of Being, and that for the most part in a more excellent and perfect manner." [1]

Principles of order, gradation, and harmony are axiomatic in the encyclopedic view of natural science. Milton might well have agreed with Nehemiah Grew that the very scale of the creatures was a matter of high speculation; but his treatment of the "gradual scale" or "scale of Nature" animated with "gradual life" as "steps" by which "we may ascend to God" agrees with major postulates in Danaeus' *The Wonderfull Workmanship of the World* and La Primaudaye's *The French Academie.* The limitation of such heathen philosophers as Aristotle is that they are bound to natural processes, "thei dooe not arise higher, neither doe thei ascende by meanes of these, as it were by a Ladder, unto God the Creatour of them." Danaeus too begins with the vegetable world, in differentiating general natural philosophy, which was to be learned out of Scripture, from the particular natural philosophy to be gathered from "woorkes of Phisitions, or of others which have written the histories of Plantes, and of lyvinge thinges." La Primaudaye says that if we survey the universe of spheres, elements, fouls, fishes, beasts, plants, grains, stones, and metals and "consider withall what a sweete harmony ariseth from all these," we may see if we have but half an eye and "feele if we be blinde, that in this rare peece of worke and frame of the world, there is most excellent convaiance without confusion, great variety concurring in unity, and diversity of all kindes without disorder." Not all encyclopedists organized their books like Maplet, by the scale of nature; but few of them failed to take advantage of the idea as it contributed to the concept of a meaningful universe, a purposive nature under God.[2]

Thus when Milton planned for his students to go from

"the History of Meteors, Minerals, plants and living Creatures as far as Anatomy," he wrote in the elaborate tradition of the encyclopedists. Even stones and minerals were part of this grand scale of being, and the classical and medieval lapidaries had found such place in the encyclopedias that Bartholomew could say "Great vertue is in herbes, but moste in precious stones." Batman echoed his original, supplemented the eighth book from Agrippa's *De Occulta Philosophia*, and added to the eleventh a section on stones "From whence hidden vertues doe proceede." A little of Milton's mineralogical lore has been touched on in Chapter I; now let us examine various lines on mining, gunpowder, potable gold, and the philosopher's stone. Most of what Milton said was generally disseminated information, including a conventional bias against mining. Taylor has shown that this hostility was at least as old as Pliny, and persisted into the late seventeenth century, as one may gather from Sir John Pettus's half-fanciful, half-defensive identification of Adam as "esteemed a *Miner* from the *Text*; where 'tis said, that God placed him in *Paradise*, and commanded him to dig or till the earth." Then with a logic perfectly understood in the seventeenth century, he sees him "also a *Refiner*; otherwise, why should it be made known to him, that the River *Pison* did encompass the Land of *Havilah* where *Gold* was, if *Adam* were not to wash and refine it from the less valuable Earth?" The customary point of attack was the evil caused by gold and silver, but under the entire complex of ideas ran a feeling against dislocating or perverting nature. Mammon originated the sacrilege:

> by him first
> Men also, and by his suggestion taught,
> Ransack'd the Center, and with impious hands
> Rifl'd the bowels of their mother Earth
> For Treasures better hid. I, 684–688

The anthropomorphic image is continued in the "spacious

wound" opened in the hill and the excavated "ribs of gold."
Comus's opposite view — that Nature's fertility in gold and
gems must be controlled by use lest it go wild and overrun
the world, challenging Jove himself — has been acutely explicated by Harry F. Robins and Brooks and Hardy. Their
analyses show how astonishingly Milton could work both
sides of a question, not as personal belief but as intensely
convincing art. Our concern here, however, is with the traditional attitude incorporated into *Paradise Lost*. In *Naturam
non Pati Senium,* Milton blamed earth herself who guiltily

Mining, from Bartholomew, De Proprietatibus Rerum, *English ed., 1495.*

concealed the gold destined to cause crimes; later, in Tubal-Cain's blacksmithing, he excludes implication of blame either way. Tubal-Cain simply finds his ore:

> (whether found where casual fire
> Had wasted woods on Mountain or in Vale,
> Down to the veins of Earth, thence gliding hot
> To some Caves mouth, or whether washt by stream
> From underground) the liquid Ore he dreind
> Into fit moulds prepar'd.[3]   XI, 566–571

In relation to this whole problem we might look at Milton's references to a specific type of mining — gunpowder. In the 1620's Milton had prophesied fame for the inventor of gunpowder, in fact, had mentioned the subject in several epigrams and the Fifth of November poem, where it is adjunctive to the undernourished proto-Satan. In *Paradise Lost* the Arch Fiend himself is credited with the invention, through lines that renew the ancient mysterious relation of dark and bright, good and evil, beauty and horror in the very soil of Heaven. His speech begins in a kind of proleptic nostalgia and moves from this momentary recall of happiness into the dark present. Satan begins:

> Which of us who beholds the bright surface
> Of this Ethereous mould whereon we stand,
> This continent of spacious Heav'n, adornd
> With Plant, Fruit, Flour Ambrosial, Gemms & Gold,
> Whose Eye so superficially surveyes
> These things, as not to mind from whence they grow
> Deep under ground, materials dark and crude,
> Of spiritous and fierie spume, till toucht
> With Heav'ns ray, and temperd they shoot forth
> So beauteous, op'ning to the ambient light.
>   VI, 472–481

Here is the scheme of chaos and cosmos, with a physical sense of the ominous minerals lying beneath the flowers and the gold. Everyone in Heaven knew there *were* minerals; only

Satan and his crew materialized evil from them. The cunning choice of *toucht, temperd, shoot,* and *op'ning* anticipates what follows; gunpowder is invented in the images before it occurs in the narrative. The metaphor is given tension by the play of *ambient light* against *spiritous and fierie spume.* Satan concludes:

> These in thir dark Nativitie the Deep
> Shall yield us, pregnant with infernal flame,
> Which into hallow Engins long and round
> Thick-rammd, at th' other bore with touch of fire
> Dilated and infuriate shall send forth
> From far with thundring noise among our foes
> Such implements of mischief as shall dash
> To pieces and orewhelm whatever stands
> Adverse, that they shall fear we have disarmd
> The Thunderer of his only dreaded bolt.
>
> 482–491

Then Raphael, in another of those dramatic interpolations that keep up the sense of narrative, comments forebodingly:

> In future dayes, if Malice should abound,
> Some one intent on mischief, or inspir'd
> With dev'lish machination might devise
> Like instrument to plague the Sons of men
> For sin, on warr and mutual slaughter bent.
>
> 502–506

The fallen angels next began to mine:

>   up they turned
> Wide the Celestial soile, and saw beneath
> Th' originals of Nature in their crude
> Conception; Sulphurous and Nitrous Foame
> They found, they mingl'd, and with suttle Art,
> Concocted and adjusted they reduc'd
> To blackest grain, and into store convey'd:
> Part hidd'n veins diggd up (nor hath this Earth
> Entrails unlike) of Mineral and Stone
> Whereof to found thir Engins and thir Balls

Of missive ruin; part incentive reed
Provide, pernicious with one touch to fire. 509–520

A great deal of mineralogical and lapidary lore, as well as the condemnation of mining, pervades these passages. Seneca had a chapter of *Natural Questions* rebuking men "that have searched out the verie bowels of the Earth to finde out Silver"; and declares himself glad to learn "that it is not of late time that Avarice hath digged into the veins of the Earth and Rocks, seeking in the darknes the ruin of Mankind." Acosta's *The Naturall and Morall Historie of the East and West Indies Intreating of the remarkeable things of Heaven, of the Elements, Mettals, Plants and Beasts which are proper to that Country* (1604), translated by E. G., quotes Boethius:

> Alas, who was the first,
> So curious and accurst,
> Who digged out of the mine,
> Mans minde to undermind,
> Heavie weights of golden ore,
> Better concealde before.

Agrippa gives a chapter in *Of the Vanity of All the Arts and Sciences* to miners and metals and repeats the formula: "certainly therefore he first found out the greatest Plague of Humane Life, that first found out Mynes of Gold, and other Veins of Metal." [4]

Milton editorializes pointedly about the gold in the soil of Hell, but passes over its existence in Heaven, together with, more interestingly, the materials for gunpowder. Putting gold, the universal symbol of royalty and virtue, into the place of horror is a fine narrative oxymoron; for "that soyle may best Deserve the pretious bane." Existence of gunpowder and gold in Heaven, however, is a proclamation of the neutrality of matter. Satan himself has described the process through which materials fertilized by the sun-like ray of Heaven develop into fruits and flowers; and he understands that by intervening he can miscreate, divert the growth of matter into evil. Raphael's practical explanation of how man acquired gold (the detailed procedure sounds almost like instruction) is a concession in its own way to the doctrine of primary and secondary causes, with the Satanic perversion of creativity a constant theme. Swan's pseudo-historical account allows for demonic instigation. He tells of the accidental invention of "that fatall dust, called *Pulvis Bombardicus*" by the Franciscan Bertholdus Swart, then cites Peucer's "continuation of *Carions* chronicle" that gunpowder "was found out by a Monk, the devil being the chiefest enginer or master-workman." The "originals of Nature," sulphurous and nitrous foam, appear in Swan's version, where brimstone and sulphur, nitre and saltpeter are synonyms. These are inactive in Heaven; it is the fallen angels who must mingle, concoct, adjust. They provide in this corruption of blameless matter one more analogue for Satan's grand plot against God and man. In Hell and in Chaos the "ever-burning Sulphur" reacts constantly; and the explosive force of the cloud that lifted Satan derived from its components fire (sulphur) and nitre. The burning marle, firm brimstone, and burnt soil of Hell correspond to Caxton's report of many great mountains there that burn night and day. Acosta's explanation of continual burning in volcanic craters reveals the traditional relation to hell fire and extends the meaning of Milton's linking of volcanic fire to Hell:

Others say, that it is hell fire, which issueth there, to serve as warning, thereby to consider what is in the other life: but if hell (as Divines holde) be in the centre of the earth, the which contains in diameter about two thousand leagues, we cannot judge that this fire is from the centre; for that hell fire (as saint *Basil* and others teach) is very different from this which wee see, for that it is without light, and burneth without comparison much more then ours.

In Milton's Hell, it will be recalled, the fires burned also without light, for from those flames came only "darkness visible." Milton included sulphur among the originals of nature also because of the common view, exemplified in Maplet, Swan, Polydore Vergil, and Fulke, that it is the father (and mercury the mother) of minerals and metals, including the naphtha and asphaltus illuminating Pandaemonium, and the metallic ore, "the work of Sulphur." [5]

Let us now return to the lore, briefly mentioned in Chapter I, about the stones and metals to which the sun is compared, for the relevant themes of the philosopher's stone and potable gold, first marking for the record such mineralogical stereotypes as the hardness of diamond or adamant, the likeness of stars to sapphires, the sweating of marble, the fitness of brass for trumpets, and the pull of the lodestone. Yet one must move carefully here. It would be a mistake, for example, to regard Milton's "sounding Alchymie" as only a metaphor for trumpet; Jonston's *An History of the Wonderful Things of Nature* proves it technical: "with the tincture of *Cadmia*" brass will look like gold, "and is called *Alchymy*." Alchemy, of course, had a turbulent history from antiquity on, and concerned itself with a good deal more than the notorious search for gold. Polydore Vergil recounts from Suidas the legend that alchemy had endured before the time of the Argonauts and that the golden fleece Jason went after "was nothing else then a certain book, that taught to turn other Mettals into gold." Sensational publications like *The Mirror of Alchimy* (1597), advertised as by Roger Bacon, multiplied belief; as late as the enlightened year 1670, there was still room for such a title as John Frederick Helvetius's *The Golden Calf, which the World Adores and Desires: in which is handled the most Rare and Incomparable Wonder of Nature, in Transmuting Metals; viz. How the intire Substance of Lead, was in one Moment Transmuted into Gold-Obrizon, with an exceeding small particle of the true Philosophick Stone.* The quest for the philosopher's stone is a secular Grail story. Occultists in particular magnified its symbolic value and believed in it as a physical possibility, and so staid an encyclopedist as Person includes in his fifth book a treatise called "Salamandra," giving specific directions for making it. John Heydon, whose titles are as wild as his work, asserts in *Hammeguleh Hampaaneah, or the Rosie Crucian Crown Set with Seven Angels, 7 planets, 7 Genii, 12 Signes, 12 Idea's, 16 Figures, and their Occult Powers, upon the 7 Mettalls* (1665) that the stone is made of gold alone and only by nature and is more sublime than those called cure-alls by the philosophers. He too gives directions for extracting the elixir of the philosopher's stone and for making potable gold. The jargon of this art appealed as greatly to late Elizabethans like Jonson and Donne as to Chaucer.[6]

The references to alchemy in Milton's prose cut two ways. "Their trade being, by the same Alchymy that the *Pope* uses, to extract heaps of *gold,* and *silver* out of the drossie *Bullion* of the People's sinnes" discredits both bishops and alchemists, like the ugly allusion to "an Alchymist of slander" in *Apology for Smectymnuus* and the "harder alchymy than Lullius ever knew" in *Areopagitica.* Here "good refiner" replaces "alchemist" as the simile for the wise man's gathering gold out of the drossiest volume. The images reappear, as so many from the prose do, in *Paradise Lost,* where they furnish a guarded analogy to angelic transubstantiation:

> nor wonder; if by fire
> Of sooty coal the Empiric Alchimist
> Can turn, or holds it possible to turn
> Metals of drossiest Ore to perfet Gold
> As from the Mine.   V, 439–443

The great figure comes earlier. Among the gems and metals compared to the sun is

a stone besides
Imagind rather oft then elsewhere seen,
That stone, or like to that which here below
Philosophers in vain so long have sought,
In vain, though by thir powerful Art they binde
Volatil *Hermes*, and call up unbound
In various shapes old *Proteus* from the Sea,
Draind through a Limbec to his Native forme.
What wonder then if fields and regions here
Breathe forth *Elixir* pure, and Rivers run
Potable Gold, when with one vertuous touch
Th' Arch-chimic Sun so farr from us remote
Produces with Terrestrial Humor mixt
Here in the dark so many precious things
Of colour glorious and effect so rare?   III, 593–612

Milton's *Elixir* is the liquid form of the philosopher's stone
that cured all diseases. But the same David Person who confidently supplied directions for making the philosopher's
stone viewed dubiously the more plausible experiment of
aurum potabile, the potable gold famous in English literature
from the time of Chaucer's Doctour of Physick. Hermeticists
naturally accepted the sun as "arch-chimic"; Heydon speaks
of its body as gold and sets down instructions for effecting
"the true Aurum potabile, and spiritual Elixir of life." Despite Person, ordinary potable gold was not thought difficult
to produce. George Ripley's *The Compound of Alchymy*
(1591) boasted the "right and perfectest meanes to make
the Philosophers Stone, Aurum potabile, with other excellent
Experiments." Gesner, *The Treasure of Evonymus* (1559),
specified, among less mentionable ingredients, the honey
and comb of a swarm of young bees, ambergris, long pepper,
and pure gold, the result after thirty days being a water to
dissolve the precious metal. Jonston said a London doctor
had brought gold to the consistency of honey; and Digby
gave four recipes for "an excellent Aurum Potabile, or Di-
gestif Gold." Wanley, *The Wonders of the Little World*,

recited the old legend of liquid gold in Roman sepulchre lamps.[7]

The images in Milton's lines here, like those about the gunpowder, branch out into the leading ideas of the poem. The key to their function is the relationships among sun, earth, Heaven, Aaron's breastplate, Hermes and Proteus, the philosopher's stone, and Satan. The first three of these form a little scale of their own, the highest stage of which, Heaven, is closed to Satan. The cosmological supremacy of the lordly sun, endlessly repeated in the poem, establishes it as a symbol of one kind of perfection in the world; what men cannot do on earth, the sun does by nature there and transcendently in its own sphere. Of all created things, it is "in splendor likest Heaven"; but it is not Heaven. Yet its brightness "beyond expression" compared to things of earth makes it a physical symbol of Heaven's special light, of Heaven itself. The failure of the philosophers to create the elixir is like Satan's failure. The bright sun is as close to Heaven as he gets on this scale, though near enough for him to recognize the hierarchical symbol and to curse its beams, having been shorn of his own and now coming to this sun himself a clouded sun. Earlier, when he was compared to the bright sun, Satan was elevated and amplified, was not less than archangel ruined, but now the true relation between him and the sun is enforced through the image of the alchemists. His quest becomes theirs, and he succeeds to the degree that they do in binding Hermes and calling up Proteus; for Uriel is deceived and man does fall. Deluded, the philosophers distort the things of nature trying to produce what the archchemic sun accomplishes naturally: whole rivers of potable gold and the elixir sought in vain on earth. Into that brightness Satan also deluded, brings a darkened and perverted will; all this clarity and absence of shadow sharpen only his physical eye. The sin of the alchemists is emulation of the sun; they try to short-cut the natural processes through which

God works; like Satan, they are self-deceived and like Satan's, theirs is finally a sin of pride. The experience will react upon him later and waken his guilty conscience, although it will not deflect him. The motif of deception runs through the whole passage. Indeed, we are mistaken if we think the comparisons to real jewels of earth will convey the sun's brightness. Such is the nature of evil that even in the bright sun, Uriel cannot detect the fraud. Aaron the true and good contrasts with fabled, elusive Hermes and Proteus; for he is paired with the sun as the philosophers with the two gods. A system of contrasts pervades the lines: reality against artificiality, physical brightness against spiritual darkness, Hebrew against pagan, the true dignity of the sun as lord of planets and natural creator against the false pride of the artful alchemists and Satan. All these implications come once we have perceived the metaphoric vocabulary imbedded in the curious and forgotten lore of philosopher's stone, the fecundating sun, and alchemy.

Comparable opportunities present themselves in the examination of medieval and Renaissance botanical lore in Milton. Not all plants lend their literary past to such a detailed history as E. S. Le Comte's persuasive study of that small unsightly root haemony, nor all flower passages to so brilliant an interpretation as Wayne Shumaker's analysis of *Lycidas.* Yet the best known in the terrestrial Paradise, the banyan tree whose leaves Adam and Eve used to cover their shame, is exceptionally important in the Christian myth, some writers identifying it (as others did the cypress) with the Tree of Knowledge. And whatever the merit of the challenge that Milton saw nature through the spectacles of books, it is clear that plants and flowers in their bookish relations contribute heavily to the metaphoric structure of *Comus, Lycidas,* and *Paradise Lost.* In the ordered universe of these poems, nearly every plant, to paraphrase Blount, carries with it the impress of its poetic maker and can read us lectures in art as well as ethics and divinity. Whether Milton read Sebastian Franck is questionable, but his practice agrees with the interpretation in *The Forbidden Fruit, or a Treatise of the Tree of Knowledge of Good and Evil which Adam at First, & as yet All Mankind doe eate death* (1640): the tree may indeed have been natural; all men partake of it, and "doe eate death, and yet neverthelesse with *Adam* and *Eve* thinke themselves to eate life, and hope to be Gods." We recall Eve:

> nor was God-head from her thought.
> Greedily she ingorg'd without restraint,
> And knew not eating Death.   IX, 790–792

This extraordinary image invokes a sudden comparison and contrast with Death, already with Sin on his way into the cosmos. Eve ravins down her proper bane; the release of inordinate appetite into the world brings on the insatiable devourer of all men. At this moment Eve is ally, victim, and instrument of Satan, a foster-sister to Death. But from her will come the devourer of Death; in the instant of her act, she is destroying herself but she is setting into motion the chain of events that will redeem her fall.[8]

In a century when everyone read Ovid and every man was either a fool or a physician, it is not unexpected that the Latin poems refer to wholesome herbs and health-giving plants, nor that the shepherd lad of *Comus* should be "deep-versed in herbs" and "simples of a thousand names." Nor is it accident that Comus knows "Potent hearbs and baleful drugs": in the symbolizing of good and evil, all nature contributes. Milton's life-long literary preoccupation with medicines and physicians, his self-medication for eye-strain and flatulence, even perhaps his association with the Cambridge botanist and tutor Joseph Mede are reflected in *Damon's Epitaph, On the Coming of Spring,* the *Second Defence,* and *Samson Agonistes.* Milton rebukes hellebore, low-growing crocus, and leaf of hyacinth for failing the master of herbs himself, Damon. The fatal compulsion to gluttony so often condemned in Milton no doubt inspired his *Commonplace Book* memorandum from Purchas that greedy Sumatrans renew their stomach "with an herb calld Arecca betula." His characterization of an opponent as one who "drunk with hellebore . . . vomits out a whole sink of foul abuse" parallels Rembert Dodoens' and Thomas Lodge's notes that an instable and dangerous variety of hellebore "causeth one to vomit up mightily." Maplet prescribes hyacinth for relief of gall; and Bartholomew, overcome by the wealth in Dioscorides and other authorities, finds crocus a specific for heart disease, insomnia, impotence, and snakebite. The *Short Title Catalogue* lists hundreds of purges and antidotes for ills of the body politic. The metaphors Milton picked up from Griffith in *Brief Notes upon a Late Sermon* were equally common: the electuary to be taken daily, the strong purgatives of the pulpit made of the myrrh of mortification, aloes of confession, and rhubarb of restitution. Although Milton did the same sort of thing when it suited him, he observes sourly of these "Physical terms" that they are "a pretty fantastic dos of Divinity from a Pulpit Mountibanck." Herbals gave long sections to these medicines; myrrh and aloes, since they were difficult to come by, were credited with many powers. Bartholomew, Batman, and La Primaudaye treat them all as purgatives.[9]

Euphrasy, rue, and fennel were popular prescriptions for eye-trouble and were extolled so enthusiastically that herbals, medical books and encyclopedias occasionally got sidetracked into unrelated properties (Batholomew reports that rue abates lust in men, excites it in women). The fennel sought by reptiles supplied Milton with a jibe in *Apology for Smectymnuus*, "gave him to see clearer than any fennel rub'd Serpent," and a piece of verisimilitude in Satan's "more pleas'd my sense / Then smell of sweetest Fenel."

Maplet, Swan, La Primaudaye, Dodoens, Lupton, *A Thousand Notable Things,* and the *Regimen Sanitatis Salerni*
treat the herbs at length. Topsell, *Historie of Serpents,* tells
how these creatures, casting their skins in spring and autumn,
"help the dimnesse of their eye-sight by rubbing their eyes
upon fennell."

The common properties of euphrasy and rue provide a
realistic foundation for the mysterious episode just before
Michael shows Adam the future of the race:

> but to nobler sights
> *Michael* from *Adams* eyes the Filme remov'd
> Which that false Fruit that promis'd clearer sight
> Had bred; then purg'd with Euphrasie and Rue
> The visual Nerve, for he had much to see;
> And from the Well of Life three drops instill'd.
> So deep the power of these Ingredients pierc'd,
> Eevn to the inmost seat of mental sight,
> That *Adam* now enforc't to close his eyes,
> Sunk down and all his spirits became intranst.
>   XI, 411–420

It is worth noting that Milton excluded fennel, despite its
consistent union in scientific books with euphrasy and rue,
for this gives another clue to his practice. In the transfer of
symbols between good and evil he was indefatigable but
selective; he avoided fennel here probably because of its
common relation to serpents and previous use with Satan.
Certainly he makes the symbolism of Michael's act overt.
After Adam's physical sight has been purged, Michael blinds
him to the immediate world with three drops from the
mysterious, almost Spenserian, Well of Life, nowhere else
mentioned or explained in the poem. There are three stages
here: a physical excess had dimmed Adam's understanding
as well as his sight; the film is removed by a kind of magic;
and then the physical sense is cleared with common herbs.
In that physically purified state Adam is prepared for the

loss of one kind of vision to gain, once more through other-worldly magic, the inner vision necessary to the return of understanding when Michael tells him to open his eyes. The whole episode is ritualistic, sacrificial, paradoxical.[10]

The symbolic goodness of nature accounts in part for the careful announcement by the Genius of the Wood in *Arcades*:

> And all my Plants I save from nightly ill,
> Of noisom winds, and blasting vapours chill.
> And from the Boughs brush off the evil dew,
> And heal the harms of thwarting thunder blew,
> Or what the cross dire-looking Planet smites,
> Or hurtful Worm with canker'd venom bites.
>
> 48–53

No one needed books to know there was war in nature, or to learn that shipmast pines grew tall (as in the account of Satan's spear). Nonetheless, as Topsell on caterpillars, palmer worms, and cankers thought it meet to say that every plant has "his proper and peculiar enemy and destroyer," so the encyclopedias repeated how the height and soundness of the pine make it suitable for masts, and how the "sturdiest Oaks" (of the dream scene in *Paradise Regained*) have deep strong roots. Geographical discovery and expansion of trade had familiarized many with the spices that sweeten the Garden of Eden; but the Bible and its commentary had long since made known the "Groves of Myrrhe, / And flouring Odours, Cassia, Nard, and Balme." These exotic blooms occupy great space in the encyclopedias for medicinal value as well as odor, Maplet remarking balm as shrub, not a tree, La Primaudaye listing cassia and myrrh with cinnamon and frankincense, Bartholomew prescribing nard for heart failure. We have seen in Chapter I how Milton turned botanical lore of a different sort into bawdy satire; he speaks in the same vein, obscurely in *Of Reformation*, bluntly in *Pro Se Defensio*. If church government is taught in the gospel, "we may

well conclude of what late standing this position is, newly
calculated for the altitude of Bishop elevation, and lettice
for their lips." Dodoens says lettuce is good against "wamb-
lings" of the stomach, which is perhaps what Milton had in
mind, though if he knew it, he would no doubt have been
thinking of Dodoens' further note that lettuce-seed eaten a
long time is an antidote to lechery. In *Pro Se Defensio* the
rapid growth and phallic shape of the mushroom are, as he
said of images in another pamphlet, "stretch'd to a figurative
construction":

To me it always appeared best to grow slowly, and as it were, by
imperceptible advances. You are that mushroom who, when only
just out of your boyhood . . . popped up professor of Greek.
. . . By and by, the mushroom having recently become tuberous,
you did not, it is true, put an end to Claudius, but you laid
Claudia on her back among the mushrooms, and the pot-herbs,
and the pot-herb tackle.

Bacon had pointed out that "such as are upstarts in state,
they call in reproach mushrooms"; but that simple analogy
is only the point of departure for this savage and involved
invective. Not least among the insults are the undertones
of poison, always part of mycological lore.[11]

Among plants with fixed literary equivalents, Milton
mentions amarant, moly, haemony (a special case), nepenthes, and that ancient figure of unity and interdependence,
the elm and vine. Moly and haemony have been so thoroughly explicated by Le Comte and Brooks-Hardy that it is
enough to remark here Le Comte's identification of the two
and the linkage of Milton's haemony with rhamus, or Christ's
Thorn, as set out in Gerard and Dodoens. The blood-red
haemony, symbol of God's grace, thus blends both the pagan
connotations of magical moly and the Christian legend of
the Redeemer's blood. Unlike Robert Greene, Milton "invented" very little science, preferring apparently to create
new combinations or to discover new possibilities in old

material, as here with haemony and in *Lycidas* with the balance (first noted by Brooks-Hardy) between "blind mouthes" and "quaint enameld eyes, / That on the green terf suck the honied showres." Nepenthes, long familiar from the *Odyssey*, is quite conventional in Comus' claim

> Not that *Nepenthes* which the wife of *Thone*,
> In *Egypt* gave to *Jove*-born *Helena*
> Is of such power to stir up joy as this.   674–676

For Swan relates from Pliny that nepenthes is "an herb which being steeped and drunk in wine, expelleth sadness." The elm and vine figure from *Of Reformation* reappears in *Paradise Lost*. The pamphleteer refuses to think "the Church a *Vine* in this respect, because, as they take it, she cannot subsist without clasping about the *Elme* of worldly strength, and felicity." The poet describes the innocent prompting of Adam and Eve in a fertility gesture that moves the pity of God himself:

> they led the Vine
> To wed her Elm; she spous'd about him twines
> Her marriageable arms, and with her brings
> Her dowr th' adopted Clusters, to adorn
> His barren leaves.   V, 215–219

No bit of botanical lore was better known — it occurs in Horace, Ovid, Virgil, Columella, Spenser, Shakespeare, Bartholomew, Batman, and Maplet — yet how strikingly Milton uses it. Adam and Eve dramatize their own relation in this act. Eve has just shown to disadvantage; her dream has divided the human pair. Now after comfort and prayer they renew their unity in simple duties: they restrain excess where any row "Of Fruit-trees overwoodie reachd too farr / Thir pamperd boughes, and needed hands to check / Fruitless imbraces"; they join vine, figure of her softness and submission, and elm. The symbolic act confirms Adam's incompleteness without

her. In this context the stereotype rehearses in singularly
appropriate sexual symbols an act which has an air of ritual
about it. Certainly no writer so conscious of its literary history as Milton was would fail to realize the traditional, cere-
monial quality of the image.[12]

We return to the famous banyan treated historically in
the first chapter. Excitement over sources has diverted editors
from remarking its extraordinary implications. Some naturalist theologians identified it with the forbidden tree; Ralegh
discusses "Becanus his opinion, that the Tree of Knowledge
was *Ficus Indica*" because the large leaves would supply the
covering spoken of in the Bible. We know from *Regimen
Sanitatis Salerni* that figs engender lust, and from Golding's
Solinus that the fruit of the banyan fig tree is "of verie
singuler sweetness." Though Milton keeps his trees separate,
employs the apple tree as the one forbidden, and expressly
denies any renown for fruit to the banyan, the existence of
the other traditions is evidence of the kind of learning he
drew from. The appeal of double duty, one tree for both sin
and sign of sin, indicates the same passion for correspondence
and poetic justice as the legend in Mandeville's *Voyages and
Travailes* that the tree of knowledge was cypress and that the
angel guarding Paradise gave Seth three kernels from it to
put under Adam's tongue at burial so that "when the tree
bare fruit then should Adam be made whole" — at the
crucifixion.[13]

The prominence given the banyan at once suggests that
there is more to the lines than meets the eye, for Milton's
epic similes are never independent decorations. Each of them,
as Whaler showed years ago, corresponds on many points
with the ideas and motives of the narrative. Mahood and
Stein describe the garden as a retreat, a shelter, a womblike
place of security out of which Adam and Eve must be born
again, ejected into the world at large. Within that temporary
home is another, the bower of Adam and Eve, and yet a third,

inside the rooted branches of this vast tree. We must examine
the lines:

> both together went
> Into the thickest Wood, there soon they chose
> The Figtree, not that kind for Fruit renown'd,
> But such as at this day to *Indians* known
> In *Malabar* or *Decan* spreds her Armes
> Braunching so broad and long, that in the ground
> The bended twigs take root, and Daughters grow
> About the Mother Tree, a Pillard shade
> High overarch't, and echoing Walks between;
> There oft the *Indian* Herdsman shunning heate
> Shelters in coole, and tends his pasturing Herds
> At Loopholes cut through thickest shade: Those Leaves
> They gatherd, broad as *Amazonian* Targe,
> And with what skill they had, together sowd,
> To gird thir waste. IX, 1099–1113

This sheltered pastoral contrasts poignantly with the frantic
distress of Adam and Eve. There is protection in the mother's
spreading arms, the high arch, the "pillard shade," and a
sense of comfortable insideness from the quick echo within
leafy walls. The tree is in the garden with us, for we see it
close; but Malabar and Decan are far distant in time (" as
at this day") and place — an implicit denial that this pro-
tected pastoral life exists any longer for the human pair.
Their act is symbolic, a synecdoche in gesture; they may not
escape to security within the tree, they may use only part of
it, ineptly ("what skill they had") to conceal themselves —
"vain Covering if to hide / Thir guilt and dreaded shame."
They feel "fenc't" with even this little, but are not. Adam
called upon the pines and cedars to hide and cover him, then
went with Eve "into the thickest Wood," and reached this
deep interior sanctuary — of which he may have only so
much token as proclaims his guilt and need. Yet there is
fecundity in the fig tree, expressed as a cycle of human generation. The twigs still bound to their mother fall to earth,
root themselves, and rise again as daughters, one more among

a hundred images of rhythmic fall and rise, rise and fall —
the theme at the center of the great double plot of the
narrative. This is Milton's advance over the "allegorizing"
of Becanus reported by Ralegh, *The History of the World*:

As this Tree (saith he) so did Man grow straight and upright
towards God, untill such time as he had transgressed and broken
the Commandment of his Creatour; and then like unto the
boughes of this tree, he beganne to bend downeward, and
stouped toward the earth, which all the rest of *Adam's* posteritie
have done, rooting themselves therein and fastening themselves
to this corrupt world.[14]

It has become fashionable to smile at Masson's senti-
mentalizing of the young Milton at Horton or the old at
Artillery Walk; yet Masson long ago found the right word in
calling *Paradise Lost* a cosmological epic. One may reject his
suggestion that it contains Milton's theory of all things. But
this chapter alone should persuade a modern reader that the
poem is cosmological, since it embraces so many particulars
bearing upon natural properties and relationships, even of
stones and metals and plants, and constantly assimilates
them through classical and medieval images and information.
We are perhaps too far away from the seventeenth century
to hope for the "universal insight into things" Milton
wanted; surely we miss many subtleties for each we do
perceive. But just as surely, it is in this recovery that we find
the materials for genuine insight into Milton's meaning
and art.

CHAPTER V

All the Beasts of the Earth:
The Animal Kingdom in Milton

ANIMAL LORE IN MILTON, like mineralogy
and botany, exhibits the stock images of antiquity, the vulgar
errors exposed by Browne and Vaughan, and the monumental
medieval glosses upon Aristotle and Pliny. Wolfgang Frantze
echoed the voices of several centuries in his *History of Brutes*,
when he proclaimed the advantages of this kind of knowledge
"not only for dispute but for the explication of Authors as
well Sacred as Prophane." The bestiaries merely intimate the
ubiquity of animal symbolism; the study of a single icon
such as the ape can be pursued indefinitely. Beast fables, ex-
empla, chivalric romances, patristic myth, the whole of medieval and Renaissance literature domesticated countless wild
animals, monsters, and fabulous beasts for plot, characterization, symbolism, exegesis, and ornament. Euphuists wove
hundreds of figures from animal lore; and the hippogrif is
surely a major character in *Orlando Furioso*. These beasts
were still alive in seventeenth-century scientific, religious, and
literary traditions. The phoenix may have lost ground to the
new rationalism; but the basilisk, which no one could look
upon without dying, was still in the prayer book and still
confidently pictured in woodcuts — presumably because it
could be killed with a mirror.

Milton stays right in this tradition, standing with Alexander
Ross, as it were, instead of Sir Thomas Browne. The patterns
of use from stone and plant lore recur in the exercise of animal
metaphor; moral and ethical values are evinced from the
slightest insect. Animal satire in the controversial pamphlets
bulks large, as Milton reviles opponents for owls and cuckoos,
asses, apes, and dogs. We shall see frequently how a detail or
a simile from the prolusions and early poems reappears in the

The beasts of the field, from Bartholomew, De Proprietatibus Rerum,
English ed., 1495.

prose and in *Paradise Lost,* as Milton's imagination returns to a figure that engaged his fancy or succeeded for him earlier. The epic is, of course, a final repository. Mineralogical lore reaches a kind of climax in the stones and metals compared to the sun, itself a central dynamic image; botanical learning culminates in the banyan-tree-of-knowledge myth, also a major symbol. The particulars spread through the antecedent works are brought together in the animals related to Satan, especially the serpent, allegorized in all cultures as a magic force, usually evil, that must be overcome or propitiated. The chain of being figures prominently in the thematic structure of an epic on the corruption of all nature; symbolic equivalents of leading ideas occur in images of vulture, whale, ant, raven, and griffin. Finally, the classical-medieval diffusion of this lore argues the same dispersion of sources seen in the preceding chapters. We find gross originals easily enough for *The Brief History of Moscovia, Christian Doctrine,* and *Judgment of Martin Bucer.* But sources are so deeply assimilated in *Paradise Lost* that there is hardly a piece of animal imagery for which several verbal parallels may not be found.[1]

We have seen too the structural function of the scale of nature in the epic argument. Raphael, Adam, and Satan repeat the encyclopedists' claim that study of lower forms of life leads to self-study and knowledge of God. Animals serve not only practical uses, as food and physic, but also point unmistakably to the Maker of all. Their hierarchy teaches man his own place in the grand scheme of life, so that by steps, as Adam says, he may ascend to God. Most of the facts may be found in Pliny and Aristotle, but their moral implications come from the heart of the middle ages and the Renaissance, and not simply because they were part of Biblical commentary. They were part of men's thinking. Allen has shown, for example, how solemnly Augustine debated embarking fish and insects among Noah's animals; indeed, a basic problem for most commentators was whether the Ark was big enough, even with Origen's three decks, for all the animals installed. But the zoological tradition upon which the time drew runs from Herodotus as well as hexamera, through Theophrastus, Nicander, Oppian, Ælian, Isidore, Vincent and Bartholomew, Gesner, and Aldrovandi beyond Topsell and his fellows. Bartholomew's restriction to animals mentioned in the Bible or biblical gloss deprived him of little. Animal lore flourished in every kind of writing; Marco Polo and Mandeville are only two of many travelers to dazzle their readers with wondrous forms and powers of distant monsters. Drayton might condemn the artificiality of Lyly in playing with words and idle similes of natural history; but it should have been the style and not the content he disparaged, for a sizable encyclopedia of science might be extracted from his own works.

Milton, then, inherited this vast Elizabethan zoo in which few specimens were suspect and all provided lectures in divinity. As to climate of belief, the credulity of any age is difficult to assess. Milton mentions scornfully the dog-headed monsters with which Spanish priests frighten the vulgar; but Edward Fenton's *Certaine Secrete Wonders of Nature* (1569) was still in libraries with its woodcut of such a beast born at Basel, and dozens of authorities testified to the cynocephali, regarding them as a minor novelty among truly marvelous monsters. A widespread superstition concerned spontaneous generation, than which no other was more deeply imbedded in the writings of theologians, serious scientists, and encyclopedists.[2]

Animal origin, particularly abiogenesis, is a good place to begin the examination of zoological lore in Milton. The graphic account in Book VII of animals spawned from sea and earth moves down the scale from "the great Whales . . . Leviathan, / Hugest of living Creatures" to the "Minims of Nature," the "Parsimonious Emmet," then up again to the serpent, significantly named last before Adam's creation. It

is the subtlest beast of all the field, sometimes frightful to
look upon, though dismissed by Raphael here as "Not nox-
ious, but obedient at thy call." Though Satan will presently
inhabit the serpent, as the reader is reminded by this emphasis, for narrative suspense Adam must not suspect temptation's form; hence the poet for a moment shows his contriving
hand in Raphael's qualification. Images of motion heighten
the description of simultaneous birth: the lion pawing to
get free of earth, the stag forcing upward his branching head,
whole flocks of cattle rising as plants. Behind this climactic
emergence of earth and sea into separate life stretch numberless handbooks of biology and many references in Milton's
prose to spontaneous generation and unnatural or monstrous
birth. Something of the sort underlies the sentence in *Reason
of Church Government*, where Rome, "as in a decay'd nature
seeks to the outward fomentations and chafings of worldly
help and external flourishes" in order to "hatch a counterfeit life with the crafty and artificial heat of jurisdiction."
The "reserv'd Manna" of *Eikonoklastes* is said to produce
worms, as if God's word ill used breeds evil instead of good.
The God-figure of the Hermetic sun, whose penetrating ray
creates even in the center of the earth, engenders the huge
python on slime; and the lines set up an immediate contrast
between God's creation of man and Satan's creation of evil.
The "wind-egg of definition" derided in *Colasterion* appears
again in *Eikonoklastes*, where the parliament is ironically
"but a Female, and without his [Charles'] procreative reason, the Laws which they produce are but wind-eggs." It
climaxes an ingenious, ugly passage of *Second Defence*:

From this connection, there followed, in due time, something
strange and monstrous — out of the common course of nature.
Not the female only, but the male conceived; Pontia a Moreling
which, for a long time after, served to exercise the Plinian exercitator Salmasius; More this addle and windy egg, from which
burst forth that tympany — the *Cry of the Royal Blood*. This was

thought at first a most delicious sup for our hungry royalists in Belgium; but now the shell is broken, they turn with loathing from the rotten and offensive contents.

In the same vein Milton had earlier combined generation from putrefaction with the related image of the *ovum aspidi* in one of many brutal indictments in *Of Reformation*:

The soure levin of humane Traditions, mixt in one putrefi'd Masse with the poisonous dregs of hypocrisie in the hearts of *Prelates* that lye basking in the Sunny Warmth of Wealth, and Promotion, is the Serpents Egge that will hatch an *Antichrist* wheresoever, and ingenders the same Monster as big, or little as the Lump is which breeds him.

God's creative act is the opposite of all this; before describing it, however, Milton reached once more into the concept of unnatural and evil birth for the "Universe of death," which God by curse "created evil, for evil only good," the place where

> all life dies, death lives, and Nature breeds
> Perverse, all monstrous, all prodigious things,
> Abominable, inutterable, and worse
> Than Fables yet have feign'd, or fear conceiv'd,
> *Gorgons* and *Hydra's,* and *Chimera's* dire.
>
> II, 622–628

Hell opposes Heaven in malignant reversal of creativeness; Satan's abode, prepared before Adam's, objectifies his avowal to bring evil out of good; irregularity and monstrosity in spite of themselves function in the great scheme of the epic. Sin and Death, monstrous, incestuous children of Satan's negative creativity, climax the catalogue of unnatural animals: she hideous half-serpent, he vulture-like in scenting the disasters that feed him, their offspring the hell-hounds into which Satan's fertility has degenerated.

By the sixteenth century, theories of spontaneous generation, of wind-eggs and serpent eggs, of cockatrice and basilisk were all worked into something like one system of belief or superstition. The wind-egg is described by Bartholomew as produced without the male but from treading by females; they are "lyttell and unsavery" and of "an evyll stynche." They are also produced by the action of the wind, which could impregnate vultures and mares too. According to Agrippa's well-worn story and Milton's little indulgence in mythmaking in *L'Allegro*, even women were susceptible to the wind's creative power. Indeed, wind fertilization of the vulture gives Frank L. Huntley the clue for integrating the whole Limbo of Vanities passage with the themes of true and false creation and the monstrosity, perversity, and futility of evil. Related in concept are the worms and lice generated from rotton wood, the gnats from horse-dung, and the mice "in Ships, out of the putrid matter which lyeth at the bottom of the Pump," all mentioned in the *History of Brutes*. Jonston gives directions for breeding bees from a freshly killed ox and relates out of Ælian that when rain falls with hail, "Mice are said to appear in the earth, half mud, half flesh." Bacon in *Sylva Sylvarum* took *insecta* to mean all creatures bred of putrefaction.

Comparable in its violation of orthodoxy or the convention of general natural law is the cock-and-serpent egg, whence came basilisk and cockatrice, those fabulously fatal monsters sometimes differentiated but by the thirteenth century often taken for the same horror. Bartholomew says "The Cockatrice hyghte Basilicus in grewe"; and *The Philosophers Banquet*, for example, tells of its birth much as Lupton does in this passage from *A Thousand Notable Things*:

About the rising of the little Dogge (beeing in Sommer) an olde Cocke doth lay an Egge, round speckled, and of diverse colours: whereof many doo thinke that the Basylike, or Cockatrise dooth come (which is a most pernicious and venemous Serpent,) especially, if that Egge be sit upon and hatched by a Tode. Which whether it be fable or not, let other judge.

Topsell equates the two in the same story, doubtfully

delivered. Swan finds it "scarce credible" but faithfully records the belief that the cock's egg hatched by a toad "bringeth forth a venimous worm, although not this basilisk." The older serpent-egg theory had its supporters; identification of that cockatrice with Antichrist was as old as "the gloss." Bartholomew, who never saw one and would doubtless have been surprised if expected to, considering the danger, knows the egg to be yellow, slimy, and stinking, and that "There the glose saythe, that of the egges of Aspidis cometh a cokatrice, and of the venemouse Jewes shalle come Antichrist." Batman, who had other troubles, added: "And of the wicked Papist the Divell." The relation of these theories to the wind-egg in Isaiah has been clarified by Robin; both were discredited by Sir Thomas Browne, but woodcuts showing the cockatrice survive from the thirteenth and sixteenth centuries and at Halle in Saxony and at Vienna are monuments to this peculiarly European animal. Milton uses cockatrice and basilisk not as articles of scientific faith but as fixed images. This is the "fiery Serpent" that killed with a look but fled the Son of God; fiery because its breath burned leaves off trees, scorched grass, and killed everything in its neighborhood.[3]

Other imaginary animals include the dragon, the gryphon, the hippogrif, and the phoenix, out of a whole calendar of mantichoras, catoblepas, bishopfish, and unicorns that Milton might have listed with his classical gorgons, hydras, and chimeras. ("Imaginary" is a courtesy title; by modern standards, all Elizabethan animals are fabulous.) Every culture of the least sophistication knows the dragon; and from Beowulf to Milton, English literature accepts it as both real and symbolic. Spenser unhesitatingly renders this mythical beast in only too much detail, but Milton contents himself with such particulars as "the scaly Horrour of his foulded tail" in *Nativity Ode*, the "guly color" and condition in *Of Reformation*, the fiery dragon, signifying Danish invasion, in *History of Britain*. Satan's symbol everywhere is the arch-dragon, especially in *Paradise Lost*. He was right to hate the beams of the creative sun, for in the old legend, the sun which engendered the python killed it; and Satan suffers a kind of death at the height of his triumph when, "Now Dragon grown" literally, he merges with his symbol. The gryphon to which he is compared in his journey through Chaos toward the world and its sun is also a solar animal, a huge half-eagle, half-lion with pointed animal ears the better to hear the stealthy one-eyed Arimaspian:

> As when a Gryphon through the Wilderness
> With winged course ore Hill or moarie Dale
> Pursues the *Arimaspian*, who by stelth
> Had from his wakeful custody purloind
> The guarded Gold.   II, 943–947

The undertones here have been worked out in part by Whaler. The eager movement of Satan toward his design equated to the relentless pursuit of the gryphon is the basic comparison here; but the interplay between Satan and the sun, gold and the sun, and the guardian gryphon and the sun all give a special intensity to the simile. Originally the gryphon was thought to fly over the earth, much as Satan, also a monstrous hybrid, now flies toward it. Agrippa might dismiss "these Figments of the *Arimaspy, Gryphons, Pigmies, Cranes*, People with Dogs Heads"; Bartholomew, Batman, Maplet, and Swan all treat it respectfully, with the gold of the early accounts extended to include precious stones, as in Olaus Magnus: "Arimaspi cum his pugnant ut lapides, qui ibi sunt, intercipiant: ex quibus sunt smaragdus, cyanem, & crystallus." Somewhere in antiquity the gryphon became symbolic of rapacity, no doubt because of its monstrous shape and size and because men had more right to gold than eagle-lions did. This fact enables us to recognize the pejorative comparison with Satan, as Milton himself shows in the earlier thrust in *Of Reformation* at "rooking Officials, with cloke bagges full of Citations, and Processes to be serv'd by a corporalty of Griffonlike Promooters, and Apparitors." The gryphon appears at one remove in *Paradise Regained.* Satan takes up the Son

> and without wing
> Of *Hippogrif* bore through the Air sublime
> Over the Wilderness and o're the Plain.
>
> IV, 541–543

The hippogrif is a second-generation monster, born of a mare and a gryphon, its habitat like its father's conveniently the northern unexplored parts of the world. It too is solar, but not so savage; in *Orlando Furioso* Rogero and Astolpho ride the hippogrif on many adventures after Atlantes has tamed it. Milton is thought to have glanced at Ariosto in the invocation to *Paradise Lost*; perhaps here he enforces another disparaging contrast between the triviality of Ariosto's theme and the importance of his.[4]

That fabulous bird, the phoenix, is of course "gazed by all," as Milton says, and renews itself in hundreds of medieval and Renaissance poems, plays, sermons, and polemics, often as a type of Christ or of immortality. With so widespread an idea, the immediate source for a given passage in Milton would seem as elusive as the bird itself; but dozens of originals have been confidently advanced. Milton knew Lactantius, Tasso, and Herodotus, few men better. Yet the survival of many parallel treatments should temper one's acceptance of Hartwell's and Hughes' selection of *De Ave Phoenice* and Tasso's poem, or Gilbert's choice of Herodotus. Milton's earliest reference seems to be that in *Damon's Epitaph*, where the phoenix on one of the cups of Manso figures as divine, unique, all brilliant blue with iridescent wings. In *Reason of Church Government*, the bird's dubious historicity becomes an ironic synonym for *never*: "it suffices me that I find it [prelaty] in his skin, so I find it inseparable, or not oftener otherwise than a Phenix hath bin seen." In *Pro Se*

Defensio occurs a contrast between borrowed feathers, the appearance of a phoenix, and the reality of the hoopoe, "with not a single plume and barely a breech." Raphael and Samson are phoenixes, the one for rarity and sunlike beauty, the other also for regeneration and the Christian doctrine of life through death. The gates of Heaven self-open for Raphael; his whole easy flight contrasts with Satan's, as he

> Winnows the buxom Air; till within soare
> Of Towring Eagles, to all the Fowles he seems
> A *Phoenix*, gaz'd by all, as that sole Bird
> When to enshrine his reliques in the Sun's
> Bright Temple, to *Ægyptian Theb's* he flies.
>   V, 270–274

Samson's life history is suggested in the triumphant summary by the Semichorus. His fiery virtues roused from under ashes into sudden flame, he came like an evening dragon to roosts and nests of "tame villatic Fowl" but as an eagle "cloudless thunder bolted on thir heads":

> So vertue giv'n for lost,
> Deprest, and overthrown, as seem'd,
> Like that self-begott'n bird
> In the *Arabian* woods embost,
> That no second knows nor third,
> And lay e're while a Holocaust,
> From out her ashie womb now teem'd,
> Revives, reflourishes, then vigorous most
> When most unactive deem'd,
> And though her body die, her fame survives,
> A secular bird ages of lives.   1697–1707

From these metaphors nine particulars about the phoenix may be extracted: it is unique and seldom seen, brilliant (blue and iridescent) in plumage, self-begotten, long-lived, Arabian, self-immolating, regenerative from ashes; and it deposits the relics of its former self in the temple of the sun at Thebes. All these traits, allowing for the confusion of

Heliopolis and Thebes, occur in extensive accounts of the phoenix and may be found in Bartholomew, Batman, Maplet, La Primaudaye, and Swan. The discrepancy between Milton's Thebes and the Heliopolis given by Batman and others may indicate his following an unknown version of the legend, as Verity thinks; or it may be explained, as does Gilbert, from the similarity of the Hebrew equivalents for the cities and from Diodorus' remark that Egyptians call Thebes Heliopolis. A stronger probability, if choice must be made, is that the accounts of Claudian and his paraphraser Tasso represent the phoenix as going to Thebes in Egypt. When one accumulates all the possibilities advanced by Miltonists and others, and adds William Browne's *Britannia's Pastorals*, in a copy of which Milton wrote "The Phoenix" beside some lines on it, there appear to be nearly fifty treatments from which he might have drawn enough for his references to this ubiquitous bird.[5]

The function of the story is more significant than its source. Raphael descends like a great legendary solar bird (Maplet among many declares it "consecrated to Sol") to instruct mankind, flying a long while before he reaches the low level of the towering eagle, a natural bird also sacred to the sun. Out of that creative center — God and the sun — comes supernatural grace, conveyed now as instruction, later by Christ, who like the phoenix dies and is resurrected. There are undercurrents in the pagan-Christian connotations of the solar bird, the god of sun and of healing Apollo, and Raphael, literally the divine healer, who would be a sun-god in any other mythology and whose advice is a kind of preventive medicine. Certainly his godlike glittering appearance (made much of here), his contra-Satanic journey to earth, and the unique grace of his divinely directed mission are symbolized and enforced by the phoenix. Its implications enlarge Raphael's part in the moral context.

In the lines from *Samson Agonistes,* the analogies with

Samson are carefully thought out. Even "dragon," commonly pejorative, fits the context and harmonizes with "eagle" as dynamic energy exploded in righteous violence upon the enemies of God. Samson, like the phoenix, achieves a new life through self-sacrifice and death. The legendary bird was not destructive since in some versions the phoenix flew under the chariot of the sun to soften its rays before they struck the earth. The rapid change here from dragon to eagle to phoenix typifies Milton's way of capitalizing upon accepted associations, then altering their image to make a new point; for the shift expresses Samson as a force expending itself, like his passion, and leaving the mind purged as by fire but renewed. A rationalist like Thomas Vaughan might decline to waste time on such an imposture; the poet lingers with the fable as a rich image for the Christian concept of gaining a life by losing it.

The minims of nature play their parts in Milton as definitely as eagles and phoenixes. For him, as for many, grasping bishops are locusts, underminers of the state are caterpillars; cankerworms are destroyers of both fruit and plant — all ancient synonyms for greed and waste. The dreaded insect was the scorpion, classified by some as a worm or serpent, and it acquired early the viperish characteristics of deception and deadly cruelty. Passages in *Of Reformation, First Defence, Eikonoklastes,* and Death's threat to Satan at the gates of Hell invoke the Old Testament whip of scorpions with which Rehoboam promised to chastise his people. The reference in *Tetrachordon* to the turning of God's bounty into scorpions carries some suggestion of deceit. *Animadversions* inverts the sequence: "they could not refine a Scorpion into a Fish, though they had drawn it, and rinc't it with never so cleanly Cookery," a proverbial metaphor paralleled in Joseph Mede's assurance that Christ "is thy Father, and will not give thee a Serpent if thou ask him Fish." Manoa skirts blasphemy in wondering if God seduces man to sin:

> Why are his gifts desirable, to tempt
> Our earnest Prayers, then giv'n with solemn hand
> As Graces, draw a Scorpions tail behind?   358–360

Bartholomew follows Isidore in calling it a "londe worme with a croked stynge in the taylle"; Maplet touches an old fable in reporting this "Serpent of the earth" called by some "flatering worme, for faire face shewed and friendly countenaunce. But if any man come neare hir behinde she payeth him home." The *Ancren Riwle* made it monstrous, a serpent with the face of a woman; in Chaucer's *Book of the Duchess* Fortune is "a fals, flaterynge beste" like the scorpion who "with his heed maketh feste" but "with his tayle he wol stynge." Chester's *Love's Martyr* repeats Maplet's phrase "cald of some the flattering worme" and adds: "The Scorpion hath a deadly stinging taile, / Bewitching some with his faire smiling face." These characteristics underlie a comment made by the Chorus after Samson has called Dalila *Hyaena,* a standard figure of flattering deception. "She's gone," says the Chorus, "a manifest Serpent by her sting / Discover'd in the end, till now conceal'd." Samson then dismisses her as a viper; but the facts suggest the scorpion, for we have seen that scorpions are classed with serpents, that they are deceptive, and that their sting is concealed in the tail. Some naturalists did debate whether serpents stung with their tails; but the weight of tradition in herpetological lore favors identifications of this manifest serpent as the bewitching, flattering scorpion-figure, with *discover'd in the end* an outrageous but irresistible double-entendre.[6]

Surely the most popular insects in Renaissance science and literature are the ant and the bee, commended in the prolusion defense of animal reasoning, the one for its instruction in household affairs, the other for its lessons in civil order. Years later in *Readie and Easie Way*, the ant becomes political analogy too, by a slight extension of Solomon's exhortation to industry. Milton condemns those who think the

nation undone without a king as having no more true spirit
and understanding than a pismire, for those diligent creatures set examples of a "frugal and self-governing democratie
or Commonwealth." The ant's domestic virtues are still
apparent; the shift from family economy to statecraft was
not unusual. The household and political sagacity alluded to
separately in the prose are united in the epic:

> The Parsimonious Emmet, provident
> Of future, in small room large heart enclos'd,
> Pattern of just equalitie perhaps
> Hereafter, join'd in her popular Tribes
> Of Commonalitie. VII, 485–489

(Milton would have agreed wholly with Jonston's assertion
that although the bloodless insects seem contemptible, "yet
there is no where a more remarkable piece of Nature's Workmanship; and Nature is no where total, more then in the
least Creatures.") "Perhaps" raises a little dilemma: Milton
wished either to qualify a too-ardent republicanism for
Raphael, who is speaking, or to keep him from appearing too
knowledgeable about events in the later world of men. The
details are common information. Maplet, for example, emphasizes the "Publicke weale" of the ant. Bartholomew cites
Avicenna to the effect "that beastes with lyttel bodyes ben
more slyghe and hardye and witty than other beastes with
greate bodyes, as hit fareth in attercoppes, bein, and amptes."
Elsewhere he moralizes for a page and a half on the domestic
and civil merits of the ant:

they make provysion and gather store agaynste tyme that com-
methe. For in sommer they gather stoore, by the whiche they
mowe lyve in wynter. . . . they lyve in company. . . . They
take greate charge of theyr comyne proffite . . . and though
amptes lyve in company, and be attendaunte eche to other, yet
have they no kynge as Aristotle sayth li. i, and Salomon saith the
same Proverb vi.[7]

Allusions to the bee follow the same progress from prolusion to epic, with the interesting difference that Milton could employ an analogy to support his own arguments and then cavil at an antagonist who did. Long after his acknowledgement of the debt of political theory to the communal habits of the bee, he refused to let Salmasius make anything of their state affairs. In *Eikonoklastes* he had quoted scornfully from *Eikon Basilike* and retorted:

They who can pick nothing out of them but phrases shall be counted *Bees*: they that discern furder both there and here, that *constancy to his Wife* is set in place before Laws and Religion, are in his naturalities no better than *Spiders*.

The implication is that Charles has no real arguments and must resort to name-calling. "*His* naturalities" implies a conveniently unorthodox or an uneducated natural history, as if to say that in every other naturality, bees are commendable creatures — Charles' use of them as a metaphor to disparage his critics simply does not apply. But perhaps Milton missed the neat point of the comparison to spiders, since he made nothing of it. Bartholomew and Batman note the characteristic constancy and love of the male for the female. The Parliamentarians are poisonous insects, says Charles, because like the spiders they make too much of constancy. Milton did not, however, miss the slips in Salmasius' analogy. First he ridicules:

'The bees,' say you, 'have a commonwealth, and so do natural philosophers call it; they have a king, but a harmless one; he is a leader rather than a despot; he beats not, pulls not, kills not his subject bees.' No wonder therefore that they revere him so. Faith, 'twas under no lucky star of yours that you made contact with those *Tridentine* bees; three toothed as they are, they show you up as a toothless drone.

This is quite in that manner of *Eikon Basilike* which he had dismissed as impertinent. Later he finds a real error:

Next you set before us for our imitation those animals that live in commonwealths, first birds, and among them bees, since these are birds, on your authority as Physiologus! 'The bees have a king.' The bees of Trent, that is, — do you not remember? All other bees, on your own admission, 'have republics.' But leave off playing the fool with bees; they belong to the Muses, and hate, and, you see, confute such a beetle as you are.

The analogy is low, as J. A. St. John complained, but in economy and variety it is half-formed verse satire. First there is the error in natural history, then the glance at Salmasius' editing of Solinus, then the painful reminder of Trent, and last the clever conversion of the blunder into a boomerang. Charles Butler's *The Feminine Monarchie* (1609) recalls the legend that "not without cause are the Bees called the Muses birds"; and thus Milton concludes the onslaught by reducing his opponent to an appropriate stand-ard image of unintelligence at opposite pole from the bee, for to the beetle the very scent of the rose was fatal.[8]

Whaler has shown by the number of analogues to the famous simile in *Paradise Lost* that bees do belong to the Muses, so to speak, and that Milton characteristically adds something to the conventional figure in being the first to liken a commonwealth of winged spirits to the whole polity of a hive. The ironic undertones should not be missed:

> As Bees
> In spring time, when the Sun with Taurus rides,
> Poure forth thir populous youth about the Hive
> In clusters, they among fresh dews and flowers
> Flie to and fro, or on the smoothed Plank,
> The suburb of thir Straw-built Cittadel,
> New rub'd with Baume, expatiate and confer
> Thir state affairs.   I, 768–775

The image reduces the demons in size before the narrative does; the ultimate collapse of pillared Pandaemonium is implicit in the oxymoron of "Straw-built Cittadel." The basic comparison of number, movement, and purpose is

only the starting point for the contrast between appearance
and reality. There are no fresh dews and flowers in Hell; the
demons are populous youth only as beginners in evil; and
their state affairs are managed for them by Satan and Beelze-
bub. The particulars of the image, available from most of
the analogues, are also present in the encyclopedias, which
shed light on the other Milton allusions too. Bartholomew
praises the bee commonwealth in which the "kynge . . . is
not armed with a stynge"; Maplet commends the social and
political organization of the hive; La Primaudaye describes
the peaceful cooperation between "king" bee and swarm;
Swan praises these "true patterns of needful government,
keeping themselves under the subjection of a king, and order
of law" because they have a commonwealth. Milton needed
no single source for such stereotyped images of ant and bee;
but unlike the common fate of hackneyed comparisons, they
are not ornamental or independent but so worked into the
texture of his statements that they become part of thematic
development in prose and poetry.[9]

Even the fish offer an archetype. Leviathan, not to be
drawn out by a hook, was in his "island-seeming treachery"
a figure for Satan, from rabbinical commentaries and the
bestiaries forward. But the finny drove so subject to the moon
in *Comus* are not very much particularized in Milton. The
conventional disparagement in *Apology for Smectymnuus*
of "all thy *Synonima's* and voluminous Papers whose best
folios are predestined to no better use than to make winding
sheetes in Lent for Pilchers" became the elaborate insult of
the epigram against Salmasius. God solemnly bids Adam
understand the same fealty from beasts and fish "Not hither
summond, since they cannot change / Thir Element to draw
the thinner Aire." Twice in the prose Milton makes use of
the remora, a small fish which, as Swan says, "cleaveth to the
bottome of a ship, and doth as strongly as strangely stay it."
In *Doctrine of Divorce* he asks, "What mighty and invisible

Remora is this in matrimony able to demurre, and to con-
temn all the divorsive engines in heaven or earth"; and in
Eikonoklastes, Charles' opponents "thought to limit or take
away the *Remora* of his negative voice, which like to that
little pest at Sea, took upon it to arrest and stopp the Commonwealth stearing under full saile to a Reformation." The
encyclopedists solemnly recorded this marvel; from the time
of Pliny it is also figurative in law cases for, as Holland
translates it, "delay of issues and judicial trialls." The contrast between the remora's size and its strength gave rise to
many moralizations upon the mystery of God's secrets; Swan,
Lodge on Dubartas, Tymme, and others use it so, Charron
naming it one of the marvelous effects or properties "not to
be imitated, no not imagined." No list of fishes would be
complete to the Renaissance poet without mention of the
dolphin, called to the surface by music in *Elegy V,* invoked
in *Lycidas,* and traditionally pictured in *Paradise Lost* as
"bended." Its sociability and love of music recur in the
encyclopedias from Bartholomew to Goldsmith. Not so well-
known as remora or dolphin, but equally attractive to Milton
as metaphor is the whale-pilot; in *Second Defence* he strikes
a double blow at More and Salmasius: "You yourself, then,
like the little fish which goes before the whale as a client
his patron, are merely the harbinger of the whale Salmasius,
who is threatening an invasion of our shores." Swan identifies
it as *Musculus* and describes its activity, oblivious to the
comic disparity which is part of Milton's point. Hippopotamus and crocodile appear in the creation story with their
characteristic epithet "ambiguous between sea and land";
Milles and Topsell, who refute sundry fables about the crocodile, record it as amphibian.[10]

The conventional figures of cuckoo, nightingale, halcyon,
crane, and vulture require notice. The "rude Bird of Hate"
in the first sonnet becomes ominous another way in *First
Defence,* where Milton pretends that the monotonous threats

of Salmasius are evidence of insanity, and that madness, which turned Hecuba into a dog, has turned Salmasius into a raving, distracted cuckoo. The reference to Hecuba is a shrewd return to the earlier jibe that Salmasius was dominated by his wife. In *Eikonoklastes* Milton amplifies the figure into a conceit including the familiar story related in *A Greene Forest* and *Speculum Mundi* of the cuckoo as "advouteresse" or "another embleme . . . in the Cuckoe is deciphered the wicked practice of adulterous men, who are not ashamed filthily to defile their neighbours bed." Says Milton: "And how unknowingly, how weakly is the using of sett forms attributed here to *constancy,* as if it were constancie in the Cuckoo to be alwaies in the same liturgie." Charles' book had made something of his martial fidelity, which Milton soon attacks as no excuse for abrogating law and just process. The cuckoo's repetition is mechanical and involuntary, not willed. It is ironical for the bird to be always in the same liturgy — the word equates set prayers with cuckoo noise — when it is itself an emblem of inconstancy. The nightingale preferred to the cuckoo in the first sonnet is like the cuckoo itself practically a dead metaphor. In defending animal reason, Milton had cited Aristotle's assertion that the nightingale taught its young the rules of music, a claim most circumstantially supported by *The French Academie.* In *Comus* it is *love-lorn* and *hapless*; but in *Paradise Lost* it is not yet Philomela, and the epithets are *wakeful, solemn, night-warbling, amorous*; in *Paradise Regained* it is now properly identified as *Attic.* Those other favorites, the halcyons who as "Birds of Calm sit brooding on the charmed wave" in *Nativity Hymn,* also roost in the encyclopedias and many another work. The sportive Sixth Prolusion refers to dinner fowl as lecherous ("after the custom of huge apes, to lie in ambush for the girls and offer violence to the women"), parrot-like ("they also push out the mange in diners"), and lousy:

Accordingly I warn you to abstain from these, for they are very effective (provided the gourmand tells the truth) in the generation of inguinal lice. . . . If they are injected into skinny horses through the fundament, they cause them instantly to become more vivacious and more speedy than if they had ten live eels in their inwards.

In the same category of casual allusion are the daw in borrowed plumes and colors and the hoopoe in *Pro Se Defensio*. But of the crane, the eagle, and the vulture, something further should be said.[11]

In Prolusion VII the geese that lessen the danger of talking by stopping their mouths with pebbles are bracketed with the cranes, which post sentries and adopt a triangular order of battle. Tillyard supposes Gosson's *Schoole of Abuse* to be the source of the first idea; but a comparison of Milton, Gosson, and this passage from Swan on cranes leaves little to choose among them:

And again it is reported, that when these birds flie out of *Cilicia,* over the mountains *Taurus,* each of them carrieth in his mouth a peble stone, lest by their chattering they should be seized upon by the Eagles.

The triangulating sentry cranes are glossed from Pliny and Cicero by most editors but are found in many repositories of animal lore. Bartholomew, Batman, Maplet, Swan, and La Primaudaye all repeat how the crane whose turn it is to stand watch "holdeth a lyttell stone in his fote, that if he happe to fall a slepe, he may be waked by fallynge of the stone." The triangular order of battle reappears as planned flight in the epic:

> Part loosly wing the Region, part more wise
> In common, rang'd in figure wedge thir way,
> Intelligent of seasons, and set forth
> Thir Aierie Caravan high over Sea's
> Flying, and over Lands with mutual wing

Easing thir flight; so stears the prudent Crane
Her annual Voiage, born on Windes.

VII, 425–431

The lore of geese and cranes apparently overlapped; as Robin notes, Ælian tells the pebble story about geese, and we have just seen it in Swan about cranes. La Primaudaye attributes to the wild geese the flight-wedge that others credited to the crane, and adds a detail that probably explains the easing of the flight with mutual wing. Wild geese fly "little and little behind like a corner, the better to gain the wind, which guideth them" and the "hindermost do commonly rest their heads upon the foremost, and when the guide is weary of going before, he commeth hindmost, to the end that every one may keepe his turne." [12]

The eagle, twice mentioned, curiously enough, in context with the phoenix, is symbolic of the power and pride of place befitting the king of birds — which is to say the top of that hierarchy. The eagle's renewing itself supplied the justly famous figure in *Areopagitica*: "Methinks I see her as an Eagle muing her mighty youth, and kindling her undazl'd eyes at the full midday beam; purging and unscaling her long abused sight at the fountain itself of heav'nly radiance." The word "muing" has given some trouble, though the sense is clear; the "fountain" and method of restoration require Bartholomew:

For in the egle the spyryte of syghte is moost temperat, and moost sharpe in acte and dede of seenge and beholdynge the sonne in the roundenesse of his cercle, withoute anye blemyshynge of eyen. . . . And herto Austin sayth and Plinius also that in age the egle hathe derkenesse and dymnes in the eyen, and hevyness in wynges. And ayenst this disavantage she is taught by kynde to seke a well of spryngynge water, and then she fleeth up in to the ayre as ferre as she may, tyll she be full hotte by heate of the ayre and by traveyle of flyght, and so then by heate the pores bene opened, and the fethers chauffed, and she falleth sodaynly in to the welle, and there the fethers ben chaunged, and the dimnes of her eyen is wyped away and purged and she taketh ayen her myght and strength.

The magic fountain here corresponds as an archetype to the mysterious Well of Life from which Michael regenerated Adam's mental sight. The life-cycle symbolism is obvious. Milton combines the fountain of water and the fountain of light into one, tightening the process and strengthening the figurative relation between sun and solar bird. With the sun and the lion, the postlapsarian eagle forms an omen rightly interpreted by Adam as one of the "mute signs of Nature" and forerunners of God's purpose:

> Aire suddenly eclips'd
> After short blush of Morn; nigh in her sight
> The Bird of *Jove*, stoopt from his aerie tour,
> Two Birds of gayest plume before him drove:
> Down from a Hill the Beast that reigns in Woods
> First Hunter then, pursu'd a gentle brace,
> Goodliest of all the Forrest, Hart and Hinde.
>
> XI, 183–189

The movement is downward, from air and hill, even as Adam and Eve were hastened by Michael to the subjected plain. The gayest plume of the human pair was their innocence; Adam once was goodliest of men. Milton not only draws the parallels; he makes Adam index them.[13]

Tetrachordon contains an ingenious analogy drawn from the hatching of ostrich eggs in the dust, and the seventh prolusion commends the Egyptian ibis for showing the value of purging, as *A Greene Forest* puts it, "with pouring in with her bill, water into her fundament." But the prescience of birds generally and of the vulture and raven in special are more substantially integrated into *Paradise Lost*. In the elegy on the Bishop of Winchester, the poet admits that birds, foreknowing though they are, succumb to death. Perhaps their prognostications of weather praised in the seventh prolusion derive from astronomy; but in a natural scale where even the rocks are sentient, an instinct of the future would seem the natural property of those higher in the chain. Mopsus in *Damon's Epitaph*, like his ancestor in the *Aeneid*, is an expert in the language of birds, the assumption being that they can tell him secrets. Folklore multiplies examples of extrasensory perception in beasts as in human beings; and from earliest times, animal knowledge of the future has been a familiar notion.

Among many ominous vertebrates, such as owls, bats, and similar fatal birds, the raven and the vulture are emphasized in Milton's treatment of Death. Before the judgment of Adam and Eve, before even the fall, Sin feels new strength, instructed by

> Som connatural force
> Powerful at greatest distance to unite
> With secret amity things of like kinde
> By secretest conveyance.   X, 246–249

Death, sequent to Sin in this as in other manifestations of the allegory

> with delight snuff'd the smell
> Of mortal change on Earth. As when a flock
> Of ravenous Fowl, though many a League remote,
> Against the day of Battel, to a Field,
> Where Armies lie encampt, come flying, lur'd
> With sent of living Carcasses design'd
> For death, the following day, in bloodie fight.
> So sented the grim Feature, and upturn'd
> His Nostril wide into the murkie Air,
> Sagacious of his Quarrey from so farr.   273–280

Foreknowledge is distributed rather warily in Milton, for the feeling of foreordination is implicit in it. God carefully explains the difference, and nothing is more central to the poem than man's freedom of choice. Milton had plenty of authority for attributing limited foreknowledge to angels like Michael and devils like the Satan of *Paradise Regained*.

Yet here the time-schedule is definite, and Sin and Death in their vague foreknowledge of man's fall participate with God. Apparently they know even earlier than Satan, for line 229 says unmistakably "Meanwhile ere thus was sin'd and judg'd on Earth. . . ." Death claims to draw a scent of carnage; Milton as narrator says he does so, like the ravenous fowl — the raven and the vulture. Bartholomew calls "divinours" to attest "the raven hath a maner vertue of meanynge and tokenynge of divination" and reports of the vulture

by smellynge he savoureth careynes that ben ferre from hym, that is beyonde the see: and ayenwarde. Therfore the Vulture foloweth the hoste, that he may fede hym selfe with caraynes of men, and of horse. And therefore (as a Dyvynour sayth) whan many vultures come and flee together, it tokeneth battayle. And they knowe that suche a battayle shall be, by some prevy wytte of kynde.

Maplet believes they can smell a carcass five hundred miles away. Swan hedges with "as some think" in relaying the same information of the raven: "by a singular instinct and naturall gift, it hath understanding of mans death, presaging it a few days before." Whether that is true or not, "this is certain, that it haunteth places of battell, with solitarie ruines." Clearly Milton was drawing on a familiar symbol of foreknowledge, and the emphasis put upon the time and distance in Death's ominous perception leaves no room for error. One must conclude either that Milton made a mistake in his poetic arithmetic (to borrow Bush's felicitous phrase) or that the foreknowledge of Death is once more part of a scheme in which the ambivalence of good and evil, God and Satan, is maintained as poetic fiction though never as moral absolute. The *instinct* credited by Sin becomes realized in the hideous nostril upturned to smell death even before it occurs. The inevitability of man's fall receives a new kind of confirmation in the extraordinary epithet *sagacious*, which combines the sense of wisdom, as if this percep-

tion were a matter of experienced knowledge, with the
original Latin *scenting*. The poet did not depend upon
familiarity with the story to sustain that inevitability; he
created it within the fable itself, affirming it in a flashback
by this episode and its image of raven and vulture.[14]

Before leaving this section of the subject, we must examine
briefly once more the generalization about reasoning in
animals and another, emphasized in *Doctrine of Divorce*,
that "many beasts in voluntary and chosen couples, live
together as unadulterously, and are truly married in that
respect." The choice between reason and instinct offered in
the Seventh Prolusion was supported by examples of the
blood-letting hippopotami, sentry cranes, schoolmistress
nightingales, political bees, and domestic ants. All these
stories are older than Pliny and Plutarch, the chief sources
for many writers. Milles, in his *Treasurie*, for instance, tells
how the hippopotamus bleeds itself by rubbing upon the
points of new cut canes and reeds. Frantze, *The Historie of
Brutes*, allows the provident pismire only imitation, not
reason; to Torquemada, *The Spanish Mandevile of Miracles*,
it is a "lively instinct" which prompts the bee, crane, and
dog. Charles Blount attributes to Democritus the opinion
"that Men have learnt most of their Arts from dumb Creatures: as that the Spider taught us to weave, the Swallow to
build, the Nightingale to sing, and divers Beasts the Art of
Physick." Lupton and Golding add further examples concerning geese, ducks, hens, cranes, panthers, and elephants.
Polydore Virgil recounts the familiar lore of ibis and river-
horse. The dying sheep in the related passage from *Lycidas*
must find their cure in a change of pastors. But their symptoms, when "swoln with wind, and the rank mist they draw,"
they "Rot inwardly and foul contagion spread," are set out
in Bartholomew, Batman, and Swan as well as Aristotle.
Every naturalist referred, credulously or skeptically, to animal
prognostication, Swan citing Ælian on the superior accuracy

of mice, Caxton crediting dolphins with warning ships of tempests. Maplet, repeating a venerable cliché, recommends the hedgehog as a wind prophet. As for marital fidelity, Milles avers we may behold this in all birds and most quadrupeds. "Adultery is hated even amongst beastes," says Nicholas Ling's *Politeuphia: Wits Commonwealth* (1598). Elephant, swan, camel, dove, even the asp are commended as perfect patterns of "chaste, mutual, and matromoniall love," to quote Swan.

But the answer to the question whether or not animals had the power to reason was not so obvious as one might expect even unorthodox Christians to reach. The usual view, echoed many times in Milton, was that animals possessed highly developed instincts but not reason; and Milton's whole concept of Adam's superiority was that his moral responsibility rested upon his unique power of right reason. The other view was the alternative Milton himself offered in the Seventh Prolusion: he cites Plutarch to the effect that a dog, reaching a crossroad, often displayed familiarity with the disjunctive syllogism. In *Paradise Lost,* however, Adam tells Eve that "smiles from reason flow, to brute denied." But earlier, God tells Adam that animals have the gift of language and the power to reason not contemptibly. The *locus classicus* is Plutarch, though Milton may have been citing him at second hand, for Plutarch's speaker goes on to say what Milton did not, that the dog's sense of smell, not his powers of logic, leads him to the correct path. The two dialogues "That Brute Beasts have discourse of Reason" and "Whether Creatures Be more wise, They of the Land, or Those of the Water" were standard sources for this debate in the Renaissance. Camerarius, Peter Charron, Blount, Huygens, and Renaudot offer the view expressed by God to Adam. Too much is made of this, in and out of Milton, for God's statement to be a Gilbertian slip; and Milton does not put lies into God's speech, even to tempt Adam. The paradox must be resolved by recourse to Milton's concept of the chain of being: as Raphael tells Adam, one first matter is constantly working up through various forms to God. In the same speech he explains that angelic reasoning is intuitive and therefore superior to human discursive reasoning. Milton's assumption in God's assertion to Adam must be that below this discursive reasoning and differing in degree but not in kind is the reasoning power of animals. Degrees of this kind jar not with moral responsibility.[15]

There are still other curiosa of natural history in the verse and prose that we should note. From Purchas, Milton transferred into his *Brief History of Moscovia* the morse that climbs rocks with its teeth and the rossomakka that "bringeth forth by passing through some narrow place, as between two Stakes; and so presseth her Womb to a disburthening." Harris Fletcher hunted this ingenious female through Bochart, Hakluyt, Olaus Magnus, Mathias Mechovita, Gesner, Topsell, and others, discovering that her device was also employed for the relief of gluttony, whereby hung many a moral lesson. Jonston calls the rossomakka as most do, *gulo*. Torquemada, in making it vomit, reverses the usual process, which is only too clear from the woodcut in Olaus. Surprisingly, Milton never used this violently emblematic figure in his mud-slinging, though delicacy certainly did not deter him; witness his advice, "Cast off from you this filthy boar of of a fellow, whose rubbing pollutes, as his stroke wounds the church" and his earlier claim that he reveals More "The pest of the people, in the church a boar no less mischievous with his tail than with his tusk oblique." These insults compound standard associations of excrement, lechery, and violence; and the allusions to More's affair with the serving girl Pontia are so plain as scarcely to require Bartholomew's assurance that the very gall of the boar "exciteth to gendrynge." Milton sardonically identifies More with the rankest of goats and the filthy hyena, "equally destructive and equally in-

famous for the blackness of its guile." Golding, Batman, Topsell repeat the substance of Bartholomew's declaration that
the hyena is an unclean beast which imitates human speech
and "begyleth and disceyveth men and ravyssheth and steleth
them, and taketh houndes, and devoureth them, as gladly as
men, and diggethe buryels and graves, and eateth the flesshe
of dead bodies that ben in them." One tradition held that
this treacherous animal changes sex, another that when it
mourns it is most guileful. These combine in Ben Jonson's
"Out, thou camelion harlot, now thine eyes vie tears with
the hyena" and Samson's savage rejection:

> Out, out *Hyaena*; these are thy wonted arts,
> And arts of every woman falls like thee,
> To break all faith, all vows, deceive, betray,
> Then as repentant to submit, beseech,
> And reconcilement move with feign'd remorse.
>
> 748–752

Similarly conventional are the reference to the lust of apes
for women in the sportive prolusion, the confidence expressed in the elegy to Thomas Young that lions spare the
trembling and prostrate, and the comparison with the camel
"to thirst inur'd" in *Paradise Regained*.[16]

Serpent lore and in a sense all of Milton's animal lore
culminate in the temptation of Eve and the transformation
of the demons at Satan's fall. Serpent imagery had been
building a long time, in and out of Milton's works: we have
touched upon it in the account of fennel and cockatrice and
have marked the encyclopedia stereotypes that permeate the
confused identities in the swarm of fiends when they are re-
born as monsters by the inverted, recoiling magic of Satan's
announcement. In the epic, Milton brings Satan through the
scale of creatures; he assumes the ominous forms of cormorant, lion, tiger, and toad; he is compared to the whale, the
vulture, and the wolf. The poisonous toad of *Colasterion*
and the toad and asp of Sonnet Twenty-one correspond in

kind and function to the low animals, full of venom, in *Pro Se Defensio,* though for the sonnet one might glance at Topsell's dictum that when an asp has eaten a toad its bite becomes incurable. The serpent-like wolf-venom spat by Salmasius of *First Defence* perhaps requires a gloss from Bartholomew's chapters "De Lupo," where it is said "woundes of theyr bytynge ben evyll, for venim cometh of them," and "Of venomous wormes," where the asp is called "Spuens, spitting, by reason that he sleeth with his spotill." And Milton discredits the irrelevant natural history of his adversaries in *Apology for Smectymnuus* by quoting contemptuously their *"Vinegar in ink is* there the *antidote of vipers"* and "Laughing in a religious controversy" is *"a thrifty physick to expell his melancholy"*; Topsell reports vinegar an ingredient in the prescriptions of Vegetius and Epigonus for snake-bite. The healing of the gashed serpent in *Animadversions* and the viper of sedition eating through the entrails of peace in *Of Reformation* are conventional enough, snapshot images like toad and asp; yet according to Victorius and Topsell, even that viper had a special name, *Caecas Colubras.* Often the threadbare allusion takes on imaginative value from its secondary connotation. The adder of Psalm 58, which Topsell says ought to be called an asp, "stoppeth one of her eares with her tail, and the other she holdeth hard to earth." Milton used it in "if we be not deaf as adders" of *Tetrachordon* and in Samson's sardonic rejection of Dalila's charms: "So much of Adders wisdom have I learn't / To fence my ear against thy sorceries." The contexts may be thought to justify pejorative value ("we would be like adders if," and "even an adder can teach me something"), yet there seems an inversion of the hieroglyph here, not unusual in Milton. The sympathetic associations contrast with Topsell's equation: deaf adders "signifie unrepentant men." A last example, the python figure in *Reason of Church Government,* mentioned also in the first prolusion before its comparison with Satan, illustrates how, like epic similes, some of Milton's prose analogies rise to eloquence through graphic diction and sustained imaginative vigor. Apollo legend and Christian specialization of evil in dragon and serpent fuse into a scourging of prelacy in a notable peroration:

Nor will any one have reason to think this as too incredible or too tragical to be spok'n of Prelaty, if he consider well from what a masse of slime and mud, the sloathful, the covetous, and ambitious hopes of Church-promotions and fat Bishopricks she is bred up and nuzzl'd in, like a great Python from her youth, to prove the general poyson both of doctrine and good discipline in the Land. For certainly such hopes and such principles of earth as these wherein she welters from a yong one, are the immediat generation both of a slavish and tyrannous life to follow, and a pestiferous contagion to the whole Kingdom, till like that fenborn serpent she be shot to death with the darts of the sun, the pure and powerful beams of Gods word.

Satan's dazzling of Eve with serpentine beauty and human speech may now be seen as part of the whole scheme of Milton's animal lore. This is the scene toward which the action, the setting, and the characters have been articulated. The prose and other poetry have trained us in the multiform allusiveness of animal lore, and what emerges here does so the same way, through the undercurrent of metaphor. For as the oldest sin of all is to be enacted, the poet establishes out of traditional serpent lore the undertone of sexual excitement thought an aspect of Eve's downfall from the time of rabbinical commentary. Empson and Stein have revived this feature of the patristic myth, and Schultz has shown the temptation to be a seduction scene, a seventeenth-century amorist's serenade.

> So spake the Enemie of Mankind, enclos'd
> In Serpent, Inmate bad, and toward *Eve*
> Address'd his way, not with indented wave,

Prone on the ground, as since, but on his reare,
Circular base of rising foulds, that tour'd
Fould above fould a surging Maze, his Head
Crested aloft, and Carbuncle his Eyes;
With burnisht Neck of verdant Gold, erect
Amidst his circling Spires, that on the grass
Floted redundant: pleasing was his shape,
And lovely, never since of Serpent kind
Lovelier, not those that in *Illyria* chang'd
Hermione and *Cadmus,* or the God
In Epidaurus; nor to which transformd
Ammonian Jove, or *Capitoline* was seen,
Hee with *Olympias,* this with her who bore
Scipio the highth of *Rome.*   IX, 494–510

Little wonder that she fell. Red and gold and green in sinuous loops and (Satan grown bolder) many a wanton wreath prepare for the miracle of language which finally deceives the Mother of Mankind. Even Joseph Mede, asking "who would not judge her a silly woman that she should think" a serpent should speak like a reasonable creature, must conclude "and yet the wisest of us all is far short of *Eve* in regard of her knowledge then." In all this flashing color and persuasive movement, thematic images recur and key words suddenly assume new focus: the green of the garden, the burnished gold and carbuncle of the sun, the grass, Satan not prone as other animals but erect like Adam and Eve. Beneath them all, hinted in "boulder now" and "wanton wreaths," works a most ancient myth. Fletcher's proposal of ultimate rabbinical origin for the entire conception of the serpent is doubtless right, though which rabbi is a puzzling question beyond all conjecture. The episode is murky in the rabbis, the symbolists who created Lilith, that other Eve whose happiness with Adam was "a death to think." Milles, who had no more Freud than Blake illustrating the fall, showed like Blake the phallic implications of the serpent. He repeats from Leo Hebraico the allegorical inter-

pretation of the serpent-tempter as carnal appetite or sensuality which

inciteth and first deceiveth the Corporall Feminine part. It is
called Corporal, when it is found any way devided from the
intellect, which is tearmed the Husband, resisting against his
strict and severe Lawes, to acquaint her selfe with carnall Delec-
tations, and darken her Native splendor, with acquisition of
superfluous and abounding riches or treasure.

The reptilian parentage of Alexander and Scipio is related
by many, Topsell and Turquet, for example. But on a single
page, Camerarius's *The Living Librarie* supplies most of
Milton's allusions, indicates by citations the widespread
dissemination of the stories, and insists upon an interpretation like Milles's:

It is not onely written in the sacred Historie, That *Adam* and
Eve being placed by God in the garden of Paradise, were deceived
(especially *Eve*) by the craftie persuasion of the Serpent; but
many Authors affirme, that Serpents have been noted to desire
the companie of women. Who seeth not therein (but more in
the action of *Eve*, than in all other) a strange efficacie and deceit
in Satan? All the Rabbins are of this mind, that the devils
(through Gods sufferance) have great power over ones concupiscence and privie members, saying, That by an Allegorie Satan is
meant the Serpent. *Philo* and the Hebrewes say, That the Serpent
signifieth allegorically, Lecherie. *Alexander* the Great held for
certaine, That his mother *Olympias* was gotten with child of
him by a Serpent, which the superstitious Pagans called *Jupiters*
Genius. Wherefore having upon a time written to his mother
thus; King *Alexander* the sonne of *Jupiter Ammon*, saluteth his
mother *Olympias*. . . . The like is reported of *Scipio Africanus*;
C. Oppius that hath written his life, *Titus Livius, Gellius*, and
Julius Higinus doe say, That a great Serpent lay with *Scipios*
mother, and was seene often in her chamber, and when any bodie
came in, he would vanish away. *Valerius Maximus* also speaketh
of it. The like doth *Suetonius* report of *Accia*, the mother of
Augustus, for hee writeth, That as shee came once at mid-night
to a certaine solemnitie, shee made her litter be set into the
Chappell; and while the other Ladies were at rest, shee fell

asleepe. Then a great Serpent crept into the litter, and while after came out againe: After which *Accia* awaking, purified her selfe as if her husband had lain with her: presently there was seene upon her skin the marke of a Dragon, which could never bee taken off, so that ever after shee refrained from going into the common Baths: and *Augustus* being borne at the end of ten moneths, was by reason thereof reckoned *Apollos* sonne. *Galerius* the Emperor, borne of clownish parents, and surnamed *Armentarius*, because he had kept cattell, bragged and tooke upon him proudly, That a great Serpent begat him, having accompanied his mother, as one had done with *Olympias, Alexanders* mother.

Milton uses the same contexts though he avoids direct statement. Satan's lust has been so established earlier in the poem and in the tradition that the inference of sexual sin is inescapable; it is confirmed as far as Milton wanted to take it in the central metaphor of Adam's anguished summary: "Defact, deflourd, and now to Death devote." [17]

The four interests proposed at the beginning of this study are thus richly documented in animal lore. First, although the range of animal allusion is nothing so generous as Lyly's or Shakespeare's, yet the full scale of nature is there. Broadbent rightly claims a special Elizabethan fascination with creatures that we take for granted but they never saw. These are endlessly described in the encyclopedias of science. Renaissance readers did have, however, what we lack, a whole vocabulary of animal emblem, hieroglyph, and symbol upon which their writers, Milton included, drew largely. What are dead metaphors to us, or simply unrecognized, were glossed for them in popular handbooks, biblical commentary, and broadside ballads. Milton's lines depend upon readymade connotations of ant, serpent, whale, crane, and cuckoo; but the controlling principle is never mere accumulation or window-dressing. Each bit of lore has its place in a small closed poetic system as well as in a chain of being. Second, the question of sources for bestiary information is really simplified, from a search among a welter of possibilities to the more plausible demonstration of what was commonly available to the general reader and how sufficient the encyclopedias and other popular materials are for the explaining of an allusion or the defining of a stereotype. Third, animal lore gives body to the abstract conception of a teleological universe and exemplifies once more how deeply integrated are the philosophical foundations of the epic narrative. Christian in effect, the world view that encompasses the scale of nature is classical in its purposiveness, its continuity, and (by inference) its plenitude.

The fourth question, toward which all these tend, has like them found answer along the way. The function of animal lore in Milton's art is to extend, expand, underline — in a word, to create the images through which his poem moves. Where nearly everything in his culture had symbolic moral significance and the mighty frame itself was magnified microcosm, animal lore offered an obligatory knowledge to poet and pamphleteer. The early poems, Latin and English, are crammed with left-overs and extensions from the schoolroom; the later work unquestionably owes some of its success in animal metaphor to these exercises. Insects, birds, fish, quadrupeds appear in their common relations, but they always function in some dominant scheme. Scarcely a detail of the creation story and its animals had escaped the commentators, professional or secular. The meticulous explanation that the Son clothed Adam and Eve "with Skins of Beasts, or slain, / Or as the Snake with youthful Coate repaid" is typical. Adam's fall transformed the frisking playmates into glaring feral antagonists. This is why we are not shocked at their fate when the God who in awful solemnity dealt a great delayed death as punishment now deals a small one as mercy. Nor are we surprised to read Mercator's conclusion that the skins were taken from brute beasts because "God had before made an end of Creating." Nor, for another example, are spontaneous generation and allied concepts only invective

in the prose or ornament in the poem; they enter the fabric
of the epic by expressing the antipathy between affirmation
and denial, fecundity and sterility, between the positive
creativity of God and the negative of Satan.[18]

The elaborate invective extends beyond literal castigation.
Faithful to his contention that by weakening public confidence in an opponent's moral behavior he could undermine
belief in his cause, Milton plied the *argumentum ad hominem*
with extravagant vulgarity in animal lore, many years before
Salmasius and his *Pliniae Exercitationes* offered special opportunities. Though few might advocate such training for a
poet, effective mudslinging does afford practice in irony, paradox, vigor of language, and the metaphor-making faculty. The
hyena in *Samson Agonistes* differs little from that in *Pro Se
Defensio*. In a cosmos where the very integrity of reason was
at stake, a constant collating of worlds through the chain of
being simply demanded zoological comparison. Not only
Hamlet knew man as the paragon of animals nor only Timon
confessed the beast in man; the writer of these defenses, knowing and confessing the same, made in them what seems now
the obvious distinction.

We have then a reiterated pattern. What Milton did with
astronomy and mineralogy and botany he did with animal
lore, not as mechanical accrual of parallels but as organicism.
Of the several matters of interest emerging from the close
reading of these allusions, one is the straight face with which
the image-making Milton could cavil at an antagonist who
tried animal analogy on him. Another is the frequent return
to images, of bee and phoenix, wind-egg and python. Each
passage we examine testifies to design and structure. We may
invoke the observations upon Oppian's *Halieuticks* by his
first English translators some fifty years after Milton's death.

Natural History is a divine speculation to the Religious, and no
less agreeable to the Curious . . . there is no Subject . . . more
conducive to the ends of Poetry, the Delight and Instruction of

the Reader. The glorious Dangers and Exploits of Heroes, the Splendor and Triumphs that attend Victory, which are the usual Subjects of an *Epic* Poem, are things that we admire in common with the gross of mankind; but to trace the footsteps of Providence among inferior ranks of Creatures, and to contemplate their constant Regularity in promoting the ends of their Creation, is an Entertainment which only refined Understandings are capable of relishing. . . . 'Tis one of the most admirable Secrets in Poety to heighten small things by a noble manner of Expression; the meaner therefore any Subject is, the more capable it is of being adorned. As there is a regular Gradation of created Beings from Man down to the lowest Vegetable, the *Naturalist* seems to have the advantage in a Subject which is capable of being improved by borrowing its Metaphors and Allusions from Objects of a superior Nature. . . . Those Faculties in the Souls of Brutes, which bear an Analogy to the Will and Passions, and enable them to act with a resemblance of the Virtues and Vices of Mankind, furnish the Poet with frequent occasions of insinuating the Precepts of Morality after the most easy and perswasive manner.

With allowances, these poets, minor though they were, might have been speaking of *Paradise Lost*.[19]

CHAPTER VI

The Structure and Surgery
of the Human Body

ONE IS NOT SURPRISED to discover that Milton's own medical history has attracted more attention than his literary physiology and psychology, for the composition of *Paradise Lost* is a biological miracle in itself. Scholars and physicians have disputed the nature of his blindness and his gout, his alleged albinism and congenital syphilis, while the metaphors of medicine in his prose have been ignored and the annotations of Newton, Todd, and Verity thought sufficient for the poems. The life records do illuminate the literary problem; Milton's personal preoccupation with medical matters certainly suggests the impulse to this kind of imagery. Except for briefly adducing these circumstances, however, the present chapter is not biographical. It concerns literary effects for which there are some literary causes — the anatomy of man is the natural next step from anatomy of stones, plants, and animals, and the ills of the body politic provoke microcosmic comparisons. Renaissance medical theory in its literary relations has been so generously reconstructed by Anderson, Campbell, Robin, and Babb that a sampling of Milton's perpetual tampering with real and literary physic will be introduction enough to a survey of his employment of humoral theory, the brain and body and their functions, and the pervasive dialectic of disease and remedy.[1]

The facts of Milton's relations with the medical profession, including Diodati, Paget, Barrow, and Parsons, have been set out by Masson and Hanford. The extraordinary letter to Philaras describing his blindness, the frequent allusions to his health in other correspondence, his mention of arthritis, flatulence, and gout in early biographies all imply that an imagery of illness and remedy might come naturally to one already absorbed in other historical or literary scientific lore. Mathematics may have been the mother of sciences, but Renaissance medicine had them all for godparents. Milton the student, who praised his vice-chancellor's profession, also urged his fellows to advance their scientific studies to "the most exact structure and surgery of the human body; and finally the godlike power and force of mind." When he came to prescribe instead of merely exhort, like a good humanist he stressed again in *Of Education* the necessity for medical study:

Then also in course might be read to them out of some not tedious Writer the Institution of Physick; that they may know the tempers, the humors, the seasons, and how to manage a crudity; which he who can wisely and timely do, is not only a good Physitian to himself, and to his friends, but also may at some time or other, save an army by this frugal and expenseless means only.

In the *Likeliest Means to Remove Hirelings*, he commended the educational system of the poor Waldensians who bred themselves in trades, "and especially in physic and surgery as well as in the studie of scripture (which is the only true theologie) that they might be no burden to the church; and by the example of Christ, might cure both soul and bodie." This image of Christ as physician was a favorite with Milton; we will meet it again. And whatever his own experience with the profession, he nearly always mentions the physician with respect, as in the rebuke to Salmasius and in allusions to the physician and dropsy (*Animadversions*), fever and palsy (*Reason of Church Government*), nausea (*Apology for Smectymnuus*), antidotes for poison (*Tetrachordon*), purgatives (*Brief Notes upon a Late Sermon*), and the skilled examination of an old sore (*Pro Se Defensio*). The physician as atheist was proverbial from classical times forward, and the profession took many a blow in the English Renaissance despite the exemplary piety of most medical literature. However anti-intellectual Milton may have been in other respects (and this case has not been proved), he did not share in the fashionable condemnation or lampooning of wide-encroaching medical science and its practitioners, though he knew a mountebank when he named one.[2]

It would indeed be strange, then, if Milton's abiding interest in medical matters failed to realize itself in images; and the prose teems with medical as the poetry with astronomical lore. Most of it is as conventional as the rest of his natural history, down to the very wording. Four centuries before the passage in *Of Education*, Bartholomew had written what John de Trevisa translated thus:

Also to heele and save effectuelly, hym nedeth to knowe and to understonde the complexyons of men, compositions, myxcyons, and medlynges, bothe of the humours and of the membres, and to understonde and knowe the disposycyons of tymes, and the condicions of the male and female, and aege. For one maner medycyne nedeth in wynter, and a nother in somer. . . . Also ayenst an hote cause nede a colde medycyne: and ayenste a colde nedeth an hote medycyne. . . . And therfore a leche and phisicien, that is wise and ware, and knoweth the evyll, tempereth the qualyte, as the quantite and qualite of the evyl axeth. Also whan he seeth that the evil cometh of replecion, he helpeth it by voidynge of the matter, and by scarse dyete. And if it cometh of abstinence he helpeth it with replecion.

So with the cosmic identities exploited in most medical treatises. Milton's comparison of earthquake to fever and ague is, we have seen, a stereotype, like the medical implica-

tions in Satan's reassurance that storms clear the atmosphere
as the sneeze does man's lesser universe. And in humoral theory Milton applied the four fixed metaphors and followed
standard conservative thought. In *Apology for Smectymnuus*
he argues against any attempt to extirpate a humor:

> no man being forc't wholly to dissolve that ground work of
> nature which God created in him, the sanguine to empty out all
> his sociable livelinesse, the cholerick to expell quite the unsin-
> ning predominance of his anger; but that each radicall humor
> and passion wrought upon and corrected as it ought, might be
> the proper mold and foundation of every mans peculiar gifts
> and vertues.

Three years later, in *Colasterion*, he repeated the warning
against unnatural change, first excusing himself for disputing
philosophy with a pork that never read any, then agreeing
that redundant humors ought to be purged, and finally then
asking "whether any man can with the safety of his life bring
a healthy constitution into physic with this designe, to alter
his natural temperament, and disposition of minde." How
much more vain "by altering and rooting up the grounds of
nature" to hope for reducing "two disagreeing mindes to a
mutual sympathy." They might change melancholy into san-
guine, he admits, though at great danger to their lives; but
what if phlegm and choler in as great a measure came instead?
In *Of Reformation* an image out of the same stock delivers
the practical ideal of political organization:

> And because things simply pure are inconsistent in the masse of
> nature, nor are the elements or humours in Mans Body exactly
> homogeneal, and hence the best founded Common-Wealths, and
> least barbarous have aym'd at a certaine mixture and tempera-
> ment, partaking the severall vertues of each other State, that
> each part drawing to it selfe may keep up a steddy, and eev'n
> uprightnesse in common.

Gradual alteration of the complexion or mixture of humors
is another matter, as Mammon's hopeful prediction shows:

the torments of the evil angels will perhaps become their elements, "our temper chang'd / Into their temper." Angelic substances may be ethereal and bleed nectarous humor only; but off-guard they describe themselves in human physiological terms. Now the encyclopedias, not to speak of treatises like Vicary's and a hundred others, discuss the humors and their disposition interminably. The background for Milton's remarks may be found in Bartholomew, Batman, and La Primaudaye, whose *French Academie* even glosses *radical humor* and *radical moisture* as the poet uses them: "it is as it were the roote of life, and hath the celestiall and quickening heate brought immediatly and directly unto it; so that when this moisture is extinguished, the heate also vanisheth, & fadeth away." The comparison from *Apology for Smectymnuus* in which set forms of prayer weaken piety just as "the daily powring in of hot waters quences the naturall heat" depends upon this sense. As an extreme in temperature, the primary physiological quality of heat, like nearly every other set of polarities, serves Milton for an image of moral opposites. In *Tetrachordon* he finds an intimate quality of good and evil in all the descendants of Adam, which like a radical heat or mortal cold unites or separates them.[3]

In this physiology, the blood distributed humors and spirits throughout the body; it was generated in the liver through heat, too much of which upset the systemic economy and impaired judgment. The "hot-liver'd Grammarians" of *Animadversions* suffer from this ailment, like the bigot in *Doctrine of Divorce* whose "will like a hard spleen draws faster than his understanding can well sanguifie." Bartholomew, noting that the liver by its heat "drawth woos and jus and torneth it into blode," recognizes the contributory function of the spleen and its repletion when "the humours wexen gleymy and harde in the holownes of the mylt." La Primaudaye assigns to the spleen the same operation of drawing gross blood. Heat and moisture, the essential qualities of life, also distin-

guish young and old blood. Comus reveals the pleasures possible when "the fresh blood grows lively"; Michael tells
Adam that at old age, a "melancholy damp of cold and dry"
will reign in his blood to weigh his spirits down and at last
consume his "Balme of Life." The image in *Comus* of the
"lees and settlings of a melancholy blood" was popular elsewhere, *The French Academie* characterizing melancholy as
"like the very bottome of a deepe, red, and thicke wine, or
like the lees in a vessell full of wine or oyle." In common with
everyone else of the time, Milton capitalizes upon the imagery
of phlegm and choler and corrupt blood, "the not letting out
whereof endangers the whole body." He uses *humor* to mean
also a disturbance of the four or a morbid condition in one
of them, and always as metaphor, abjuring the "hydropic humours not discernable at first from a fair and juicy fleshiness
of body" or "luxuriant humors which wealth and excesses
have caus'd to abound." From these fever arose; the corruption of each separate humor, says La Primaudaye, breeds a
special ague; thus the continual fever from the blood, the quotidian from phlegm, the tertian from choler, and the quartan
from melancholy. When Milton mentions "all feavorous
kinds" in *Paradise Lost* he means more than these four, of
course; for the number varied from book to book. Batman,
for example, added fourteen to those described by Bartholonew. The most sophisticated Renaissance pharmacopoeia offered no specific; hence the proverbial cast to Milton's parallel
in *Reason of Church Government*: "such endlesse question,
or rather uproare is arisen in this land, as may be justly term'd
what the feaver is to the Physitians, the eternall reproach of
our Divines." Milton nowhere betrays any acquaintance with
Harvey's discovery; his references to the blood and its functions and to the humors are traditional and almost always in
figurative context. Like the good Aristotelian he could be
upon occasion, he introduced the homeopathic theory of
tragedy into the preface to *Samson Agonistes*, with its corre-

sponding analogy: "for so in Physic things of melancholic hue and quality are us'd against melancholy, sowr against sowr, salt to remove salt humours."[4]

In the thorny Fifth Prolusion, where he argues the dreary question of partial forms in addition to the whole, Milton uses the soul of man as illustration and follows the Aristotelian classification:

Lastly, if in all parts, for example, of a man partial forms were to be increased in number, surely from these one whole form distinct from the rational soul will arise, whence that will be either the form of the inanimate or corporeity, or the form of a mixture, to grant which in addition to the soul in man is quite beyond belief, or it will be either the sensitive or vegetative soul.

This conception corresponds to gradations in the chain of being; for though the soul is single, its nature is triple and Milton is quite accurate in denoting the creatures developed out of earth as "living Soule." The vital force realizes itself in the vegetative soul, common to plants, animals, and men; in the sensitive soul, possessed by animals and men; and in the rational or reasonable soul that identifies man. Milton qualifies reason in animals through the principle of gradation; thus these three souls are in degree "more spiritous and pure." The rational soul recapitulates the other two, so to speak, just as the higher links in the chain recapitulate the lower. One of the infrequent appeals to natural science in *Christian Doctrine* recognizes this; spirit, being the more excellent substance, contains the inferior "as the spiritual and rational faculty contains the corporal, that is, the sentient and vegetative faculty." Each soul of the three controls certain powers or faculties: the vegetative soul inspires the functions of the body, the act of living; the sensitive soul accounts for the powers of movement, sense perception, mental response, and memory; the rational soul alone enjoys the faculties of reason and will. With minor variations, this is standard medieval and Renaissance doctrine, repeated, as Babb indicates, in many textbooks. *De Proprietatibus Rerum,* more widely read as a medical authority than the great *Speculum Naturale,* gives the third book to the soul, with a chapter apiece on vegetative, sensitive, and rational. *The French Academie* splits the rational into *cogitative* ("proper to brute beasts, whom some think to be partakers after a sort of reason") and *reasonable.* The faculties are exercised by the soul through the instrumentality of *spirits*: natural, located in the liver; vital, in the heart; animal, in the brain. Symmetrically enough, these three also relate to the hierarchy of nature; and though his classification is unsteady, Milton confirms the gradation:

> flours and thir fruit
> Mans nourishment, by gradual scale sublim'd
> To vital Spirits aspire, to animal,
> To intellectual, give both life and sense,
> Fansie and understanding, whence the soule
> Reason receives, and reason is her being.
>
> V, 482–487

Robin supposes that Milton omits mention of *natural* spirits; but these are contained in *flours and thir fruit,* for as Bartholomew says "in plantes the werkynge of the vertu, that hight natural is the comen werkyng that gendreth, fedeth, and maketh to grow." The additional kind, *intellectual,* probably resulted from some such distinction as Bartholomew's between these powers of the soul "Racio, reason, that demeth betwene good and evyll" and "intellectus . . . understondynge and inwytte." The "cordial Spirits" in the account of Eve's creation are *vital* by derivation. Satan attempts to taint "Th' animal Spirits that from pure blood arise"; and Samson learns that torment preys upon the "purest spirits" of the mind."[5]

We should consider here some examples, supplementary to those in Chapter I, on imagination and the cells of the brain. Milton knew that "all the faculties of the Soule are confined of old to their several vessels, and *ventricles,*" that the five watchful senses register impressions upon the fancy, located in the first cell, and that these are judged by the reason before being passed on to memory in the third cell. The wild work of fancy in assuming reason's charter, as it does in Adam's analysis of Eve's dream, had received expression earlier in *Colasterion*. A physiological simile combines with the psychological to characterize an opponent's attack: "like a generous Wine, only by overworking the settl'd mudd of his Fancy, to make him drunk, and disgorge his vileness the more openly." Satan at the ear of Eve succeeded in reaching the "Organs of her Fancy" to forge illusions, and (if Tillyard's latest opinion is to be accepted) in tainting the animal spirits so that "inordinate desires" were aroused. A passage in *Animadversions*, punning ingeniously on blushing and inconvenient pregnancy, takes external influence upon the fancy for granted:

> A man would thinke you had eaten over-liberally of Esau's red porrage, and from thence dream continually of blushing; or perhaps to heighten your fancy in writing, are wont to sit in your Doctors scarlet, which through your eyes infecting your pregnant imagination with a red suffusion, begets a continuall thought of blushing.

The suggestions of whoredom, venereal disease, and illegitimate offspring are made, of course, by *scarlet, infecting*, and *begets*. Dreams produced by the fancy in its natural function might also come from immediate influence of good and evil angels. Satan is tied to second causes in *Paradise Lost* but not in *Paradise Regained*, where with ugly dreams he disturbed the Son's sleep. The *Commonplace Book* notes that demons "in dreams told some persons that they too were among those who were destined to die by this plague." God and his servants also work directly. As early as *Comus*, liveried angels are prepared to instruct the chaste "in cleer dream, and solemn vision." Satan boasts that he lends advice to men by portents and dreams; Michael, in a parallel to Satan's evil disturbance, calms Eve with gentle dreams; and she learns that God is "also

in sleep, and Dreams advise." The controversy over Satan's
power owed some of its intensity to the great mass of dream
lore in the encyclopedias and medical treatises. Bartholomew
knew that corrupt blood and vapors infected the cell of fancy,
and that "evyll dygestyon" caused poor sleeping. The point is
of some interest, for the fifth book opens with the assurance
that Adam's sleep was "Aerie light, from pure digestion bred
/ And temperat vapors bland," as if to keep in the margin a
natural explanation of Eve's awaking now as she did later,
"as from unrest." The first sleep after the fall, it will be remembered, was a nightmare "bred of unkindly fumes." A
final point of importance is that Eve's dreams were not Milton's first efforts in that kind; once again he was returning to
a device in which he had had some practice, for there are
dream visions in the third and seventh elegies and the fifth of
November poem, where the Tempter appears to the pope.[6]

Let us remark other physiological features and the variations wrought upon imagery from digestion and from reproduction, the latter of exceptional interest because Milton drew
so often upon the unpleasant lore of monstrous birth, miscarriage and abortion, and hermaphroditism. One ancient motif
in the physiology of Adam and Eve is the imperfect and extra
rib from which she was created. When Adam describes her
origin to Raphael, it was from a rib "with cordial Spirits
warme" from the left side, near the heart. But when he blames
Eve, she is

> all but a Rib
> Crooked by nature, bent, as now appears,
> More to the part sinister from me drawn,
> Well if thrown out, as supernumerarie
> To my just number found.   X, 884–888

Verity notes the old tradition that Adam had thirteen ribs on
one side, but the lines go beyond that to suggest the ominous
emblem in "crooked by nature" (physical deformity manifests moral imperfection), drawn from the evil part of Adam.

This too is traditional, as Institor and Sprenger's misogynistic *Malleus Maleficarum* shows in explaining why women are more vulnerable to temptation than men. There was an error in the composition of Eve, "since she was formed from a bent rib, that is a rib of the breast, which is bent as it were in a contrary direction to man," and through this defect she is imperfect animal (Adam calls her "fair defect / Of Nature") — "she always deceives." Bartholomew notes that the left side is called *sinistra*; and Bacon argues its inferiority from the location of the liver on the right. Not to be overlooked are the implications that the *cordial spirits* are in effect a weakness, that Adam recognizes after the fall the duality or ambiguity of his nature, and that he flatly asserts his imperfection as he came from the hand of God. But Milton's ideas and even language had been anticipated. Joseph Swetnam's *The Araignment of Lewde, Idle, Froward, and Unconstant Women* (1615) had in happy malice marked Moses' statement: "He also saith that they were made of the ribbe of man, and that their froward nature sheweth, for a ribbe is a crooked thing good for nothing else, and women are crooked by nature, for small occasion will cause them to be angry." And Ester Sowernam in *Ester hath Hang'd Haman: or an Answere to a Lewd Pamphlet entituled, The Arraignment of Women* (1617), takes the charge to its logical conclusion:

Admit that this Authors doctrine bee true, that woman reciveth her froward and crooked disposition from the rib, Woman may then conclude upon that Axiome in Philosophy, *Quicquid efficit tale, illud est magis tale,* That which giveth quality to a thing, doth more abound in that quality. . . . So, if Woman receaved her crookednesse from the rib, and consequently from the Man, how doth man excell in crookednesse, who hath more of those crooked Ribs?

What Ester hammers out, Milton leaves to inference. Adam recognizes the evil in himself, yet only as imperfection. This is not blasphemy or heresy or oversight, but a remarkable unification of patristic and physiological lore with something like popular belief to dramatize a moral truth — that the origins of Adam's fall coexisted with his creation.[7]

Functions like respiration and hearing receive some expression, and references to sight occur with expected frequency. Generally they are conventional, though not always so nor always bookish. The first prolusion remarks that the hearing is sharper at night; Samson hears "the sound of words, thir sense the air / Dissolves unjointed." The impossibility of teaching the mind to do contrary acts toward the same object at the same instant is as impossible as to "teach our faculty of respiration to contract and to dilate it selfe at once"; and Adam realizes in a fine image that prayer against God's absolute decree "No more availes then breath against the winde, / Blown stifling back on him that breathes it forth." Samson's agonized query was a current physiological commonplace:

> why was the sight
> To such a tender ball as th'eye confin'd?
> So obvious and so easie to be quench't,
> And not as feeling through all parts diffus'd,
> That she might look at will through every pore?
>
> 93–97

In the same kind is the arrow picked up from More in *Pro Se Defensio*. "*Qui nulli tum fuerant oculi, nunc exemptiles & Lamiarum sunt*" ("The eyes which before were no eyes, are now removable and like those of a witch") goes back in literary history to the myth of Jupiter's special courtesy to Lamia. Plutarch mentions it in the *Morals*, and one may be led by Milton's known acquaintance with this volume to suppose it the source. But it may be found in many places, notably in Gesner's *Historia Animalium* and Topsell's *Historie of Serpents*, the latter retelling from Varinus that "Jupiter having pitty upon her, gave her exemptile eyes that might be taken in and out at her own pleasure." Topsell cites Plutarch as affirming Lamias to be "Phairy women" capable of assuming any form.

In addition to these senses, an imagery of digestion and rejection occurs often in the prose and reappears in a striking analogy in *Paradise Lost*. The prelate in *Of Reformation* has a "canary-sucking, and swan-eating palat"; when Charles reaches the point where his conscience in "unnatural *dyscrasie*" will digest poison and "keck at wholsom food, it was not for the Parliament, or any of his Kingdoms to feed with him any longer"; the antagonist in *Second Defence* "vomits out a whole sink of foul abuse collected, with the help of an index to Plautus, from the mouths of slaves and mountebanks"; the conservatives in *Of Reformation* return to the constitutions of Edward VI, "belching the soure Crudities of yesterdayes *Poperie*." The most daring of these allusions is the castigation of those whose devotion "most commonly comes to that queazy temper of luke-warmnesse, that gives a Vomit to God himselfe." The comparison implied throughout between the natural functions of the body and political action or logical thinking depends upon the same assumptions about natural and moral law expressed by the analogy in *Areopagitica*: "Wholesome meats to a vitiated stomach differ little or nothing from unwholesome. . . . Bad meats will scarce breed good nourishment in the healthiest concoction." The parallel is taken a step further in reporting of Cambridge University that, from what both she and her sister "hath of long time vomited, . . . the worser stuffe she strongly keeps in her stomack, but the better she is ever kecking at, and is queasie. She vomits now out of sicknesse, but ere it be well with her, she must vomit by strong physick." The most extraordinary of these pathological configurations is an extended, fantastically bound complex of elaborately ironical charity, dog-vomit, gluttony, and madness wherein the diseased system cannot retain truth:

And since there be a crew of lurking raylers, who in thir Libels,

and thir fitts of rayling up and down, as I hear from others, take
it so currishly that I should dare to tell abroad the secrets of thir
Aegyptian Apis, to gratify thir gal in some measure yet more,
which to them will be a kind of almes (for it is the weekly vomit
of thir gall which to most of them is the sole meanes of thir feeding) that they may not starv for me, I shall gorge them once
more with this digression somwhat larger than before: nothing
troubl'd or offended at the working upward of thir Sale-venom
thereupon, though it happ'n to asperse me; beeing, it seemes,
thir best livelyhood and the only use or good digestion that thir
sick and perishing mindes can make of truth charitably told
them.

Beneath this violence moves an assumption of the unity of
truth with morally healthy minds. One unity implies another.
So when Milton came to affirm the real concoctive heat of
angels, he played upon a familiar theme; the digestion of
spiritual beings reasserts the unity of matter, and Raphael
returns to the process for a figure of the assimilation of knowledge. The physiological basis of imagination, reason, and
memory are implicit in the analogy between brain and stomach.

> But Knowledge is as food, and needs no less
> Her Temperance over Appetite, to know
> In measure what the mind may well contain,
> Oppresses else with Surfet, and soon turns
> Wisdom to Folly, as Nourishment to Winde.
>
> VII, 126–130

The hungry sheep in *Lycidas* received instead of honest gospel
the "rank mist" that inflated and rotted them. Thus, though
the particulars differ, poem to poem and pamphlet to pamphlet, the fundamental physiological process remains the
center of the analogy.[8]

Fecundity and creativity, extolled as early as the elegy on
the coming of spring, form a dominant motif in *Paradise Lost*
in the opposition of Christ and Satan. The emergence of life
from the dust of the earth, the origin of Adam and Eve, the

dynamic opulence of the garden, indeed, the whole narrative, symbolize the struggle between positive and negative creativity. When Milton reached the composition of *Paradise Lost*, he had had long experience in formulating analogies from animal and human reproduction. The motifs of miscegenation, hermaphroditism, and disnatured conception occur in the prose and have their counterpart in the epic. "Counterfeit life" and animal reproduction engaged his interest early, and the inclusion of the human process was a natural concomitant. For one example, a metaphor in *Reason of Church Government* anticipates the infernal trinity: "Heresie begat heresie with a certaine monstrous haste of pregnancy in her birth, at once borne and bringing forth." For another, *Doctrine of Divorce*, which here reads in its eloquence like *Areopagitica*, relates the birth of truth:

Though this ill hap wait on her nativity, that shee never comes into this world, but like a Bastard, to the ignominy of him that brought her forth: till Time, the Midwife rather than the mother of Truth, have washt and salted the Infant, declar'd her legitimat, and Churcht the father of his young *Minerva*, from the needlesse causes of his purgation.

The Minerva-figure was to be parodied in the birth of Sin; here the favorable comparison participates in a complex fusion of church practice, the judgment of time, tribal disapproval of by-blows, and technical details of accouchement. Bartholomew, who offers a chapter on nearly everything, provides one "Of a mydwyfe" who "wassheth awaye the blode of the chyld, and baynyth hym with shalte and hony, to drye up the humours, and to comforte his lymmes and membres." Milton attacked the metaphor by reference to another kind of midwife in *Eikon Basilike*: "they plaid the hasty *midwives, and would not stay the ripening, but went streight to ripping up, and forcibly cut out the abortive Votes.*" The king's *miscarriages* of business are condemned; and in a remarkably poetic sentence, his sincerity is impugned: "And thus his pregnant *motives* are at last prov'd nothing but a Tympany, or a Queen *Maries* Cushion: For in any Kings heart, as Kings goe now, what shadowie conceit, or groundlesse toy will not create a jealousie." The tympany was as old as Aristotle, cited by Batman in his fifth book: "And sometime the woman supposeth that she goeth with childe: and she beareth in her wombe some manner lumpe wonderfully shapen." The phantom pregnancies of Mary Tudor seem to have been honest mistakes; but she was accused so often of simulating the condition that "Queen Mary's cushion" became proverbial. The "prodigious Births of bodie or mind" of *Paradise Lost* owe something to this management of metaphor in the prose; but before returning to that theme, we must review those extravagant insults in which Milton calls Salmasius an hermaphrodite.[9]

True to his advice that one should study the exact structure of the human body, Milton frequently speculated upon the phenomena of animal and human hermaphroditism. Some of this adheres to the allusions to wind-eggs in *Eikonoklastes*, where he combines in a startling imaginative effect a legend of Julius Caesar with Charles' rejection of parliament:

And if it hath been anciently interpreted the presaging sign of a future tyrant, but to dream of copulation with his mother, when can it be less than actual tyranny to affirm waking, that the parliament, which is his mother, can neither conceive or bring forth any authoritative act without his masculine coition.

Robert Allott, *Wits Theater of the Little World* (1599) supplies an explanation of the cryptic allusion: "Caesar dreamed, that hee lay with his mother, which the Sooth-sayers interpreting, the earth to bee his mother, sayde, That hee should bee conquerour of the world." The implication here is some kind of ambisexual nature in parliament. Milton perforce dealt directly with the condition in arguing divorce. *Tetrachordon* disputes the familiar crux *In the Image of God created he him*. It might be doubted why the text reads *him*,

says Milton, and "not *them,* as well as *male and female them.*"
It could not have been *male and female him*

> however the Jewes fable, and please themselvs with the accidental
> concurrence of Platos wit, as if man at first had been created
> *Hermaphrodite*: but then it must have bin male and female
> created he him.

In rebuking Salmasius for an error in the ornithology of quail,
Milton seizes the statement "*Gallus gallinaceous* wields imperial power over both males and females" and puns his way
into invective. How can that be, he asks, since Salmasius himself, who is Gallic and only too cocky, does not rule his wife?
If the gallinaceous cock be king over many females, Salmasius
must be some other kind because he is a slave to his hen. "For
the matter of books," he continues, "nobody publishes huger
dunghills, and you deafen us all with your crowing over them;
that is the only point in which you resemble a true cock." In
First Defence he exclaims: "Help, Lucina! Mount Salmasius
is in labor! It is not for nothing that he was married by a he-
wife. Mortals, expect some huge monstrous birth." In *Second
Defence* he pays the compliment to both his adversaries, first
introducing "Salmasius, or Salmasia (for of what sex he was,
was rendered extremely doubtful, from his being plainly
ruled by his wife, alike in matters regarding his reputation,
and in his domestic concerns)." A few pages later he broadens
the little myth to include More's seduction of the serving girl:

> In the meantime, Salmasius, not unlike in fate to Salmasis (for
> as the name, so the tale is not unapt), unconscious that More,
> whom he had associated to himself, was an hermaphrodite, alike
> capable of procreation and of parturition, not aware of what
> More had begotten at home, he fondles in ecstasy what he had
> brought forth — namely the book in which he so often found
> himself styled great.

This is the "addle and windy egg, from which burst forth that
tympany — the *Cry of the Royal Blood.*" The union of Hermes

and Aphrodite had long been part of travel lore when Milton
bandied the ideas. Torquemada, *The Spanish Mandevile of
Miracles*, refers to Aristotle and Pliny in his discussion of
hermaphrodites and tells of Egyptian women producing multiple births, some of them bisexual. These creatures occur in
most extended accounts of monstrous births, though *The
Voyages and Travailes of Sir John Mandevile*, in a chapter on
the great island "called Dodyn, where are many men of evill
condition" is more concerned to be explicit about another
island where folk "are both men and women, and have members of both, for to engender with, & when they will, they use
one at one time, & another at another time, and they get children when they use the members of a man and they beare
children when they use the members of a woman." [10]
Much of this kind of material reappears in *Paradise Lost*.
We have seen one resolution of this speculation upon monstrous births in the description of Hell as a universe of death
where nature breeds perverse, "all monstrous, all prodigious
things." After the fall, miscegenation enters the cosmos where
good and bad are matched, abhorring to join, and by imprud-
ence mixed produce the deformed births of body or mind.
Medieval pneumatology appears in the lines on Baalim and
Ashtaroth

                               those male,
These Feminine. For Spirits when they please
Can either Sex assume, or both.   I, 422–424

This assertion perhaps helps explain Raphael's embarrassed
reply to Adam's query about angelic intercourse, though it
will bring little comfort to Milton's equally embarrassed ad-
mirers. It is hard to see only innocent curiosity in Adam's
unexpected rejoinder to the lecture on sex, or less than physical union in Raphael's equivocation between human and
angelic love.

Whatever pure thou in the body enjoy'st
(And pure thou wert created) we enjoy

In eminence, and obstacle find none
Of membrane, joynt, or limb, exclusive barrs:
Easier then Air with Air, if Spirits embrace,
Total they mix, Union of Pure with Pure
Desiring; nor restrained conveyance need
As Flesh to mix with Flesh, or Soul with Soul.

VIII, 622–629

Adam forgets this in his challenging of God's motives after the fall:

O why did God,
Creator wise, that peopl'd highest Heav'n
With Spirits Masculine, create at last
This noveltie on Earth, this fair defect
Of Nature, and not fill the World at once
With Men as Angels without Feminine,
Or find some other way to generate Mankind?

X, 888–895

As in so many cruxes in *Paradise Lost*, the solution seems to lie within the chain of being or system of hierarchies. The lines on angelic love form an addendum to critics' complaints that the war in heaven is a blemish on the poem. The problems are related in their reference to the substance of angels. The usual excuse that Raphael is rendering spiritual conflict in corporal terms "as may express them best" is but partly relevant; hence it is refreshing to see that the war has recently been called a good epic battle in itself. Similarly, it is not enough for the critic to justify Milton's inclusion of angelic intercourse merely on the ground that it was a contemporary intellectual interest. The concepts of one first matter for all things and of graduated refinement in nature and function make angelic loving the logical (not to say inevitable) concluding question in a discussion of imperfect human love, which follows, though at some distance, the discussion of imperfect human reason. Adam's last query — why did God provide only this way of increase — is indeed a question to be asked; among many, La Primaudaye answered it, without preventing Sir Thomas Browne, for example, from asking it indirectly again. *The French Academie* credits all to the wisdom of God in adjusting generation to "force and infirmitie .... so that the one can do nothing without the other in generation." The occurrence of these ideas in the poem partially results from their presence in the traditional knowledge with which Milton was working. But it also results from their organic usefulness in projecting the problem of good and evil through images of creation and negation, fecundity and sterility, the ambivalence (but not relativity) of moral issues in the human cosmos. Through all runs a common referent: good is natural, normal, self-balanced; evil is unnatural, deformed, miscreative, and dependent for its very definition upon good. Mutants and deviates from ordinary sexual identity and reproduction, like monstrous births and hermaphrodites in poetry or prose, reflect this central verity from one more mirror of science.[11]

The dialectic of disease and remedy so frequently met in Milton's prose issues from such postulates as the cosmic correspondence of man with the great world and the inescapable equation of disease with disorder, health with harmony and unity, and remedy with curative measures in church and state. Order is not only heaven's first law, but man's. Not all prose metaphors shine inwardly like the inspired comparison of a good book to the precious life-blood of a master spirit; but even this shares an identity of substance, the same nature, method, and purpose with medical images in the violent character assassinations of the *Defences* and the rigidly argued political analogies of other tracts. Diseased flesh and blood imply always the opposite: the possibility of order in men and institutions. *Of Reformation* is not alone in being governed by an image of the healthful relationship of Christ and the Church; the insistent analogy between the law of nature and the law of God is expressed so heavily in medical-anatomical images as to become almost a myth in itself in *Doctrine of*

Divorce, discussed at length in the next chapter. Nor is the poetry lacking in medical metaphor, though astronomy and cosmology provide the dominant symbols of order in *Paradise Lost*. The palace revolution in which passion snatches the rule of man from reason is an image combining biological, civil, and moral order. To discover its outlines, we must examine comparisons such as the sore on the political or ecclesiastical body that betrays corruption within, the dropsy or gout that makes a monster of unregulated institutions, and the mental anguish and madness that are the last and worst infirmities in man or state.

We begin with *Eikonoklastes*, where Milton characteristically accepts a metaphor and turns it against the inventor:

He is accurate *to put a difference between the plague of malice, & the ague of mistakes, the itch of noveltie, and the leprosie of disloyaltie.* But had he as wel known how to distinguish between the venerable gray haires of ancient Religion, and the old scurffe of Superstition, between the wholsome heat of well governing, and the feverous rage of Tyrannizing, his judgement in State-physic, had bin of more autoritie.

In this context, it is a mistake for Charles to convert state government into state physic; for if he is so ignorant in the one, he must be worse in the other. In *Of Reformation* the church has been envenomed with a "universal tetter of impurity" like "all the inward acts of worship" of the superstitious man, whose fear and hope, fixed only upon the flesh, render him carnal; for those acts "run out lavishly to the upper skin, and there harden into a crust of Formallitie." Moral corruption is a "universall rottennes, and gangrene in the whole *Function*." Milton needed no book for this, but the bookish quality of the figure may be seen in Bartholomew's statement that "kynde putteth out from the inward partis the matter that is infect to the skyn" with the result that sometimes "it is greved with scales, and sommetyme with ytchynge, with drye scabbes and wete." In an age of Bible-readers the "spiritual leprosie" of *Means to Remove Hirelings* is as familiar as the "speckled vanity" and "leprous sin" of *Nativity Ode*. Milton's agility and equanimity in working from both sides of the same image of diseased skin as symptomatic of internal disorder appear in *Apology for Smectymnuus*. In one place he announces:

For if the sore be running upon me, in all judgement I have scapt the disease, but he who hath as much infection hid in him, as he hath voluntarily confest, and cannot expell it, because he is dull, for venomous Atheisme were no treasure to be kept within him else, let him take the part hee hath chosen, which needs must follow, to swell and burst with his own inward venome.

Here he relies on the aphorism about the impostume: "Whan it is broke," says Bartholomew, "it is no drede of peryll." But a few pages later Milton conveniently describes the outward sign in another fashion. The "tetter of Pedagoguisme" upon his opponent reveals "that his brain is not meanly tainted with that infection." He is technically right in distinguishing between a rash and an open ulcer; and it is the precision in nomenclature that enables him to enforce the contrast.[12]

Two generalizations about the imagery of internal disorders require notice. One is that the references to internal diseases implied by sores support the logical statement, in much the same way that elements of the epic similes repeat and extend the central comparison. In *Pro Se Defensio* the adversary's gentle touch upon his own actions is done "with so much art, so much like an old practitioner, that anyone may perceive there is a sore underneath." It will presently be seen how pronounced was Milton's employment of these two elements — the physician and the hidden malady. The conflict of appearance and reality takes other forms in this category of science. The analogy found for the evil of sin within the letter of the law exemplifies the insight with which Milton's mind fetched similitudes from nature. What is true in physic, he says, will be found as true in policy: "that as of bad pulses those that beat most in order are much worse then those that keep the most inordinat circuit; so of popular vices those that may bee committed legally, will be more pernicious then those that are left to their own cours at perill." The motto *No Bishop, No King*, which Milton was not prepared to accept when writing *Of Reformation,* is "a meere ague-cake coagulated out of a certaine Fever they have" — where the fears of the bishops are equated with distempered minds, fever in Milton being almost always synonymous with frantic illogicality and unreason. In *Comus*, the Attendant Spirit's description of mortals who strive "to keep up a frail, and Feaverish being," though less complex, belongs to the same category. The expression "dangerous Ruptures of the Commonwealth . . . which cannot be without some inward flaw in her Bowels" is inescapable rather than imaginative and fit for *A Letter to a Friend. Animadversions,* on the other hand, Milton's most remarkably ingenious pamphlet, supports very well the quick play of "'tis fear'd you have *Balaams* disease, a pearle in your eye, *Mammons* Praestriction." The word *pearl* moves two ways: the technical term for a kind of blindness which prevents the bishops from seeing truth, and the symbol of the greed which precludes even an interest in the truth. Moral corruption figures repeatedly as obesity, dropsy, tumors, and excrescent flesh. In *Doctrine of Divorce*, the man who swallows the book of Custom "puffs up unhealthily"; worldly prosperity is condemned in *Reason of Church Government* as "puffing up the soul with a slimy fleshinesse, and weakening her principal organick parts."

The second generalization about this medical imagery is that each comparison looks forward or back to a central image; or to put it another way, somewhere in the prose will be a fully developed analogy to which others may be referred as to a point of origin. *Colasterion* continues the figure of pathological obesity in "one who will expect other arguments to bee perswaded the good health of a sound answer, then the gout and dropsy of a big margin." The "puffed up tumour of a man" in *Pro Se Defensio* repeats the "noysom, and diseased tumor of Prelacie" that must be "cut away from the publick body" in *Of Reformation*. Bartholomew and La Primaudaye describe dropsy as a bloating caused by "errour of the vertue of dygestion in the holownesse of the lyver"; and the first book of the famous John Banister's *Workes* (1633) identifies dozens of tumors. *Animadversions* contains the most extended development of the image in which the initially promising appearance of health conceals an inner distemper that swells at last into something like a dropsy:

> but his [Cyprian's] personal excellence like an antidote overcame the malignity of that breeding corruption which was then a disease that lay hid for awhile under shew of a full, and healthy constitution, as those hydropic humours not discernable at first from a fair and juicy fleshinesse of body, or that unwonted ruddy color, which seems graceful to a cheek otherwise pale, and yet arises from evil causes, either of some inward obstruction, or inflammation, and might deceav the first Phisicians till they had learnt the sequell, which Cyprians dayes did not bring forth, and the Prelatism of episcopacy which began then to burgeon, and spread, had as yet, especially in famous men, a fair, though a false imitation of flourishing.[13]

For most of these pathological allusions, an ordinary dictionary will suffice; some require the clinical detail of the encyclopedist. A case in point is Milton's warning: "Take care, More, take care, that after your Pontian sweats, you do not contract a gravedo in your head or a polypus in your nose." Batman says that polypus is a superfluity of flesh growing out of the nostrils, bred of redundant humours; and Pierre Le Loyer, *A Treatise of Specters* (1605), defines gravedo as a disease which stops the head and nostrils like polypus. All the authorities agree that it is a loathsome and stinking affliction, and this might be thought sufficient insult. But Batman says also that polypus comes of hot humours, a fact which explains the reference to the tumbling of Pontia and the polypus as a kind of punishment. Le Loyer adds that such stoppages lead to corruption of the fantasy, making it subject to "false Impressions and Specters," a fact that enlists this detail in support of other charges of More's brainsickness and wild effusions. A last ambiguity, certainly not too subtle for Milton, arises from the fact that, as Banister reports, the growth is "of substance loose and fungous, like the flesh of the fish called *Polypus*." The associations of Pontia as sexual object, *Pontus* as sea, and fish as sexual symbol coalesce with those of repellent odor and insanity to produce an attack of extraordinary ingenuity and economy.

The central image of the tumors and excrescences to which polypus relates is, of course, the extended fable of the wen, perhaps a climax of Milton's references to tumors, and also an illustration of the conversion of metaphor into analogy or allegory by a narrative treatment. The multiple cross-references to microcosm and macrocosm, the body of man and the body politic, the bishops, the king, and the people move the figure three ways at once. Mindful of the tradition in which he was writing, Milton calls on Menenius Agrippa for help and begins:

Upon a time the Body summon'd all the Members to meet in the Guild for the common good (as *Æsops* Chronicles averre many stranger accidents) the head by right takes the first seat, and next to it a huge and monstrous Wen, little lesse then the Head it selfe, growing to it by a narrow excrescency. The members amaz'd began to aske one another what hee was that tooke place next their cheif; none could resolve. Whereat the Wen, though unweildy, with much adoe gets up and bespeaks the Assembly to this purpose. That as in place he was second to the head, so by due of merit; that he was to it an ornament, and strength, and of speciall neare relation, and that if the head should faile, none were fitter then himselfe to step into his place; therefore hee thought it for the honour of the Body, that such dignities and rich indowments should be decreed him, as did adorne, and set out the noblest Members. To this was answer'd, that it should bee consulted. Then was a wise and learned Philosopher sent for, that knew all the Charters, Lawes, and Tenures of the Body.

On him it is impos'd by all, as cheife Committee to examine, and discuss the claim and Petition of right put in by the Wen; who soon perceiving the matter, and wondring at the boldnesse of such a swolne Tumor, Wilt thou (quoth he) that art but a bottle of vitious and harden'd excrements, contend with the lawfull and freeborne members, whose certaine number is set by ancient, and unrepealable Statute? head thou art none, though thou receive this huge substance from it, what office bearst thou? what good canst thou show by thee done to the Common-weale? the Wen not easily dash't, replies, that his Office was his glory, for so oft as the soule would retire out of the head from over the steaming vapours of the lower parts to Divine Contemplation, with him shee found the purest and quietest retreat, as being most remote from soile, and disturbance. Lourdan, quoth the philosopher, thy folly is as great as thy filth; know that all the faculties of the Soule are confined of old to their severall vessels, and *ventricles*, from which they cannot part without dissolution of the whole Body; and that thou containst no good thing in thee, but a heape of hard, and loathsome uncleannes, and art to the head a foul disfigurment and burden, when I have cut thee off, and open'd thee, as by the help of these implements I will doe, all men shall see.

Similar to this story is the fable of the belly and the members, a Renaissance commonplace; the invocation to Menenius Agrippa points to Plutarch or Livy as the ultimate source, but the homily was available in *Coriolanus* and *1 Corinthians*, not to mention Thomas Tomkis' *Lingua; or the Combat of the Five Senses for Superiority* (1607). *The French Academie* typifies popular analogy between the body and the state:

Wherefore a sound body of a good constitution is like the body of a whole people and societie, that hath the members agreeing well together, so that every one keepeth his ranke, not hurting one another. But a sick and diseased body is like the body of a mutenous and seditious people, that breaketh the order it ought to keepe, and goeth beyond appointed bounds. Therefore wee have a goodly image of peace, and of that peaceable life whereunto men are created and borne, in the disposition and temperature of the humours and members of the body, whereby we ought to learn what great account we are to make of peace, amitie, and concord, and how we ought to hate and abhorre all warre, discord and dissention, seeing the one is as it were health and life, and the other as disease and death.

Milton uses physiological lore to illustrate a civil condition and to argue the usurpation of bishops; La Primaudaye uses the body politic to explain the physiological fact. The one is a specific example, the other a general comparison; but the fundamental assumptions are the same. Often in the prose, Milton's metaphors verge like this into allegorical narrative. The Eros-Anteros myth of *Doctrine of Divorce*, to be considered in the next chapter, is an example. Here the fable of the wen illustrates the tendency fully developed, the master image, so to speak, to which other prose figures of puffed or insolent flesh may be referred.[14]

Diseases of the mind, like those of flesh and entrails, form a little category of their own, sometimes combining with the others to create a sense of complete disorder. The "dizzy megrim" of *Doctrine of Divorce* comes from a distempered stomach; and in arguing against the restraint of lawful liberty, Milton declares: "As by Physick we learn in menstruous bodies, where natures current hath been stopt, that the suffocation and upward forcing of some lower part, affects the head and inward sense with dotage and idle fancies." This vigorous if unpleasant image has its poetic counterpart in the effect of the forbidden fruit on Adam and Eve; they suffer an indigestion and "grosser sleep / Bred of unkindly fumes." The language of the prose resembles La Primaudaye's explanation that when the liver is not purged or when "veines are stopt" it decays by "retayning stil the excrements thereof from whence the vapours ascending up to the braine trouble it very much and cause it to fall into very strange & foolish conceiptes." Le Loyer declares that blood prevented from passage in women at term "troubleth the braine in such sorte, that (as *Hippocrates* saith) it causeth many of them to have idle fancies and fond conceipts, and tormenteth them with diverse

imaginations of horrible specters." Bartholomew finds the
cause of giddiness "to moche plentie of humours . . . [which]
meve in the heed with ventosyte that comyth up from the
body, or fro the stomack to the brayne." In *Samson* the aber-
ration is divinely directed; but one should note Milton's inclusion of gluttony and drunkenness, for these causes of God's
intervention could also induce frenzy. While the Philistines
are "drunk with Wine, / And fat regorg'd of Bulls and Goats"
and prefer their idols

> Among them he a spirit of phrenzie sent,
> Who hurt thir minds,
> And urg'd them on with mad desire
> To call in hast for thir destroyer   1675–1678

Belief in direct punishment by supernatural agents died
hard. Batman, adding to Bartholomew's chapter "Of the
phrensie, and the causes and remedyes thereof," finds it
"very daungerous to cure, if the vitalls be over ruled by a
strong spirit" and "a token of a deepe displeasure from God,
when it remaineth unto the ende in the possessed." Milles,
as it were anticipating the "blindness internal" of the lines
on the Philistines, recites in his *Treasurie*:

So blinde is the wisedome and pollicy of man, when God de-
termineth to punnish him: for then, the first blow that God
commonly giveth him, is in the braine, whereby he taketh from
him his judgement, that he may run headlong upon his own
ruine.

Salmasius and More are charged with madness, of course;
and Samson is heavy with mental anguish, lamenting that
torment is not confined to the flesh, on which already wait
ills innumerable. His discourse restates an old and admittedly
unrealistic query; for Plutarch's question "What passions
and maladies be worse, those of the soul or those of the body"
allowed but one answer. The distinctive feature to the lines
is their perfect integration with the dramatic narrative and

hence the freshening of the stereotyped debate. Readers perceiving what Samuel Johnson missed, that the middle of the poem occurs in Samson's mind, see the following as no digression or ornament but a thematic statement of Samson's situation. The qualification "Though void of corporal sense" at once recognizes the element of pseudo-controversy and validates the relation of mental suffering in physical terms. Torment, says Samson,

> must secret passage find
> To th'inmost mind,
> There exercise all his fierce accidents,
> And on her purest spirits prey,
> As on entrails, joints, and limbs
> With answerable pains, but more intense
> Though void of corporal sense.
> My griefs not only pain me
> As a lingring disease,
> But finding no redress, ferment and rage,
> Nor less then wounds immedicable
> Ranckle, and fester, and gangrene,
> To black mortification.
> Thoughts my Tormenters arm'd with deadly stings
> Mangle my apprehensive tenderest parts,
> Exasperate, exulcerate, and raise
> Dire inflammation which no cooling herb
> Or medcinal liquor can asswage,
> Nor breath of Vernal Air from snowy Alp.   610–628

It is clear from what we have seen of Renaissance physiology and psychology that Milton is working with conventional particulars; it is also apparent that the images of diseased skin and organs, met earlier in the prose, here exemplify the more hideous maladies of the mind. Earlier Samson had been promised "Salve to thy Sores" in the form of counsel or consolation, for "apt words have power to swage / The tumors of a troubl'd mind"; but at this stage the "healing words" of his friends have not been "as Balm to fester'd wounds." [15]

The obligatory passage in any discussion of Milton's medical lore is the catalog that Michael reveals to Adam, wherein converge so many allusions:

> Immediately a place
> Before his eyes appeard, sad, noysom, dark,
> A Lazar-house it seemd, wherein were laid
> Numbers of all diseas'd, all maladies
> Of gastly Spasm, or racking torture, qualms
> Of heart-sick Agonie, all feavorous kinds,
> Convulsions, Epilepsies, fierce Catarrhs,
> Intestin Stone and Ulcer, Colic pangs,
> Daemoniac Phrenzie, moaping Melancholie
> And Moon-struck madness, pining Atrophie
> Marasmus, and wide-wasting Pestilence,
> Dropsies, and Asthma's, and Joint-racking Rheums.
>
> XI, 477–488

These evils derive by natural and moral logic from excess in meat and drink, and are the penalty of Eve's inabstinence, as Milton sustains the conservative attitude that disease, by God's allowance or direction, punishes sin. The sins are clear enough; the kinds of diseases, like Dryden's last verse, have not yet been sufficiently explicated. Verity and others gloss *Atrophie* and *Marasmus* (probably tuberculosis; the text here lacks a comma). We have already noticed "all feavorous kinds," melancholy (which Bartholomew distinguished as an infection of the middle cell of the head, with privation of reason), and madness (foremost cell, with privation of imagination). But "Phrenzie," "Dropsies," and "Spasm" contain much more than has been noted. Agrippa's *Three Books of Occult Philosophy* records four varieties of frenzy — from the muses, from Dionysius, from Apollo, from Venus. Lodge's *DuBartas* recognizes three sorts of dropsies: one arising from a humour dispersed through the body, another from excess wind and humour "wherein the upper parts are extenuate, and the lower are tumified," and a third from wind in the belly. Batman adds to Bartholomew's chapter "Of the Crampe":

There are foure kindes of Spasmos or cramps, the first is named Emprosthotonos, the which is when the head is drawne downward to the breast. The second is named Thetanos, & that is when the forhead & all the whole body is drawen so vehemently, that the body is unmoveable. The third is named Opisthotonos, & that is when the head is drawn backward, or the mouth is drawne towarde the eare. The fourth kind is named Spasmos, the which doth drawe the sinewes verye streight & asperusly in the feete and legges.

The phrase "all maladies / Of gastly Spasm" unquestionably refers to such a classification as this. The passage as a whole operates in a context not only of medical lore but of literary tradition and of immediate narrative function. Editors have recognized the similarity of this set piece to catalogs of disease in the ancient writers, in *Piers Plowman*, and in Du-Bartas. Milton's survey cannot compare for length to the latter's seven quarto pages; but his expansion of the 1667 version by three lines suggests special concern with it. He frames it with Michael's introduction blaming Eve and subsequent ungoverned appetite, Adam's overflow of pity for the sufferers, and Michael's stern repetition of man's particular and general responsibility. It becomes a lurid example of the wages of sin, a fall and punishment in little. The experience contributes to Adam's maturity without mitigating his blame.[16]

The other side of the question, remedies for ills of man and state, provided the impulse for dozens of metaphors and half-formed allegories in the prose, many of them recurrent. The dominant motif, even more common than the "strong purgatives" Milton frequently advised, is the stringent or corrosive medicine needful to the cure of religion or commonwealth. The knife is the last resort in civil or ecclesiastical polity. Each "radicall humor and passion" may be

wrought upon and corrected; and "there bee many drugs
to purge those redundant humors and circulations that commonly impair health." Nothing will cure the Remonstrant
"but some familiar and Kitchin phisick." Moral as well as
medical relativity seems implied in *Reason of Church Government* that prelaty is "not such a kind of evil, as hath any
good, or use in it, which many evils have, but a distill'd
quintessence, a pure elixar of mischief, pestilent alike to
all." Many a "sovran ointment" and "strong physick" appear:
leeches, tartar, vitriol, mercury, aloes, rhubarb, and myrrh.
The Latin poems ofter refer to the healing power of herbs.
Something has been said in Chapter IV about the remedies
for sight; to these should be added the request in *Reason of
Church Government* for "some eye-brightning electuary of
knowledge, and foresight" and that in *Of Reformation* for a
"sovrain eyesalve" to purge "that intellectual ray" God has
planted in us. Later, if not at this time one may expect exactitude in Milton's references to diseases and remedies of the
eye; the *drop serene* of the personal allusion in *Paradise Lost*
translates the *gutta serena* of the physicians, even as the opening of the twenty-second sonnet paraphrases it. Throughout
these medical metaphors some equivalents often recur. Milton equates the minister or magistrate with the physician,
the citizen with the patient, and the disease with heresy, sin,
or civil disorder. Here is one illustration of the method:

For publick preaching indeed is the gift of the Spirit working as
best seemes to his secret will, but discipline is the practick work
of preaching directed and apply'd as is most requisite to particular duty; without which it were all one to the benefit of souls,
as it would be to the cure of bodies, if all the Physitians in London should get into the severall Pulpits of the City, and as-
sembling all the diseased in every Parish, should begin a learned
Lecture of Pleurisies, Palsies, Lethargies, to which perhaps none
there present were inclin'd, and so without so much as feeling
one puls, or giving the least order to any skilfull Apothecary,
should dismisse 'em from time to time, some groaning, some lan-

guishing, some expiring, with this only charge, to look well to themselves, and do as they heare.[17]

Milton employs the same figure among the many medical configurations in *Reason of Church Government*. Later he was to offer his first divorce pamphlet to the "cure of an inveterate disease crept into the best part of humane societie; and to do this with no smarting corrosive, but with a smooth and pleasing lesson, which receiv'd hath the vertue to soften and dispell rooted and knotty sorrows." But here an extended analogy with mental disease recognizes the need for drastic therapy in the state; it is founded on the copybook aphorism older than Horman's *Vulgaria*: "Physicions heale sore sykenessis with sharpe medicynes." Punishment or censure, says Milton, is not an evil but a saving remedy.

Thus then the civill Magistrate looking only upon the outward man if he find in his complexion, skin, or outward temperature the signes and marks . . . of injustice, rapine, lust, cruelty, or the like, sometimes he shuts up as in frenetick, or infectious diseases; or confines within dores, as in every sickly estate. Sometimes he shaves by penalty or mulct, or els to cool and take down those luxuriant humors which wealth and excesse have caus'd to abound. Otherwhiles he seres, he cauterizes, he scarifies, lets blood, and finally, for utmost remedy cuts off. The patients which most an end are brought into his hospital, are such as are farre gone, and beside themselves (unlesse they be falsly accus'd) so that force is necessary to tame and quiet them in their unruly fits, before they can be made capable of a more human care.

Systematic exploration of the analogy continues through several pages, as state gives way to church and every equivalent applies.

The civil magistrate confers to the healing of mans mind, by working only by terrifying plaisters upon the rind & orifice of the sore . . . not once touching the inward bed of corruption, and that hectic disposition to evill . . . Which how insufficient it is to cure the soul of man, we cannot better guess than by the art of bodily physick. Therefore God, to the intent of further healing mans deprav'd mind, to this power of the Magistrate, which contents it self with the restraint of evil-doing in the external man, added that which we call censure, to purge it and remove it clean out of the inmost soul. . . . God . . . hath committed this other office of preserving in healthful constitution the inner man . . . to his spiritual deputy . . . who being best acquainted with his own flock, hath best reason to know all the secretest diseases likely to be there . . . . for neither doth the physitian doe all in restoring his patient, he prescribes, another prepares the med'cin, some tend, some watch, some visit.

Most of these medicines and procedures are in Bartholomew's thirteenth-century discourse on remedies for the frenzy, a testimonial to both the bookish conventionality of Milton's analogy and the slow progress in treatment of mental disorders. First the patient's head is shaved and washed in vinegar and he is "well kepte or bounde in a darke place." He is bled, and his shaved head "plasterd with lounges of a swyne or of a wether," and "at the laste if purgations and electuaries suffisen not, [he] shall be holpe with crafte of Surgery." La Primaudaye speaks in Milton's tongue when he asserts that "as God hath provided corporall medicine for the body, so he hath prepared spirituall Phisicke for the soule against all the diseases thereof."

In *Reason of Church Government* appear other parallels to the incompetence of "that restraining and styptic surgery which the law uses" not against the malady but outward symptoms. The minister, however, sends in "those two divine ingredients of most cleansing power to the soul, Admonition and Reproof," the only drugs or antidotes to purge the mind. Therefore, as soon as the Christian patient, "by feeding otherwhere on meats not allowable" falls into sickness, the minister tries "some gentle potion" of admonishment. If that fails, he lays "neerer siege to the entrenched causes of his distemper." Finally, "one while he shakes his stubbornesse with racking convulsions nigh despair; other whiles with deadly corrosives he gripes the very roots of his faulty liver to bring him to life through the entry of death." Excommunication "is a rough and vehement cleansing med-cin," to be prescribed where the illness is obdurate, "a morti-fying to life, a kind of saving by undoing." If the convales-cent sinner brings "his bill of health, that he is now cleare of infection and of no danger to the other sheep," he is nursed by his brethren; but he that would hide his faults from such a "wholsome curing as this . . . is like a man that having foul diseases about him, perishes for shame, and the feare he has of a rigorous incision to come upon his flesh." [18]

Tetrachordon elevates the comparison to Christ. For "as the Physician cures him who hath tak'n down poyson" not by the middling temper of nourishment but the other ex-treme of antidote, "so Christ administers heer a sharpe & cor-rosive sentence against a foul and putrid licence." The civil officer that for utmost remedy cuts off an arm or leg or a man practices a surgery like the philosopher's dissection of the wen, or the general cashiering and excision from the body politic of the "noysom and diseased tumor of Prelacie." This desperate remedy is nature's teaching, "to divide any limb from the body to the saving of its fellows" even though it deform the whole. How much more is it her instruction to cut off not a true member but "a sore, the gangrene of a limb, to the recovery of a whole man?" Bartholomew's ad-vice is the same; it is better, he says, that one corrupt part be burned or cut away than that all be destroyed. Indeed, the entire complex of medical images and analogies is quite com-monplace. The Biblical Father-figure often appears in a surgeon's gown; even handbooks of set comparisons paral-leled physician and minister as Milton did. Robert Caw-drey's *A Treasurie or Store-house of Similes* anticipates most of his language:

As a carefull and skilfull Surgion, who having Patients that are diseased with sundry greevous woundes and sores, and having provided drawing Plaisters and Corasives for the same, dooth not commit them to his Patients, that they should lay and applie them to their sores and wounds, least they should withdraw and keepe back the same plaisters from their sores and wounds, and so seek to free themselves from the smart and griefe which would ensue and follow upon the laying to of the said plaisters and corasives to their festered sores and wounds; and therefore he wil not trust them therewith, but doth himselfe both lay and apply the same plaisters and corasives to their sores, and will himselfe cut out the corrupt and rotten flesh that groweth in their wounds: Even so it is not inough that a Preacher. . . .

In the heyday of the parallel passage, Cawdrey's duplication of the basic comparison of surgeon and minister, together with such particulars as corrosives and plasters, festered sores, and excision of corrupt flesh, would have been indisputedly entered in the register of Milton's sources. Its true value, however, is to promote clearer understanding of Milton's practice, for it shows him working with a common vocabulary. His enlarged prose similes are developed beyond Cawdrey's, and in his hands the argument from analogy served every purpose from invective to exhortation.[19]

The conclusions issuing from this survey of medical lore in Milton confirm those already spoken. The number of allusions is large; the range of information and the depth is narrow and small. Whatever he may have known out of books or experience, he used only conventional, comparatively shallow medieval and Renaissance commonplaces in physiology, psychology, and medicine. The ingenuity with which these are manipulated in the prose, like the unfailing unity with which they inform the major poems, is another matter; and it is here that Milton as artist reveals himself. The bulk of medical-anatomical metaphor and simile in the prose is enough to suggest a prevailing way of looking at civil and ecclesiastical relations. The problem becomes one of exploration rather than identification; the cosmic equivalents of health and order, disease and negation, remedy and reform operate within a vast Platonic concept of the ugliness and deformity of evil, the regularity and beauty of good. Working these out in their contexts is the final critical exercise toward aesthetic comprehension; but the background of the image is part of its definition.

So it is that the dozens of passages in which Milton's language repeats the technical terminology of *De Proprietatibus* or *The French Academie* support the view that his medical allusions are traditional, even old-fashioned, familiar and acceptable to a mid-seventeenth-century reader if not to a late seventeenth-century scientist. His enthusiastic program of study never realized itself in medical science as it did in history. This is a literary and moralized kind of natural philosophy, not experimental or speculative. In the prose it is a rhetorical vocabulary, symbol and image integrated with argument. In *Paradise Lost* it conforms to the pattern of total unification; physiological data recapitulate the ethical and moral assumptions — the crooked rib is as much a part of the whole story of the fall as the *felix culpa*, the logic of illness from intemperance is as inexorable as the punishment of Adam's sin.

The function of science in Milton's thought and art has been a corollary to the preceding surveys of the cycle of natural philosophy, which were occupied mainly with establishing the kind, the scope, and the provenience of Milton's information. Now we are prepared for systematic examination of its aesthetic and rhetorical function, and for answers to the questions posed at the beginning of the study. Chapter VII considers the part science plays in the content and form of a pamphlet of the middle prose period, *The Doctrine and Discipline of Divorce*. The final chapter may be allowed a test case for the critical perspective in which the whole study has been undertaken. In a modified formalist critical approach, the results of the historical and descriptive methods are assimilated into the exposition of *Paradise Lost* as a fusion of science with character, narrative structure, and theme.

CHAPTER VII

Precepts of Beneficence in Prose

T HE PROSPERITY OF THE PROSE has been an agreeable and instructive development of the excitement thirty years ago over the new Milton implied in Saurat's title. Discovery then of an intellectual content in the poetry beyond Raleigh's purview sent professional readers into the supposed thornforest of the pamphlets. The complexities of political and religious thought found there encouraged many to return to *Paradise Lost* with new conviction of its specific gravity. Since then the prose has reinforced the claim of the poetry to respectful attention as a body of ideas. One unexpected result of this enthusiasm has been that another outcry against the heresy of the didactic has caused us, astonishingly enough, to defend a literary interest in the moral seriousness of the poem. A more felicitous outcome has been the appearance of the complete canon with a monumental index and the beginnings of a heavily annotated edition of all the prose. With a full text before them and a guide that amounted to a concordance, the next stage for scholars was determined. They took to heart Raleigh's observation that Milton was preoccupied in his controversial tracts with themes and ideas that later pervaded his epic. Almost at once old prose became new gloss writ both large and small, with Kelley's full-scale comparison of *Christian Doctrine* and

Paradise Lost its outstanding contribution. The development of Milton's thinking and its milieu was steadily clarified by Willey, Wolfe, Barker, and Haller.

So much industry, however, was doubtless bound to produce error. Distinctions between prose and poetry about questions of belief tend to disappear between the parallel passages, an inclination accelerated by study in the history of ideas. Recurrence of a motif in tract and poem does establish the continuity of Milton's interests, even a kind of harmony of his gospels, as we have seen, But inferences from repetition should be psychological or cultural — about Milton's habits of mind or the relationship of his thought to his time. Or the conclusions may be textual and canonical; thus Tillyard recommends a date for *L'Allegro–II Penseroso* close to that of the first prolusion because of echoes, but Le Comte disallows it from the general practice of verbal recurrence throughout the prose and verse. Yet it is surely a mistake to emphasize Milton's ideas as beliefs at the expense of his effects in poetry, and it is dangerous to the integrity of his poems to regard the prose as Milton's deliberate annotation of his verse instead of an anonymous dictionary from which definitions may be drawn to explain literal meaning. Overemphasis of unit-ideas in the prose that are repeated in the poems promotes a misleading sense of Milton's modernity, for it is tempting to select those that speak to our condition. We need greatly Tillyard's *Elizabethan World Picture* and Bush's *Paradise Lost in Our Time*; we can dispense with Knight's *Chariot of Wrath*.[1]

There is, however, a further approach to the prose that has lately received something of its due, although we are not yet entirely in command of Milton's thought there, nor of its influence. But to go with Sensabaugh's book about Milton's impact upon later seventeenth-century political thought, studies of the prose as prose have begun to emerge; and we have been advised of the rhetorical features, diction, and imagery. Quite properly Milton's changing attitudes toward Christian liberty or the decay of the world or the Trinity is a matter of concern. But we are becoming concerned also for the prose expression itself, its structures and its rhetoric, even as in *Paradise Lost* we have increasingly emphasized the poetry. Allowing for such essays as Gilman's formal analysis, the concern generally means seeing both prose and poetry as artifact; in particular, it means seeing them as symbolic and metaphoric and multidimensional, not merely factual or testimonial. Doubtless every reader has a working conviction of what Milton really believed in *Areopagitica* and *Paradise Lost*, and it is scarcely necessary to remark the insistent moral purpose impelling everything he wrote. Yet in the poem, as Rajan says, the question of Milton's beliefs should never arise; the only requirement is to make certain suppositions for the duration of the poetry. In the prose, a less formal artifact, the question does arise because of the common assumptions we make about factual and argumentative prose and because of Milton's strong autobiographical and confessional habit there. Even so, the formality with which he addresses himself to his subject should warn us not to identify the world view there with Milton's own daily world view, nor to attempt establishing from the prose the attitudes of a poem written at the same time. We do better by our responsibility as students of his art when we explore the ways in which the prose is made effective by those devices of language and style that occur in all good discourse.

Here the obvious caveat against forced merging of genres must be stressed. Even in the highly structured and eloquent prose appearing intermittently in all the tracts and sustained throughout *Areopagitica*, the rhetorical processes and devices do not equal in number or intensity those in the poetry. They display enough family resemblance, however, to warrant close consideration, enough and more to justify Eliot's left-handed compliment to the prose as half-formed poetry.

Given Milton's constant recourse to natural philosophy as we have seen it, the dominant figures, the structure of metaphor, and the rough-cast epic similes, as they derive from natural science, fairly demand exploration. One inducement to such examination comes from studies of the prose vocabulary like Neumann's descriptive survey and Ekfelt's close reading of graphic diction. Another develops from Price's modestly professed explication of incidental imagery in *Areopagitica* and Wolfe's discovery of a governing image in *Of Reformation*. Still a third, somewhat oblique, inducement emerges from the emphasis on prose in Banks's book on imagery and Le Comte's on recurrence — the one confined to formal figures in conceptual categories, the other to images as part of a system of verbal echo. Here we will see Milton invite a different kind of analysis at the outset and maintain that opportunity throughout. We will witness a structuring closer to the mode of poetry than of prose, for the highly formal organization of *The Doctrine and Discipline of Divorce* lends itself admirably to this kind of investigation.[2]

We have noted the extraordinary range of scientific lore in the prose, how astronomy, botany, zoology, mineralogy, and physiology are drawn upon in their customary associations for illustration, argument, invective, and the other devices of controversy. Medical and anatomical allusions recur with great frequency. It has been suggested that anyone writing about political ills will make the expected comparisons with human maladies; but the emphasis in *Of Reformation* and *Eikonoklastes* on fevers, flesh and skin diseases, insanity, and other ailments goes beyond the casual to the insistent and the directive. In *Eikonoklastes* and the *Defences*, for example, stress falls upon disease and distortion rather than remedy: distemper, palsy, abortion, false pregnancy, and miscarriage. In these pamphlets Milton argues more against an opponent than for an idea, and the morbid associations would appear to be part of his strategy.

Now let us examine *The Doctrine and Discipline of Divorce*, to illustrate some of the ways in which materials quarried from natural science work as a feature of Milton's deliberate technique of prose argument, and to suggest a structural function of the imagery. The concern is with figurative language in general, and not only with formally constructed tropes; for much of the material cited is, strictly considered, but half-formed metaphor. It should also be clear at this stage that the four major problems defined in the introduction have a tendency to flow together. The previous chapters have shown that we cannot talk of the aesthetic function of science without talking of its philosophical origin; that before we try to say what science does, we must say what it is and whence it derives.[3]

What Milton does in poetry he does in prose — less often and less powerfully, to be sure, but as he tested many of his ideas first in the prose, we are not surprised to find poetic construction there. Certainly he was aware of the differences in genres and of the demands of decorum, no man more so. But the logical faculty, as Rosemond Tuve has shown, does not exclude the imaginative; and it is suprising only, I believe, to discover how much of the poet is here. Many of the arguments in *Areopagitica*, for example, have little or no significance today, but the poetry in it speaks to us. Milton describes getting "the power within me to a passion," a power expressing itself, to take the most famous single example, in such a statement as "who kills a Man kills a reasonable creature, Gods Image; but hee who destroyes a good Booke, kills reason it selfe, kills the Image of God, as it were in the eye." This figure is recognizable as the way of poetry, not prose, but it is found everywhere in good prose of any period and especially in Milton's. The same intensity occurs in *The Doctrine and Discipline of Divorce*. Perhaps it is not so sustained as in *Areopagitica*, but Milton's method is in many ways what we would call the poetic method. Even con-

structions like the epic simile are frequent in this poet's
prose: the myth of truth in *Areopagitica,* the huge wen in *Of
Reformation,* and here, in addition to that of Custom and
Error, the allegory of Eros and Anteros.[4]

Milton indicates at the outset that he intends an imaginative or poetic as well as a formally logical method in his
pamphlet. He calls the opening discourse of Custom and
Error an allegory, and later says that he will use in his argument "allegorick precepts of beneficence fetcht out of the
closet of nature." He interprets allegorically the myth of
Eros and Anteros, which he defends as "no meer amatorious
novel," for "to be wise and skilful in these matters, men
heretofore of greatest name in vertue, have esteemd it one
of the highest arks that human contemplation circling upward, can make from the glassy Sea whereon she stands."
This comparison would fit into the very fabric of *Paradise
Lost.*[5]

Milton deals here with four kinds of law: canon, civil,
divine, and natural. His case rests upon the identity of the
laws of God and nature as opposed to mere canon law, and
upon the recommendation of this twofold mandate to Parliament, the makers of civil law. He must show, as he says, that
it is against nature and therefore against God's will that the
temperamentally incompatible remain yoked in an artificial
and unnatural union. His references to Selden's *De Jure
Naturali* show that he is in agreement with the traditional
opinion of natural law as proceeding from God, and in
Christian Doctrine he defines the unwritten law of God as
that law of nature originally given Adam. To Milton, Christian liberty, as Woodhouse and Barker have shown, was
" 'the liberty we have in Christ' [which] frees the Christian
from all external authority." A most interesting feature of
this line of reasoning is the Christian Milton's pagan emphasis upon sins against nature rather than sins against grace.[6]

Milton's fundamental comparison, carried all through the

tract, amounts to this: canon-law impediments to divorce have created diseases in human society which result in a distortion of nature; Milton's proposals are remedies drawn from nature and natural law. The reasoning in canon law is described as indigestion, disorder of the humours, sores, blots, megrims, and the like. The law of nature is manifested in salves, medicines, and soothing treatments. Constantly expressed or implied is the comparison between truth as health and error as disease, with canon law a pollution, an unhelpful remedy, a producer of still further disease by force exerted against the bent of nature. A sort of inner framework to the pamphlet is evident in the frequent reference to nature as the creative power of the universe and as the created universe itself. The very words "nature," "natural," and "unnatural" recur in twenty-seven of the thirty-six chapters, some eighty-nine times in all. A measure of this recurrence might be expected, but if Empson were searching for the significant words here, he would find them to be "law" and "nature." Milton refers to "blameles nature," the "unreducible *antipathies* of nature," the "radical and innocent affections of nature," Christ's "fundamental and superior laws of nature and charity." "What is against nature," he concludes, "is against Law, if soundest Philosophy abuse us not." Astronomy, anatomy, and medical lore are combined into an explicit statement of the blindness of canon law and its adherents, the diseased condition of enforced marriage, and the cures and remedies consistent with the axiom, expressed here and later, that God and nature bid the same.[7]

The instability of categories based on vehicle or substance, such as medical or astronomical images, is well known and perhaps best demonstrated by Rosemond Tuve, who justly argues for the study of function. But one will find a general agreement in content among the images discussed here: they all relate, both tropes and mentioned particulars, in some fashion to natural philosophy, to what Milton regarded as natural science. Since my intention is not to classify images but to show how natural science serves as a resource for imagery and how that imagery works in the tract, the following groups are only a convenience for illustrating scientific or pseudo-scientific origins.

The astronomical and the medical-anatomical images are central; others, through their use, partake of the content of these two, and this interrelation of function is the crux of Milton's technique. One group of images, roughly astronomical in content, with emphasis on the clear light of truth as opposed to the darkness of error and sin, relates in function to a group that concerns impediments to true sight: mists, blots, robes and clothing, obscurities. Taken together, they communicate the want of insight by the defenders of canon law. A third group of images, on the flowing of water and light and their stoppage or the restraint of nature in any way, connects the previously mentioned groups with the figures from anatomy and medicine, of disease and remedy, the dislocation or distortion of nature to which all these other images relate and refer. There are of course figures and particulars which do not fall into these groups or relate directly to natural science, but these are few. Most of the images amplify either the evil of the situation or the naturalness of the cure.[8]

First astronomy. Milton may have been out of date in offering to devise *"Prutenick* tables" to mend the astronomy of the expositors who alleged "foule *Hypotheses* to save the *Phaenomenon* of our Saviours answer to the Pharisees"; but the astronomical content of the allusion and its use are unmistakable. So is his reference to the truth, which is as impossible to soil as is a sunbeam. Marriage should not exist only "to remedy a sublunary and bestial burning"; and it is a violence against the "reverend secret of nature . . . to force a mixture of minds that cannot unite, and to sowe the furrow of mans nativity with seed of two incoherent and uncombining dispositions." He refuses to attempt an astrological explanation of incompatibility: "But what might be the cause, whether each ones allotted *Genius* or proper Starre, or whether the supernall influence of Schemes and angular aspects or this elementall *Crasis* here below, whether all these jointly or singly meeting friendly, or unfriendly in either party, I dare not, with the men I am likest to clash, appear so much a Philosopher as to conjecture." Eros, "soaring up into the high Towr of his *Apogaeum*, above the shadow of the earth . . . darts out the direct rayes of his then most piercing eyesight," and later "repairs the almost faded ammunition of his Deity by the reflection of a coequal & *homogeneal* fire." In arguing that sin and true law are *"diagonal contraries*, as much allowing one another, as day and night together in one hemisphere," Milton says, "if it be possible, that sin with his darknes may come to composition, it cannot be without a foul eclipse, and twylight to the law, whose brightnesse ought to surpasse the noon." [9]

The blind side of Eros on earth and his piercing eyesight in his own sphere, "the clear light of nature in us & of nations," and the "Pharisiack mists rais'd between the law and the peoples eyes" similarly exemplify the systematic metaphorizing of appearance and reality. The "thick-sighted" cannot perceive the evils of enforced marriage because of a "blindnes in Religion." The obstacles to true vision are "swoln visage," "blots and obscurities," veils, blurs, and stains, "impostures, and trim disguises" as well as sottish blindness. A law that prohibits divorce and thus encourages sin is "no Law but sin muffl'd in the robe of Law, or Law disguis'd in the loose garment of sin." The link between this sort of comparison and the medical-anatomical appears in Milton's mention of "the troubles and distempers which for want of this insight have bin so oft in Kingdomes, in States, and Families." [10]

The free movement of light and truth and the dangers in

blocking or stifling natural motions are variously expressed. Milton writes of the mind "from whence must flow the acts of peace and love," of the tainted fountains of doctrine, of the "promiscuous draining of a carnall rage," of the "issues of love and hatred distinctly flowing through the whole masse of created things." Canon law, he says, places "more of mariage in the channell of concupiscence, then in the pure influence of peace and love, whereof the souls lawfull contentment is the onely fountain." In testifying that what is against the law of nature is against the law of God, and that lawful liberty ought not to be restrained, he draws this figure: "As by Physick we learn in menstruous bodies, where natures current hath been stopt, that the suffocation and upward forcing of some lower part, affects the head and inward sense with dotage and idle fancies." Canon lawyers argue "as if the womb of teeming Truth were to be clos'd up, if shee presume to bring forth ought, that sorts not with their unchew'd notions and suppositions." Moses "commands us to force nothing against sympathy or naturall order." The "adamantine chains" which bind the unhappily married, which "clogge a rationall creature to his endlesse sorrow," create not two souls in one flesh but "two carkasses chain'd unnaturally together . . . a living soule bound to a dead corps." [11]

This restrictive force appears in references to the remora, to fetters and bonds, and perhaps most vividly in a daring, epic-like, deliberately mixed figure near the end of the tract:

To couple hatred therefore though wedlock try all her golden links, and borrow to her aid all the iron manacles and fetters of Law, it does but seek to twist a rope of sand, which was a task, they say, that pos'd the divell. And that sluggish feind in hell *Ocnus*, whom the Poems tell of, brought his idle cordage to as good effect, which never serv'd to bind with, but to feed the Asse that stood at his elbow. And that the restrictive Law against divorce, attains as little to bind anything truly in a disjoynted mariage, or to keep it bound, but servs only to feed the ignorance, and definitive impertinence of a doltish Canon, were no absurd allusion.

One more such image of restraint and stoppage will provide a transition to the disease-and-remedy clusters which dominate the tract. Near the end of his argument, Milton writes: "Let us not be thus over-curious to strain at *atoms*, and yet to stop every vent and cranny of permissive liberty; lest nature wanting those needfull pores, and breathing places which God hath not debar'd our weaknesse, either suddenly break out into some wide rupture of open vice and frantick heresie, or else inwardly fester with repining and blasphemous thoughts, under an unreasonable and fruitless rigor of unwarranted law." [12]

The imagery from anatomical and medical lore underlies all the other types in the pamphlet. Milton's deliberate recourse to this material is demonstrated in his declaration "that which is true in Physick, wil be found as true in policie: that as of bad pulses those that beat most in order, are much worse then those that keep the most inordinat circuit, so of popular vices those that may be committed legally, will be more pernicious then those that are left to their own cours at perill." The pattern is set early when Milton says Custom's "sudden book of implicit knowledge . . . of bad nourishment in the concoction, as it was heedlesse in the devouring, puffs up unhealthily, a certaine big face of pretended learning, mistaken among credulous men, for the wholsome habit of soundnesse and good constitution; but is indeed no other, then that swoln visage of counterfeit knowledge and literature, which not onely in private marrs our education, but also in publick is the common climer into every chaire." Medical metaphor enforces the point of a later question: "Did God for this come down and cover the Mount of *Sinai* with his glory . . . to patch up an ulcerous and rott'n commonwealth . . . [and] to wash the skin and garments for every unclean touch?" The origin of truth is described as human birth: "Though this ill hap wait on her nativity, that shee never comes into the world, but like a Bastard, to the ignominy of him that brought her forth: till Time the Midwife rather than the mother of Truth, have washt and salted the Infant, declar'd her legitimat, and Churcht the father of his young *Minerva*, from the needlesse causes of his purgation." The continuing equation of moral truth with a kind of natural-philosophical or scientific truth as found in medical lore emerges also in the passage on diseased thought: "And what though others out of a waterish and queasy conscience because ever crasy and never yet sound, will rail and fancy to themselves, that injury and licence is the best of this Book? Did not the distemper of their own stomacks affect them with a dizzy megrim, they would soon tie up their tongues . . . till they get a little cordiall sobriety to settle their qualming zeale." He believes that his book "undertakes the cure of an inveterate disease crept into the best part of humane societie: and to doe this with no smarting corrosive, but with a smooth and pleasing lesson, which receiv'd hath the vertue to soften and dispell rooted and knotty sorrowes." And finally in another of those mixed, prose-epic-similes noted earlier, Christ is distinguished from the canonists with their "unhelpful Surgery." He is

like a wise Physician, administering one excesse against another to reduce us to a perfect mean. . . So heer he may be justly thought to have giv'n this rigid sentence against divorce, not to cut off all remedy from a good man who finds himself consuming away in a disconsolate and uninjoy'd matrimony, but to lay a bridle upon the bold abuses of those over-weening *Rabbies*; which he could not more effectually doe, then by a countersway of restraint curbing their wild exorbitance almost into the other extreme; as when we bow things the contrary way, to make them come to their naturall straitnesse.

Later the contraries are posed again: "this obdurat disease cannot bee conceiv'd how it was the more amended by this

unclean remedy, is the most deadly and Scorpion like gift
that the enemy of mankind could have given to any miserable
sinner." [13]

These many references to natural science constitute a
framework through which the prose argument is made effective. The logical emphasis on natural law against canon law
is produced by a structure of scientific and semi-scientific
metaphors and particulars. Milton the theocentric humanist
was well aware of the limitations of natural knowledge, but
he was no less aware of its moral implications than were
compilers like Swan and La Primaudaye. His use of such
material in this tract is not by accident or for ornament, but
rhetorical, which is to say poetical. The sciences appealed to
him as a logician and as a poet. By the end of the pamphlet,
Milton has in effect created a symbolic statement of his case;
for metaphor, even submerged metaphor, repeated and extended, becomes symbol. The figurative elements express
the argument, in effect *are* the argument. Divorce actually
and in a sense outrageously is represented by Milton as a
form of natural order to which "God and nature signifies
and lectures to us not onely by those recited decrees, but
ev'n by the first and last of all his visible works; when by his
divorcing command the world first rose out of Chaos, nor
can be renewed again out of confusion but by the separating
of unmeet consorts." [14]

Structure in prose, like structure in verse, is not mere
external arrangement; nor is the poetry of this tract a matter
of occasional purple passages. *The Doctrine and Discipline
of Divorce* is in two books, in thirty-six chapters, divided
logically according to the branchings of subject. The introduction and most of the content follow well-known rules of
rhetoric. But there is the other kind of structure, too, the
inner form created by motifs in scientific imagery that make
the argument as well as support or embellish it. And the
preliminary allegory gives us our warrant for this sort of

study if we need it. To the encyclopedists, natural science had as one of its purposes the discovery of nature's truth as the physical manifestation of moral truth; and Milton's use of this material is consistent with their objectives. His systematic exploitation of scientific lore as a unifying and formative force in *The Doctrine and Discipline of Divorce* suggests that his prose has an even stronger claim to attention than has been thought. Perhaps, if this demonstration has been persuasive, one will say with an intent quite different from Eliot's in his belated and ungracious palinode, that Milton's prose is really close to half-formed poetry.[15]

CHAPTER VIII

Natural Philosophy and Paradise Lost

FORMAL DISCUSSION of the natural science in *Paradise Lost* begins most properly with the creation story in Book VII. The celebrated dialogue on astronomy, which has attracted more notice as science, really originates there. For Milton was following hexameral tradition in extending the Genesis account by details from natural philosophy; the commentaries had brought abundant secular learning to bear upon the work of the six days and had indeed translated a mass of zoological and other lore from classical and medieval culture to the Renaissance. Kirkconnell rightly distrusts the tendency to regard *Paradise Lost* as chiefly hexameral; yet this section of Book VII forms a metaphorical matrix for the whole poem. It is the central passage to which all other passages of scientific lore may in some sort be referred, for its location in the narrative and its content conform to some of the grand strategies of the epic. Its position between the fall of the angels and the fall of man is crucial, and details of natural philosophy incorporated into it assert the major importance of scientific lore as a vocabulary of metaphor in amplifying or specializing descriptive, psychological, and thematic elements of the poem.

We have partially recovered that vocabulary in two of its contexts. One is the milieu of science: in identifying and

explaining most of Milton's particulars from the encyclopedias of science, we have seen that they are commonplace,
classical-medieval in origin, medieval-Renaissance in implication, part of a popular cultural lag, an old order not yet
superseded in either common imagination or the literature
of science. The second context is Milton's own prose and
poetry, where we have observed these particulars providing
much of the learning demanded by the epic as a form, deep-
ening the relations between parts, and functioning in the
way metaphor always does. "The language of poetry and of
science was one when the world was one." Here the respecta-
bility of the scientific detail is irrelevant, unless the poet
qualifies, as he does with classical mythology, where the
parallels are displayed and then dismissed as false. The effect
of that rejection is at once the recognition of a continuity
in human or imaginative experience (in *Paradise Lost* I,
Mulciber is *like* Mammon) and the denial of literal truth in
the myth ("thus they relate, Erring"). In the unmodified
poetic context, however, the phoenix differs from the eagle
only in degree; and the ulcer is merely more visible than the
cell of memory. To distinguish between true and false in
this is to confuse contexts, for in metaphor everything is
true. Milton's much debated choice of old instead of new
science for his figures was inevitable. Beginning now with the
hexameron in Book VII, we may inquire how the same kind
of lore operates in the setting, characterization, and thematic development of *Paradise Lost*.[1]

The pivotal position of Book VII, 210–634, amounts to
this, that it follows immediately the war in Heaven, a partial
destruction of angelic solidarity, and precedes the human
counterpart of that negation, the major element of the
double plot, Adam's denial of his relation to God, to nature,
and to Eve. If one says with Stein that the war in Heaven is
a metaphor, then he must affirm that the creation story is
too. As a redaction of revealed truth it is of course historical;

but as part of a poem it is part of a structure. Here God's positive creativity is balanced against its opposite, which is not sterility but negative creativity. Milton had elsewhere said he could not praise a cloistered virtue; here he could not use an inactive evil. Satan is never quiet, for destruction is not passive; his restless thoughts never fail of release into action. It is evil, perverted, anarchistic; but it is action. In like manner, the creation of the universe not only brings good out of evil, but actively opposes evil. The defection of angels is momentarily overwhelmed in the swarm of life that rises from the fecund earth. As one of the four grand elements in the celestial cycle (fall, creation, fall, atonement), this passage declares part of the theme of the poem, and as a derivative and dependent of the hexameral tradition, it includes a great deal of natural philosophy. The parts share the function of the whole; scientific details are part of the language in which God's creativity expresses itself. The scientific vocabulary appears in the very first image of Chaos "Outrageous as a Sea, dark, wasteful, wilde," in which all direction and dimension are lost and the Pole is mixed with the Center. The golden compasses, "Earth self-ballanc't on her Center," even the "black tartareous cold infernal dregs" purged away are in the language of science. The relation of pre-solar light "Sphear'd in a radiant Cloud" to that of the sun, the question of the firmament and the waters above — these too are expressed not as in Genesis but as in hexameron and encyclopedia. So with the view of earth as female to the warm impregnating waters, and the survey of grass, herb, tree, vine, and bush. La Primaudaye's title page to volume three is so like this as to be an hexameron in miniature; in this regard, Bartholomew, Caxton, and Swan are analogues to *Paradise Lost*. The work of the fourth day is, like the others, described in lines for some of which no gloss of science is needed ("And sowd with Starrs the Heav'n thick as a field"). But many other lines involve such scientific questions as whether the planets "augment / Thir small peculiar" from the fountain of light itself, the sun. Creatures of the sea, animals, the "Minims of Nature" are rendered in details from the bestiary and encyclopedic traditions, even as we have seen. Typical of these are the gills and trunk of the whale, the cranes flying in wedges, and the parsimonious emmet, "Pattern of just equalitie" to man yet unborn. Milton compresses volumes into lines; but the hexameron is unmistakable, and the scientific details are intrinsic to the development.

Learning had so pervaded the hexameral and epic traditions that Milton could not have sung creation or fall without adducing the variety of lore accumulated upon the content of the story and required by genre. Almost every subject introduced is attended by details out of natural philosophy that are related to others in the account of creation. The description of Hell with which the poem opens invokes mineralogy, the theory of earthquakes and volcanic action, the nature of light and darkness. At creation, the earth erupted animals, the stars and planets bore the light to which the "darkness visible" of Hell is a contrast. The soil of Heaven is potentially explosive. The Garden is an arboretum and menagerie in which Adam and Eve are integrated by allusions to elm and vine and "fairest unsupported Flour," to animals among which Adam might have found a mate, and to nature's apparently disproportionate emphasis upon the earth instead of the wheeling stars. Establishment of planetary motions at creation supplies exposition for Raphael's remarks in Book VIII and anticipates the cosmic disorder of Book X, where the sun had first his precept so to move and shine as might affect the earth with extremes. The action of *Paradise Lost*, occurring in the stupendous frame of the universe over the four stations of Heaven, Hell, earth, and Chaos, demands an inter-cosmic comparison of worlds. The materials of metaphor derive as easily from heliocentric theory as geocentric; and nothing is clearer than that Milton found an infinite universe in a cosmos somewhat uncertainly Ptolemaic. From this point of view, earth is an insecure citadel invaded by Heaven and Hell alike for an unequal contest in which man's free choice gives temporary advantage to evil. A survey of the twelve books will show how scientific components of character and theme as well as of setting relate in content to the story of creation, which is itself a preliminary establishment of postulates before earth is invaded by Chaos at man's fall.[2]

Each book contains passages outstanding for their scientific allusions. In the first they are the description of Hell, the cosmological characterization of Satan, the fiery hill that "Shon with a glossie scurf, undoubted sign / That in his womb was hid metallic Ore, / The work of Sulphur." The second contains the technical account of Chaos, "the secrets of the hoarie deep." The third ends in details of the outside shell of the world, the mineralogical description of the sun, and the "preview" of creation afforded by Uriel. In the fourth, the Garden attracts numberless scientific particulars, and Satan's effort to tempt Eve by reaching the organs of her fancy is a physiological and psychological process. The fifth book opens with Adam's dream analysis and continues with Raphael's explanation of the chain of being which sets the stage, thematically, for his relation of Satan's revolt. The sixth delivers in technical language the paradoxical invention of gunpowder from materials in the soil of Heaven. Book VII is the hexameron; Book VIII features Raphael's sketch and dismissal of cosmological alternatives. The ninth contains the serpent lore attached to Satan, the tremendous banyan-tree simile, and the storm of passion that follows the fall. The tenth presents in the vocabulary of the encyclopedias the dislocation of the cosmos, ambiguously rendered ("Some say . . . som say"). In Book XI, the catalogue of diseases relates to the creation story as a denial of the immor-

tality implied there. And the twelfth concludes in the ambivalent mist and the comet-sword that threatens to parch
Paradise. These highlights focus attention in an epic where
the scientific is not the central world view, but on the other
hand is almost never absent from the language in which that
Christian humanist world view is delivered.[3]

As to characterization, one has only to recall the epic
images associated with Satan, Adam, and the rest to perceive
how natural philosophy enlarges and deepens their impression. Everything related to Satan operates in the extraordinary dialectic of good and evil. He is compared to Leviathan,
to a comet, a wolf, a toad, a serpent; images of sun and moon
cluster about his form. Upon discovery by Ithuriel and
Zephon, he flares like gunpowder. His tortuous journey
through Chaos, his apostrophe to the sun, his return voyage
between Cancer and Scorpio, his serpent identity before and
after the fall partake of the natural history and cosmology
long established in imaginative and scientific literature.
Adam and Eve are similarly described. They move in an
atmosphere created in part by Adam's explanation of the
fancy, by the changes wrought in their physical universe, by
Michael's purging of Adam's visual nerve. Their fall is
physiological and psychological as well as moral and ethical.
The indecisive debate upon systems of the universe, which
typifies the function of scientific lore in the epic, likewise
extends the characterization of Adam, commonly portrayed
as endowed with all the arts and sciences. These hundreds of
details from science, not to speak of patristic and classical
myth and sacred and secular history, account for the sense
of depth and breadth of recondite knowledge, distressing
even to Addison not fifty years away from the poem.

The bearing of this lore upon thematic content is extensive. For one major example, the hierarchical concept of
order and gradation, set out in the speeches of Adam, Raphael,
and Satan as the chain of being, finds its thematic origin in

Divine Providence and its conceptual center in the creation story, where order is earth's first law also. The chain or stair, as Maplet and Browne call it, objectifies the spiritual gradations from animal to angel and their corresponding degrees of moral responsibility. Conviction to the serpent none belongs; to Eve much; to Adam most. The multiple manifestations of good and evil as order and disorder, obedience and rebellion, humility and pride, receive extra dimension from the uniform movement of heavenly bodies, from the distinction between man and lower animals, from the very image Raphael uses of root, stalk, stem, branch, bud, and odor. In this cosmos sin is a violation of nature as well as of God's will, and all unnatural things are evil. The fundamentals of this unifying hierarchical theme are imbedded in the account of creation, from the Son's imposition of silence upon the troubled waves of Chaos to the origin of Eve.

Another example of thematic expression in the terms of science is the three-fold concept of light as essential, material, and divine — this last the light "by which the poet inwardly sees," as Allen puts it. The standard moral equivalents — light as good and dark as evil — recur unceasingly; and the movement between them keeps up symbolic significance along with physical description. The demons think to imitate God's light as he their darkness. Satan, in broken splendor like an obscured sun, has not yet lost all his original lustre; hence he can utter tears such as angels weep. Repeatedly light is rendered in technical language; and the exactitude implied by scientific terminology supports the moral statement. Light and motion are, it should be noted, the prime characteristics of astronomy and cosmology. When Theodore Banks says that Milton has very few astronomical images, he means formally constructed similes and metaphors; for it is quite clear that astronomy and cosmology provide the basic, pervasive imagery of the whole epic. For a single further example, the thematic affectiveness of astronomy appears in

the impressions of spatial enlargement, cosmic immensity,
natural law, Divine design, and order. To each of these the
images of light are fundamental. The whole universe, therefore, is a symbol in its complexity and integration for what
goes on in the poem. The themes of decline and regeneration, of fall and atonement, of the punishment for sin are all
similarly expressed, never solely through figures from science
but seldom without them.[4]

The basic mode of *Paradise Lost* is ambivalence. One
obvious manifestation of this is the symbolism, quite conventional at its simplest level, where bower, serpent, and tree
exist in both the "real" world (the literal narrative) as place–
character–thing and in the other world of significance as
innocent sexuality, malignant subtlety, and taboo. It is a
truism that setting, characters, and action share this duality
inherent in all art, as Milton's unflagging parallels from
classical literature indicate. Loss of innocence, alienation
from the god, atonement, and regeneration are so common a
set of themes that even twentieth-century readers see how
Milton could accept the historicity of Adam and yet narrate
his experience as universal. The symbolic values range from
the simple identity of light with good to the complex implications of the banyan tree or the sexual element in Eve's fall.
Even without invoking archetypes or solar myths (and it
would be an error to suppose the seventeenth century ignorant of either), one may perceive how Milton capitalizes upon
cosmic correlatives by imaging the fall as a convulsion in
nature or Raphael as a phoenix figure. By this time the
world of experience had been allegorized and symbolized as
thoroughly as the Bible, and similarly without losing its
hard literal identity. It was usable, like the characters in the
poem, in the relation of an action; and like them it possessed
the qualities that make sense of any action. Everything is
at least two-valued, and the posing of alternatives is axiomatic
to the whole frame of free choice. The paradox of the fortu-

nate fall may seem to confuse values in practice, but they are never forgotten in the design. The narrative offers a double plot in the two rebellions, even a double man in Adam and Eve. Adam himself is dualistic: body and soul, reason and passion, flesh and spirit, but synthesized in practical action, and predestined for monism as body refines into spirit. The heavenly powers are in two arrays; Adam's choice is between two alternatives; all that Satan does is undone by Christ.

The central image to these alternatives is the dialogue on astronomy in Book VIII, where the options are given and dismissed. Whether earth move or heaven, says Raphael, imports not: "Sollicit not thy thoughts with matters hid." The existence of the options prefigures the choices open to Adam; their dismissal affirms their limitation for metaphorizing the greater dilemma. Theologically and dramatically the moral opposites have to be maintained as opposites while they are being blurred in metaphor; for unless evil has the appearance of good, temptation is impossible and we are left with an implausible theme and an uninteresting action. The scientific content of the poem flows up to and away from the hexameron in Book VII; the poetic method is most clearly illustrated from science in the dialogue in Book VIII. It receives one expression in the careful balancing of Heavenly against infernal councils, trinities, volunteers. It receives another in the kind of ambiguity that culminates in the concluding image of comet-sword and parching Paradise. Milton never abandoned the principle in *Animadversions* that "the light of grace [is] a better guide than Nature"; but he seldom missed a literary opportunity to relate the two, affirming through hundreds of scientific allusions that "God and Nature bid the same." Ambivalence as characteristic of man's place in the chain of being was widely recognized by Christian humanists like Pico della Mirandola and was still prominent in even the decaying optimism of the seventeenth century. Man for his soul belongs with the spirits, for his body with the beasts; he links both orders as he centers each, and that status proclaims the ambiguity that makes him "the nodus of the universe." [5]

This practice of alternative, option, ambivalence, or ambiguity precipitates a remarkable interrelation of parts, and the cohesion of scientific details remarkably integrates the diverse elements of the epic. Thus the alternatives in Raphael's dialogue are posed again in the cosmic alterations effected by Adam's sin, the axial dislocation of sun or of earth. The two methods of fire-making proposed by Adam are a simple enough epic expansion, like the two methods of mining ore ascribed to Tubal-Cain; but in this context they belong in the same mode as Milton's locating gold in Hell, which deserves the precious bane, and in Heaven, where it forms the pavements at which unfallen Mammon stares. The fire-making is option, the location of gold is ambivalence; they meet as parallel structures meet, by inference, and as a double commentary on the theme of appearance and reality. In this sense the instability of Baalim and Ashtaroth, now male, now female, is typical. Satan may assume the forms of cormorant or serpent; his reality remains the same, and the rapacity of the bird, like the subtlety of the reptile, proclaims it. Nature may seem disproportionate, but in a physical universe centered by man she is not. Michael will have to rebuke Adam after each revelation, as he judges each by its appearance.

Related to this dualism are other principles of composition, such as symbols that reappear in several relations or in opposing contexts of good and evil. The preceding chapters have shown how often Milton returns to a scientific motif; and scarcely anything occurs in *Paradise Lost* without repetition on the same or another level. The comparison and contrast create the parallelism by which the complexity of the moral question is set forth. The two accounts of creation and the two temptations of Eve, more than narrative repetition, are part of a pattern in which the structure of events gives force to meaning. Uriel and Satan parallel Raphael and Adam; ironically, Satan by his own criteria actually profits no more from this instruction than his counterpart Adam. In Eve's first temptation she took Satan for Adam ("Rose as at thy call"); in the second she accepts him as her guide and disposer instead of Adam. The transfers of symbol involved in Satan's likeness to the sun or the cherubim's to the demons are likewise part of that pattern. The major effect of all this ambiguity and duality is of course paradox. Contradictions in appearance and reality are moral and ethical as well as physical, and even before Lovejoy, *Paradise Lost* was recognized as nothing if not paradoxical. Failure to admit paradox accounts for much of the critical difficulty over the character of Satan. The principles of ambivalence and recurrence described here are exercised constantly in the scientific elements of the poem. They testify to the profundity of its themes, just as the substance in which they operate affirms the truth of Milton's solution as if it were scientific fact. Any science does this, not only new science. The most famous of all Donne's images of exactitude, the stiff twin compasses, comes from the old, not the new philosophy.

Chapter by chapter we have seen how scientific lore informs and structures the epic. The "shapeliness" of *Paradise Lost*, to use Mahood's phrase, exists not only in the neat concentric spheres but also in the order of its universe, the disposition of its story among the three major figures, the paralleling of character and incident, the high-level poetic justice of its conclusion. The whole learning of *Paradise Lost* argues for that shapeliness. Milton obtains the impression of an articulated cosmos of infinite space precisely because he began with the established cosmological system already assimilated into literature and then introduced alternatives within it. The arcs of movement described as creating this shapeliness, the rhythms of action detected by Mahood, have their foundation in a clear picture of the cosmos, an organic whole in which minims of nature find their place no less than giant constellations. One can hardly imagine the poem divested of these and reduced to its speeches like a play. Yet even the speeches (Uriel's creation story, Raphael's instruction, Satan's soliloquies) contain much of what Milton thought of as imaginative truth. The concept of hierarchy that is a thematic center of *Paradise Lost* had its most common manifestation in natural philosophy, the interdependence of elements, the gradations of being, the simplest facts of *natura naturata*. Milton levied upon these inexhaustible stores for a cosmic setting, heroic characters, the great argument, even the plot. The result is at once a conviction of the oneness of truth, of the union of God and nature, of the first man's perfect accord with his world and then his reconcilement to its shattered postlapsarian state. In such detail and with such power does Milton present this pattern that the conflicting forces are finally seen actually to complement each other. Satan the false god is as essential to the poem as Christ the true. The dualism of order and restraint that Marjorie Nicolson finds so characteristic of Milton should be regarded as another aspect of the governing strategy, for it epitomizes the ultimate conflict between law and nature. God and external nature bid the same; yet human nature, however minutely analogous to the macrocosm, by its very faculty of free choice runs counter to both law and nature. Miss Nicolson sees a perhaps unconscious contradiction between Adam's Ptolemaic world and Milton's Galilean sun, moon, and Milky Way elsewhere in the poem. "In the astronomy of *Paradise Lost*," she writes, "Milton, whether he realized it or not, broke the Circle of Perfection." She describes this, I think properly, as Milton's response to the aesthetics of the new space. I should take it farther. Milton's breaking of the circle is a deliberate ambiguity, not only consistent with the theme but contributory toward the narrative design implied in the many other dualities, alternatives, and options in characterization, setting, and plot. The first problem, posed at the beginning of this study, was to identify, describe, and explain the science in Milton. Previous chapters have made quite clear that Milton's works contain a tremendous amount of scientific lore, most of it contemporary property and most of it shallow and bookish. True, his most startling effects in this kind are to be observed neither in nature nor in books, as when he speaks of the quaint enameled eyes of flowers, the eruption of Aetna, or the appearance of the underside of uprooted hills. But these are infrequent. In poetry and prose he relies on established metaphor, or the established materials for it; most of his allusions may be explained from encyclopedias of science like Bartholomew's *De Proprietatibus Rerum,* Caxton's *Mirrour of the World,* and Swan's *Speculum Mundi.* His range is broad, not deep, conventional, not recondite. Milton shows an interest literary rather than professional; his early curiosity in science never advanced to the experiments of a Royal Society nor the speculations of a Descartes or Hobbes. Somewhere between the school exercises and the first anti-prelatical pamphlet, Milton settled upon the older vocabulary of science. Here and there a contemporary allusion to Galileo or the plurality of worlds recalls the original ambition; but from that point on, the science in his works is mainly classical in origin, medieval in implication, literary in function. To one who sees the progress of science as a cultural index, Milton's practice seems old-fashioned and anti-intellectual. To one who sees the epic as an artifact of tremendous scope, committed to reaching back into antiquity, Milton's practice seems reasonable and inevitable. For the story of Adam and Eve was imbedded in a literature of science from which at this time it could scarcely have been separated; the new philosophy lent itself easily to the metaphysical conceit; but a conceit cannot be expanded into an epic. It is not too much to say that the aesthetic truth of Milton's narrative depended upon its occurrence in the cosmic setting that had given it significance for so many years, and the encyclopedias of science, products of the same tradition as the narrative, serve as touchstones for its scientific content.

The second question, of sources for Milton's science, has certainly been answered. Francis Johnson, Arnold Williams, and lately Watson Kirkconnell have decried the search for the immediate origin of commonplace elements in *Paradise Lost*. On the evidence of the encyclopedias, the same is true for the science in all his works. Behind him lie Pliny and Plutarch, Ovid and Aristotle; but in between come countless reinterpretations, highly moralized and fitted into a Christian cosmos, where classical teleology becomes a function of the Christian concept of God's design. All might not be right with the medieval and Renaissance world; but God was unquestionably in his Heaven, and men should proceed upon the conviction that He would provide means for the evolution of body to spirit. Thus we identify source areas, not particular books; neo-Plinyism, not Pliny. Though the encyclopedias are not the sole repositories of scientific lore, for it enriched the hexamera, DuBartas, drama, lyric, and polemic, they are certainly the ultimate source from which the middle-class Renaissance reader formed his understanding of nature. The similarity between the encyclopedias and Milton's works argues for the integration of even *Paradise Lost* into the cultural context of its time. For all the activity of Bacon and Galileo, this was what seventeenth-century men commonly held. The heliocentric shock might call all in doubt for a Donne, but the element of fire remained in the vocabulary long after the philosophers had eliminated it from the cosmos. Milton's style perhaps required a fit audience; but he never lost any readers of his own time because of scientific novelty. Addison and Johnson lived in what was in effect another country; and the degree to which their time had lost touch with Milton's appears in their complaints about his needless ostentation of learning. They saw Milton's interaction of pagan and Christian world views as Gothic instead of (as we would call it) baroque. The energy and tension held in balance, though scarcely lost upon generations which revered his sublimity and parroted his tricks, seemed incorrect and certainly made them uncomfortable. Something of Milton's style, then, depended upon his sources; and for science these ultimately derived from the classics, but passed first through the refinement and adjustment of medieval Christianity. Milton recognized their vitality and their propriety to his narrative, for very little in seventeenth century print was really secular. The particular source disappeared; the great genre of scientific literature to which it belonged survived. It is on this large body of lore that Milton drew.

The third problem, the place of science in Milton's thought, is beset with special difficulties. Despite Milton's own warning that an author's characters are not his spokesmen and despite common critical refusal (until the present age) to accept Shakespeare's protagonists so, the modern tendency has been to obscure Milton as artist in Milton as propagandist. The matter is complicated further by the transparent resemblances between ideas in Milton's prose, particularly *Christian Doctrine*, and those in his poems, particularly *Paradise Lost*. And it is distorted by the temptation to extract a systematic worldview from a work of art and then re-introduce it, so to speak, as if it so existed in the poem. It is ridiculous not to assume that he believed in God or Satan; but it is unliterary to assume that he believed in them as they occur in his poem. Even the passages put in by Milton as narrator, his editorializing upon the action, must be taken as literary, not testamentary. As Kirkconnell says, the sources of *Paradise Lost* are Homer and Virgil, not Basil and Jerome. Every writer is identified with his work; and the reader is impelled by the nature of the

subject and of Christian humanism to equate the positive,
affirmative elements in the poem with Milton's personal
views. Yet this reduction of literature to spiritual autobiography is dangerous. The moral values are not lost if we
restrict them to the poem; the world view is not less valid
because it emerges in fragments from a poem instead of from
a personal philosophy. The extremity of this kind of bargain-
hunting is the effort to discredit Milton as a person by asserting the unfairness of his treatment of Satan or the unconscious meaning of *Paradise Lost*. We can better attend to the
moral issues of his poems if we recognize them as artifacts,
literary constructions, made things in which the basic assumptions are authorized by a kind of common law. Even the most
autobiographical of poems is depersonalized, for that kind of
detachment is implicit in the creative process itself. Until the
writer can disengage himself from his material, he cannot
order it as art; the *furor poeticus* has method in it. We have
been taught, and by no admirer of Milton, that poetry is not
the spontaneous overflow of powerful emotion recollected in
tranquillity. Involuntary art is a real contradiction in terms,
not a paradox.

What this amounts to is that the poem, not the man, is our
province. On that basis, the world view of the poem is a theocentric Christian humanism in which science has a large share
as metaphor. We must be chary of particularizing that world
view, as a comparison of the infinite detail of *Christian Doctrine* and the limited specifications of *Paradise Lost* must
show. In the tractate Milton located Hell outside the earth
for sound theological reasons. In *Paradise Lost* he placed it
outside the ordered cosmos for literary effect, that of shoving
evil as far away from earth as was the throne of God. Then he
counteracted all that space with the most refined analogies
between the two, binding them together, not to deny their
distinction or to confuse moral values, but to proclaim and to
picture the true nature of evil, which is perversion, distortion,

and deformity. Milton's suspicion of intellectualism has been over-documented. If, in a poem based on the Christian humanist assumptions, it is anti-intellectualism to subordinate all learning to man's prime duty to God, then the case is proved. But it is not proved to those, like Bush, who see the disparagement of astronomical controversy in *Paradise Lost* and of classical culture in *Paradise Regained* as perfectly consistent with the acceptance of an ordered universe in which learning and art have their hierarchies too. The poems "believe" in science the way they believe in classical mythology: the real truth is not in it except as it is analogue. Raphael must be balanced by Michael; the one assuring Adam "To ask or seek I blame thee not" because nature lies open before him like a book of God's works, the other commending him for having learned a lesson which is the sum of wisdom, beyond mastering the stars and all secrets of the deep. Michael's adjuration comes at a critical point in a poem ceaselessly invoking this kind of science; its significance should not be overlooked, for it is almost the final statement of the due bounds of knowledge. Astronomy is not disparaged; it is really praised as the highest standard by which the even higher knowledge can be indicated. The key to this view of Milton's anti-intellectualism is Adam's discovery that by contemplation of created things he may ascend to God.[7]

Medieval elements in the science of *Paradise Lost* have been established by correspondences between Milton and Bartholomew, Caxton, and others. The primary effects of that medievalism are to identify the cosmos of the poem with both the Middle Ages in which the encyclopedias developed and the Renaissance in which their lore was widely disseminated. A secondary effect is to suggest the universality of that cosmos; Aristotle, Aquinas, and Shakespeare would have recognized it. So in limited fashion would the groundlings and Oliver Cromwell. Tillyard is unquestionably correct in saying that the origins of the Renaissance spirit go right back into the authentic Middle Ages and that "the Middle Ages did not end with either a bang or a whimper in the fifteenth and early sixteenth centuries" but continued into the next side by side with the rise of the new science. It is not too much, then, to attribute considerable importance to the function of natural science in the thought of the poem. Natural science is consistent with the demand for learning in the epic; supports the closed moral system of Christian humanism; corroborates the hexameral elements; and binds the poem to the past and present of its seventeenth-century readers.

The same observations hold true for *Paradise Regained, Samson Agonistes*, the other poems, and even, as far as science enters the world view of the prose, for that too. If the universe of *Paradise Lost* is considered as only roughed in, then the other compositions are even sketchier. Rajan is quite wrong in believing that Milton chose to revive the symbolism of a dying culture; he capitalized upon a symbolism still very much alive. There were of course few survivors of the old science among the professional scientists in 1667, and the transition was certainly in progress on social and intellectual levels. But the continued publication of old science makes a little premature John Eachard's ironic pronouncement to the clery that "he that has got a set of Similitudes calculated according to the Old Philosophy and Ptolemy's system of the World, must burn his commonplace Book and go a gleaning for a new one." Indeed, Eachard himself declines to choose "which Philosophy the Old or New, makes the best Sermons. . . . There have been good Sermons, no question, made in the days of *Materia Prima* and *Occult Qualities*: and there are doubtless still good Discourses now under the Reign of *Atoms*." The change from old to new science was much faster than that from Middle Ages to Renaissance, yet it was likewise gradual and likewise had its Savonarolas. In *Paradise Regained* and the rest, much was left to inference; those poems did not require a cosmological system as part of their substance. In *Paradise Lost* the formulations had to be made, not because they were unfamiliar to its readers but as part of the mode of existence in a poem whose subject was the first man. The old scheme, at least in outline, was so embodied not merely or primarily because analogues of the story did but because the universe it organized was still meaningful.[8]

The place of science in Milton's art is our final query. We have seen that the relations of Renaissance science and literature pose some rather special queries, not least of them the critical methodology for dealing with the way science enters literature. The pioneer work of the 1930's in literary psychology, astronomy, and natural history occupied itself quite properly with recovering the facts of science and identifying them in literature. This was, so to speak, the monographic stage of research, characterized by collection, explanation, annotation. There were studies of the humours and Shakespeare's characters; surveys of the changing history of astronomy and medicine; rediscovery of Pliny; observations of the new philosophy in Donne, the old in Milton. The monographic phase overlaps into the next, the stage of synthesis and generalization, like the recent work of Allen, Kocher, and Duncan. For the historian of ideas this is sound progress toward the statement of milieu, of a writer's participation in it, of its effect on his world view, of his relation by it to other writers and thinkers. Asked how science gets into literature, the historian would seek the answer in trends of thought, in culture-patterns, in biography. But the conclusions reached in these pursuits would not, I submit, tell us much about how science really enters the work of art. From the historical or cultural points of view the answer may be discovered in the nature of the subject, the environment in which the work was done, the poet's education, the poet's sources. But from a completely literary point of view, these songs are partial. They may be thought to answer why science is there, but not how; or if how, then they do not answer in literary terms. A poem about a whale or a planet will embody a good deal of natural history or astronomy as part of the ontology of whale or planet, part of the aesthetic substance, whether that science be assimilated or not. But the lore of whales and planets in a poem about the fall and regeneration of man must find other justification. One object of the preceding chapters has been to establish that justification by inquiring what science actually does in *Paradise Lost*. Its presence is dependent, operative, functional; science becomes literature from its part in such literary concerns as plot, character, setting, theme, tone, and image.

The external facts, direct results of the monographic stage, are necessary to establish what elements of *Paradise Lost* are science. Paradoxically, we need that information to isolate temporarily what we would examine for its inseparable integration with literary context. But the central objective lies within. To see how science enters the poem we have had to see what it does toward interrelating and extending the literal narrative statements. Two recent opinions of Milton's cosmology illustrate the point. McColley concluded that Milton introduced and condemned the geo-heliocentric controversy as a rebuke to seventeenth-century speculative rationalism. Mahood suggested that the spheres within spheres of the roughly Ptolemaic universe contributed to the sense of order and shapeliness of the narrative itself. If McColley's conclusion is valid, and if we stop there, then we may question whether the Raphael-Adam dialogue is really assimilated into *Paradise Lost*. If it does not share in the design or the tensions and conflicts of the poem it is a digression (as some have felt); and the explanation of its presence is biographical or psychological, not literary. Similarly, to say that science was in the air and that no poet, least of all so learned a one as Milton, could fail to show its influence is to make a safe and even interesting generalization; but it is not truly relevant as aesthetic or literary explanation. We have seen, however, that McColley is wrong. The dialogue expresses the ambivalence of Adam's situation; it is a hypothetical choice, one he does not have to make, but it is one of many presented him and we see him a divided man long before his actual fall. Quite possibly Mahood may be wrong too, even as she is certainly incomplete. But she is working with the relationships of object (physical universe) and theme (concept of order) in the poem, and it is these realationships that I have tried to follow and develop.

The demand for learning was united with the hexameral characterization of Adam as endowed with all the arts and sciences, and at the fall he lost information as well as innocence and understanding. This double emphasis upon erudition may account historically and genetically for the scientific lore in the poem, but if critical inquiry ends on that fact, it is still incomplete. For the poet must encompass that learning in a special, aesthetically plausible, causative way. Science, like history or mythology, must act with and upon the themes and structure. Thus in *Paradise Lost* the accretion of knowledge is promoted not only by genre and subject but by one of its central themes and formative elements, the hierarchy of existence or chain of being. This concept is a theme because it objectifies that order which is Heaven's first law; it is a structure because its recurrence unifies and relates many episodes. It is scientific as well as theological. Its employment to convey Adam's relationship to God involves much collateral lore about the links of the chain. In that engagement the scientific facts become imaginative symbols and subsurface metaphor.

Laboratory science, such as it was in the century, had even less effect upon Milton's literary imagination than upon Sir Thomas Browne's. But the place in Milton's art of bookish science is confirmed by the total intention of this cosmological epic, and the total intention includes like all literature the tension between the inner and the outer life of man. But it extends beyond. It takes not one world but all worlds; it implies not knowledge but all knowledge. It encompasses sacred history, divine revelation, theology, philosophy; in every sense the total intention of *Paradise Lost* is heroic. Its design is ambitious beyond many analogues and prototypes, and its author declared it original, a thing unattempted before him in prose or rhyme. He did this possibly because he was including the four great stories in the celestial cycle, but probably because he was giving that cycle its most deliberately literary form. The kind of truth *Paradise Lost* is must be reached as in all literature through literary means — through the imaginative relevance of its parts to the inner life of the man at its center. This is the final meaning of structure, texture, organicism, unity, any quality we use to denote art; and it includes reversal of values, ironic assertion and denial of relationship, ambivalence, all the devices of rhetoric and poetic exercised in among others the vehicle of science.

One reason for the failure of *Paradise Lost* with respectful readers in every generation is the apparent breakdown of communication within the poem of what seems asethetically intractable fact (free will, anti-Trinitarianism, astronomical debate) and the genuine human condition, imaginatively presented. Science figured not a little in Raleigh's catalogue of dead ideas. The poet must create the connections, and the reader must perceive them. The textbook case for this kind of failure is Melville's inability to unify cetological lore and the tensions of Ahab and Ishmael. With *Paradise Lost,* however, the failure has lain with its readers, first because their literary experience has not prepared them for assimilating the genre. In committing his insight to the form he did, Milton at the outset, knowingly or not, gave every advantage to oblivion. It is the last English epic, and the world has grown away from the primary qualification for reading it, response to the form.[9]

A second reason for the failure, and one which concerns science, is the modern loss of the sense of universe, the essential oneness of things, of God with nature, man with God, man with nature. This idea of unity survives as religious or philosophical concept, but not as the feature of literary experience; it is not an asethetic habit. *Paradise Lost* creates in literary modes what it assumes philosophically — the participation of all outer and inner experience, all objects of sense or thought, all hierarchical gradations in a dynamic evolving singleness. The poem expresses this not transcendentally, which is to say not seemingly nor in a mist, the common gloss of philosophers, but physically and materially. Modern man usually lacks the instrument, the ear to hear what in the poem speaks to this singleness. Whatever his philosophical or psychological qualifications, he lacks the unified literary sensibility. The scholar's reconstruction of systems of thought, climates of opinion, historical background, literary milieu, the critic's naming of parts, analysis of metaphor, discovery of structure — all are ear-training. This is not to say that the modern reader must believe in that harmony to hear it; yet it is not enough to make the obligatory gesture of good will, to "accept" the relationship, merely to grant the poet his postulates. What is required is an act of imagination, not of will. The reader must see how that universeness, that singleness, is made true in the poem. The office of the critic and scholar together is to show it happening, to unwrite the poem, to make it a process of discovery for the reader.

This has been the object of examining the science in Milton: to discover the literary, the presentational, the imaginative relationship of materials isolated for the purpose from their context but worked back into it. Scientific lore not only functions in immediate contexts, but also proclaims in its every occurrence the perfect organic wholeness of the total poetic experience. Science is literal in defining setting and developing characters; symbolic in expressing the inner meaning of their experience. It foreshadows, anticipates, recalls, amplifies. The paramount physical facts of the prelapsarian universe are that it all came from God and tends to return, and that it exists in a perfect order. The moral facts are micrometrically congruent with these. The place of science in Milton's art, then, is like that of theology, mythology, Biblical history, but with its own identity. Like them it supplies analogues, parallels, metaphors, symbols, the perception of which recovers to the imagination in this one regard the harmonious vision, the literary habit of mind which can respond to the poem. Unlike theology and the rest, the special identity of science is not abstract knowing or theorizing, but immediacy: it names things in a special way. Metaphors from science do not simply create fair pictures in the air; they lend to their context the sense of precision, objectivity, something like mechanically verifiable truth. They create a physical sense of order. The world of the poem is shapely because of them; the poem itself is shapely because of them. The original statements have been lost through a failure of knowledge, which can be recovered; the original insights have dimmed through a failure of attitude toward literary experience, which must be trained. Retracing the subsurface movement of science and exploring the many modes of its entrance into the whole poem, as we have done here, re-establish the connections and illuminate the literary function of those precepts of beneficence Milton fetched from the tremendous cabinet of nature and unified into the wide deep vision which is *Paradise Lost*.

Notes

Notes

I have compressed documentation by accumulating references in the text and grouping them here, shortening titles, and omitting place of publication for works issued at London. In each note Milton entries appear first, in order of occurrence in the text; others follow in the same scheme; last are additional comments and cross-references. After the first full citation in text or note, books and articles are indicated by author's name, with catchwords where necessary. I have used the Columbia Milton (cited as *Works*), with comparisons (chiefly silent) to the Yale edition of the prose now in progress (Wolfe, *Yale Prose*, I) and Fletcher's photographic facsimile. Idiosyncrasies of sixteenth- and seventeenth-century printing have been allowed to stand, except for regularization of *u, v, i, j* and the expansion of a few contractions.

CHAPTER I — THE COMPENDIOUS METHOD OF NATURAL PHILOSOPHY; THE ENCYCLOPEDIC TRADITION

1. *Works* XII, 171, 265; IV, 283; *PL* V, 511–512.
2. I refer to William B. Hunter's articles on matter, Harry F. Robins' on the waters above the firmament (which he kindly let me see in MS), and J. B. Broadbent's on Paradise. For Addison see *The Spectator*, ed. G. Gregory Smith (Everyman's Library, 1907, 1934), II, 177–178; James H. Hanford, *A Milton Handbook*, 4th ed. (New York, 1946), p. 224.
3. Historians of culture have dealt extensively with the tradition of the encyclopedia of science through the Middle Ages and Renaissance. My account owes a good deal to Charles H. Haskins, *Studies in the History of Medieval Science* (Cambridge, Mass., 1922); Lynn Thorndike, *A History of Magic and Experimental Science* (4 vols. New York, 1929–1934); George Sarton, *Introduction to the History of Science* (2 vols. in 3, Baltimore, 1929–1931); Henry O. Taylor, *The Mediaeval Mind* (2 vols. New Haven, 1919); Louis B. Wright, *Middle Class Culture in Elizabethan England* (Chapel Hill, 1936). Wright's chapter "The Strange World of Science" is still the most useful description of Renaissance encyclopedias for students of literature. It is also a wholesome corrective to Basil Willey's *The Seventeenth Century Background* (1942), which, despite the attention given to such a transitional figure as Joseph Glanvil, underestimates the importance to literature of the traditional science.

4. E. W. Gudger, "Pliny's *Historia Naturalis*, the Most Popular Natural History Ever Published," *Isis* 6:269–281 (1924), reports fully on sources, editions, redactions. Salmasius edited Solinus' *Polyhistor*, based on Pliny, in 1629, as Milton grimly reminded him in alluding to the "Plinian exercitator," *Second Defense, Works*, VIII, 37.

5. Ernest Brehaut, *An Encyclopedist of the Dark Ages, Isidore of Seville* (New York, 1912).

6. Adelard of Bath, *Dodi-Ve-Nechdi, Uncle and Nephew*, trans. and ed. by Hermann Gollancz (1920); *Alexandri Neckam De Naturis Rerum*, Rolls Series No. 34, ed. Thomas Wright (1863). For Thomas of Cantimpré's *De Natura Rerum* I have relied on Thorndike, II, 376–379. F. S. Bodenheimer, "On Some Hebrew Encyclopaedias of the Middle Ages," *Archives Internationales d'Histoire des Sciences*, No. 22 (1953), pp. 3–13, shows the relation of the *Dodi-Ve-Nechdi* paraphrase of Berachya Ha-Nakadan to its original, Adelard's *Quaestiones Naturales*.

7. Gerald E. SeBoyar, "Bartholomew Anglicus and his Encyclopedia," *JEGP* 19:160–189 (1920); *Medieval Lore from Bartholomaeus Anglicus*, ed. Robert Steele (1924), pp. 181–182.

8. F. ccclxxxviiir of the 1535 ed., which I use here. Louis B. Wright, pp. 552–553; Foster Watson, *The Beginnings of the Teaching of Modern Subjects in England* (1909), pp. 180–181; Steele, p. 4. Francis R. Johnson, "The Elizabethan Science of Psychology," *English Studies Today*, ed. C. L. Wrenn and G. Bullough (Oxford, 1951), p. 118, confirms *De Proprietatibus Rerum* as one of the best sources for the ordinary Elizabethan's general knowledge of psychology.

9. *L'Image du Monde de Maître Gossouin*, ed. O. H. Prior (Lausanne et Paris, 1913), p. 11. I use Prior's ed. of Caxton's translation, EETS, e. s. CX (1913). See George C. Taylor, *Milton's Use of DuBartas* (Cambridge, Mass., 1934), p. 10; *CHEL*, II, 357; *Popular Treatises on Science Written during the Middle Ages in Anglo-Saxon, Anglo-Norman, and English*, ed. Thomas Wright (1841), p. viii; Francis R. Johnson, *Astronomical Thought in Renaissance England* (Baltimore, 1934), p. 70. No settled practice is followed in author entries for Renaissance books. The *Short Title Catalogue* lists *Mirrour of the World* under Vincentius Bellovacensis instead of Gossouin or the translator Caxton, Mexia's *Treasurie* under translator Thomas Milles, *The French Academie* under author La Primaudaye. I have followed title pages when they seemed clear, precedent when it was more sensible, and convenience when it was not.

10. Maplet, p. 8. This title-page appeal was common. William Bourne, in *A Booke Called the Treasure for Traveilers* (1578), f.*4v, is typical: "I doo not intende to make any booke to teach them that are cunning and learned: But the only cause of my writing of this booke is, to instruct and teach them that are simple and unlearned." Maunsell, *The Seconde Parte of the Catalogue of English Printed Books* (1595), p. 11; Louis B. Wright, p. 555; Hyder Rollins, "John Grange's *The Golden*

Aphroditis," Harvard Studies and Notes in Philology and Literature, 16: 177–178 (1934).

11. Steele, p. 4; Louis B. Wright, p. 553; Batman, f. ¶ r; Seager, *Natural History in Shakespeare's Time* (1896), p. vi; Ruth L. Anderson, *Elizabethan Psychology and Shakespeare's Plays* (Iowa City, 1927), *passim*; John W. Draper, "Jaques' 'Seven Ages' and Bartholomaeus Anglicus," *MLN*, 54:273–276 (1939), and many other studies; Carroll Camden, "Memory, the Warder of the Brain," *PQ*, 18:52–72 (1939); Rosemond Tuve, "A Medieval Commonplace in Spenser's Cosmology," *SP*, 30:133–147; A. W. Verity, ed., *PL* (Cambridge, 1910, 1929), II, 659, 680; Merritt Y. Hughes, ed., *PL* (New York, 1935), p. xlviii. R. T. Gunther, *Early Science in Oxford* (1925), III, Pt. 1, 152, cites *Batman uppon Bartholome* and *De Proprietatibus Rerum* as important textbooks in zoology.

12. La Primaudaye, p. [643a]. Louis Bredvold, "The Sources Used by Davies in *Nosce Teipsum*," *PMLA*, 38:745–769 (1923); Anderson, *passim*; Camden, p. 52; George Buckley, *Atheism in the English Renaissance* (Chicago, 1932), p. 93; Hardin Craig, *The Enchanted Glass* (New York, 1936), pp. 10, 119, 179, 223; Johnson, *Astronomical Thought*, pp. 260–261; London, *Catalogue*, ff. U3v, D4r, E3r, F4r. H. C. Hart's series in *N&Q*, 10th ser., 4 (1905) and 5 (1906) shows numerous Greene and Marlowe borrowings from early editions of *The French Academie*. Irving Ribner uses La Primaudaye's analysis of pride in "The Tragedy of *Coriolanus*," *English Stud.*, 34:1–9 (1953).

13. Louis B. Wright, pp. 559–561; Watson, p. 192; Johnson, *Astronomical Thought*, pp. 275–277. London, f. Y2v. Herschel Baker, whose emphasis on strength of tradition in *The Wars of Truth* (Cambridge, Mass., 1952) properly modifies Basil Willey's attitude, uses Swan as typical of seventeenth-century enlightened conservatism. *Speculum* was not anachronistic as a title; the *Short Title Catalogue* lists dozens of "mirrour" and "speculum" books.

14. *Theatrum Mundi* (1574), preface; *Wits Theater of the Little World*, f. 155r. Allot's claim was conventional; even Thomas Sprat, *The History of the Royal-Society* (1667), p. 6, echoed it.

15. Cawdrey, ff. A3r–v; Torquemada, t. p.; Topsell, t. p.; Lodge, ff. *1r–v; Widdowes, 1631 t. p. The *Short Title Catalogue* incorrectly ascribes the Torquemada to Ferdinando Walker; see ff. A3r–A4v for Walker's indentification of Lewis Lewkenor as the translator. Cawdrey's recommendation would have carried little weight with that neo-Augustan supporter of the simple style in sermons, John Eachard, who complains, *Works* (11th ed., 1705), p. 54, of extravagance and triteness in "that imprudent way of speaking by Metaphor and Similitude."

16. Person, pp. 178, t. p.; DuPlesis, f. A1or; Comenius, pp. 3–4; Sherley, f. A6r; Blount, t. p., f. A4r; Grew, f. A5r; Topsell, *The Historie of Serpents* (1608), p. 94. The encyclopedic genre did not, of course, end with the seventeenth century. Philip Shorr, *Science and Superstition in*

the Eighteenth Century (New York, 1932), shows the considerable survival of medieval science in Ephraim Chambers' *Cyclopedia of Arts and Sciences* (2 vols. 1728) and Zedler's *Grosses Vollstandiges Universal Lexicon* (64 vols. 1732–1750), concluding, p. 74, that "the two encyclopedias still bear a close resemblance to their earlier medieval prototypes." Goldsmith's *History of the Earth and Animated Nature* (1774), though based on moderns like Linnaeus and Buffon, alludes often to the old naturalists and pseudo-science; its organization is characteristic of its forebears. Goldsmith says that delight in reading them moved him to emulation: "The ancients, indeed, and Pliny in particular, have anticipated me in the present manner of treating natural history. . . . I have followed their manner, rejecting the numerous fables which they adopted, and adding the improvements of the moderns, which are so numerous, that they actually make up the bulk of natural history" (York ed., 1808, I, xi). Elizabeth Stubler pointed out to me that Arthur Hughes, "Science in English Encyclopedias 1704–1875," *Annals of Science*, 7:340–370 (1951), deals with animistic mineralogy and comet lore in Chambers.

17. *PL* X, 560–570; *Works* V, 263. See Hughes, p. 334; Whiting, *Milton's Literary Milieu* (Chapel Hill, 1939), p. 58; Verity, II, 596–597. Batman, f. 256v; Bartholomew, f. clxxixv, repeated by Batman, f. 193v; Caxton, p. 90; *Defensative*, ff. 3v–4r; *The Voyages and Travailes of Sir John Mandeville* (1625), f. G3r; Swan, p. 296.

18. Milles, pp. 661–662; Caxton, pp. 80–81; Maplet, p. 17; La Primaudaye, p. 850; Swan, pp. 288, 290; Person, pp. 42, 33–54; Bartholomew, f. ccxxxvr; Widdowes, p. 27; Wanley, p. 225; Agrippa, pp. 50–52. George F. Kunz, *The Curious Lore of Precious Stones* (New York, 1938), p. 347, notes that chrysolite was assigned to the sun by Rautzau, *Tractatus de Genethilacorum Thematum Judiciis* (Frankfort, 1633); Kunz's chapter "On Ominous and Luminous Stones," pp. 143–175, combs antiquity for legends of rubies and other gems of supernatural brightness and efficacy. Edgar H. Duncan, "The Natural History of Metals and Minerals in the Universe of Milton's *Paradise Lost*," *Osiris*, 9:386–421 (1954), provides the most comprehensive historical study of Milton's mineralogy in its ultimate genetic relationships.

19. Thomas Warton, ed., *Poems upon Several Occasions by John Milton* (1785), pp. 146–147, with most editors agreeing upon Gerard as source; Henry J. Todd, ed., *The Poetical Works of John Milton* (4th ed. 4 vols., 1842), II, 389; Charles Firth, "Sir Walter Ralegh's *History of the World*," *Proceedings of the British Academy* (1917–1918), pp. 427–446; Whiting, pp. 87–88; Robert R. Cawley, *Milton and the Literature of Travel* (Princeton, 1951), p. 99; Maplet, p. 78; Swan, pp. 274–275; Bartholomew, ff. cclxv; Batman, ff. 291r–v; Golding, f. Eeiir; Jonston, p. 141.

20. *Works* VIII, 33, 264. Allan H. Gilbert explicates the passage in "Milton's Defense of Bawdry," *SAMLA Studies in Milton*, ed. J. Max Patrick (Gainesville, Fla., 1953), pp. 58–59. Bartholomew, ff. ccxliir,

cclxxxviir; Batman, f. 272r, 319v–320r; Maplet, p. 106; *Regimen Sanitatis Salerni* (1634), p. 107. If Milton knew the occasional identification of the Genesis fig tree with the sycamore, as he probably did, the further complication of puns must have pleased him. I am indebted to Mary Goddard for reference to George Herbert's *The World* 11–12 as a contemporary example of the belief.

21. Thomas Newton, ed., *PL* (5th ed. 2 vols., 1761), I, 26; Todd, II, 262; Verity, II, 376; Hughes, p. 15; James H. Pittman, "Milton and the Physiologus," *MLN*, 40:439–440 (1925); P. Ansell Robin, *Animal Lore in English Literature* (1932), p. 124; Whiting, p. 81.

22. Bartholomew, f. clxxxviv; Caxton, pp. 88–89; La Primaudaye, pp. 781–782; Swan, pp. 360–361. Albert S. Cook, ed., *The Old English Elene, Phoenix, and Physiologus* (New Haven, 1919), pp. lxiii–lxxxv, supplies additional versions of the whale-island story from Arrian, Strabo, Pseudo-Callisthenes, Rabbah barbar Hana, Arabian folklore, and the Greek *Physiologus*, Pseudo-Eustathius, Basil, Ambrose, Pontopiddan, and Hakluyt. The "two holes (of a cubite long, which they have neere to their nostrils)" mentioned by La Primaudaye help explain the term "Trunck" in *PL* VII, 416, which editors do not gloss. The blowing of the whale was a standard feature of description. Timothy Granger's *A Moste True and Marvelious Straunge Wonder, the lyke hath Seldom Ben Seene, of XVII Monstrous Fishes, Taken in Suffolke, at Downam Brydge* (1568) relates: "Upon theyr heds were holes, as big that a man might put in both his fistes at once, out of the which they did spoute a great quantitie of water whyle they were atakinge, that they had almoste dround ii boates men and all with spoutynge of water: for the water wold assende uppwarde from the fisshes, as hie as any house, and so fall doun & weet all them that were within theyr reache most cruellie." Between Book I and Book VII, Milton apparently decided that the whale was the largest of animals. In I, Leviathan is "of all his works . . . hugest that swim th' Ocean stream"; in VII the qualification is dropped: Leviathan is "Hugest of living Creatures." And when behemoth is mentioned it is as "biggest born of earth" (VII, 471).

23. Swan, p. 485, 482; Bartholomew, f. cccxr; Batman, f. 342v; Torquemada, f. 154r; Topsell, *Serpents*, pp. 147–151, 198–200, 232; Golding, ff. Siv–Siir; Maplet, p. 96.

24. Todd, II, 125; G. C. Taylor, pp. 28–29; Edwin S. Greenlaw, "A Better Teacher than Aquinas," *SP*, 14:212 (1917); Bartholomew, f. xiiir; Batman, ff. 14v–15r; La Primaudaye, pp. 414, 410, 415. William B. Hunter, "Eve's Demonic Dream," *ELH*, 13:255–265 (1946); "Prophetic Dreams and Visions in *Paradise Lost*," *MLQ*, 9:277–295 (1948), shows many parallels between Milton's practice and seventeenth-century dream theory.

25. Bartholomew, f. lxxxixr; Batman, ff. 90v, 104r; La Primaudaye, p. 396; *The Works of Sir Thomas Browne*, ed. Simon Wilkin (1906), I, 410–413. *The Problems of Aristotle, with Other Philosophers and Phisi-*

tions (1597), f. B3*v*, gives a similar answer to the question *Why do men sneese?*

26. Gilbert, "Milton's Textbook of Astronomy," *PMLA*, 38:305–306 (1923); Nicolson, "Milton and the Telescope," *ELH*, 2:17–21 (1935); McColley, "Milton's Dialogue on Astronomy: the Principal Immediate Sources," *PMLA*, 52:732 (1937); Johnson, *Astronomical Thought*, p. 108. Vandermast, the German magician in *Friar Bacon and Friar Bungay*, ix, 29–33, cites "Hermes, Melchie, and Pythagoras" to affirm that "terra is but thought / To be a punctum squared to the rest." Neckam, p. 34; Caxton, p. 59; Taylor, *Meditations from the Creatures*, p. 92; Carpenter, *Geography* (Oxford, 1625), p. 121; Lodge, p. 125; La Primaudaye, pp. 4–5. See also John Wells, *Sciographia: or the Art of Shadowes* (1635), f. 2*v*; William Pemble, *A Briefe Introduction to Geographie* (Oxford, 1658), p. 14; Recorde, *Castle of Knowledge* (1556), p. 10; Renaudot, p. 54. Milton's distinction between "world" (universe) and earth is commonplace; see William Cuningham, *The Cosmographical Glasse* (1559), pp. 6, 9.

27. Bartholomew, f. cxxxviir; La Primaudaye, p. 722; Caxton, pp. 134, 235. The shadow cone was a standard illustration for an eclipse of the moon; see Pemble, p. 7. It became a literary commonplace as well. See Joseph Beaver, "Lanier's Use of Science for Poetic Imagery," *AL*, 24: 528–529 (1953), and my addition, "Lanier's Cone of Night: an Early Poetic Commonplace," *AL*, 26:93–94 (1954). It is characteristic of Milton's method that he would employ such a figure from the old astronomy in a poem that alludes to the telescope and the worlds in and beyond the moon. An even more remarkable affair is the microscope in *PR* IV, 56–60. Apparently Milton did not understand this instrument at all, for Satan says he has so well disposed his "Aerie Microscope" that the Son may behold "Outside and inside both" of distant houses. Yet one cannot be sure that Milton did not have some kind of authority. Leonard and Thomas Digges, *A Geometrical Practical Treatize Named Pantometrie* (1571), describe just that sort of optical glass. See my article, "Milton's 'Aerie Microscope,'" *MLN*, 64:526–527 (1949).

CHAPTER II — THE HARMONY OF THE SPHERES

1. E. M. W. Tillyard, *The Elizabethan World Picture* (1944) provides a composite of traditional cosmology, emphasizing hierarchy, cosmic identities, planes of existence, and orchestration of nature; many of his illustrations come from Milton. The most valuable recent work on Milton's universe is the series of articles by Walter Clyde Curry and William B. Hunter. See Curry's "Milton's Scale of Nature," *Stanford Studies in Language and Literature* (Stanford, 1941), pp. 173–192; "Milton's Chaos and Old Night," *JEGP*, 46:38–52 (1947); "Milton's Dual Concept of God as Related to Creation," *SP*, 48:190–210 (1950); "Some Travels of Milton's Satan and the Road to Hell," *PQ*, 29:225–235 (1950); "The Con-

sistence and Qualities of Milton's Chaos," *Vanderbilt Studies in the Humanities*, 1:56–70 (1951); "The Genesis of Milton's World," *Anglia*, 70:129–149 (1951); and Hunter's "Milton's Materialistic Life Principle," *JEGP*, 45:68–76 (1946); "The Seventeenth Century Doctrine of Plastic Nature," *Harvard Theol. Rev.*, 43:197–213 (1950); "Milton's Power of Matter," *JHI*, 13:551–562 (1952). The most thorough discussion of the waters above the firmament in Milton's system is Harry F. Robins, "The Crystalline Sphere and the 'Waters Above' in *Paradise Lost*," *PMLA*, 69:903–914 (1954).

2. Paul H. Kocher, *Science and Religion in Elizabethan England* (San Marino, 1953), shows definitively how the generation of scientists before Milton, for all their impassioned study of second causes, acknowledged as Christians the original Divine impulse in nature. For the conservative attitude in Genesis commentary see Arnold Williams's chapter "Science and Pseudo Science" in his valuable pioneer study *The Common Expositor: An Account of the Commentaries on Genesis 1527–1633* (Chapel Hill, 1948), pp. 174–198. Except for Mersenne, the commentators are like the encyclopedists; they "add nothing to the scientific knowledge of their day; they only mirror the dominant concepts of the culture of which they were a part" (198). The conventionality of Milton's astronomical information is established by Grant McColley, "The Astronomy of *Paradise Lost*," *SP*, 34:209–247 (1937), and Johnson, *Astronomical Thought*, pp. 284–285.

3. Prolusion VII, *Works* XII, 265; Prolusion III, 171. Compare Person's praise of natural philosophy in *Varieties*, p. 2: "seeing by it we arrive at the perfect understanding (at least so farre as humane wit can reach) of all the secrets that Mother Nature containeth within her imbrace, whether in the Heavens, Aire, Seas, Earth, and of all things comprehended within or upon them." Person believed like Adam that "knowledge of natural things and of their causes, leadeth us (as it were) by the hand to the search of their Author and Maker." Contrast John Huarte's admission that young men, as Aristotle says, are not ready for this study, *Examen de Ingenios. The Examination of Mens Wits* (1594), pp. 7–8. On celestial journeys see Curry, note 1 above; Marjorie Nicolson, "Milton and the Telescope," *ELH*, 2:14–15 (1935), for the suggestion that this instrument inspired the technique of lifting the reader to heights and vantage points; Josephine W. Bennett, "Milton's Use of the Vision of Er," *MP*, 36:351–358 (1939), for parallels from Book X of *The Republic*; and *The French Academie*, pp. 4–5.

4. Although early editors and commentators glossed passages in plenty, systematic exposition of Milton's cosmology did not appear until the nineteenth century. Patrick Hume did anticipate modern research by citing Galileo; and Pearce, replying to Bentley, did draw notes from an astronomical paper in the *Philosophical Transactions* of the Royal Society. But it was Thomas Keightley who offered in 1855

the first extended description. Masson's 1874 edition contained a more thorough account. John A. Himes in 1878 and Homer Sprague in 1879 set out diagrams differing from Masson's; and Maria Mitchell in 1894 surveyed the astronomy of the poem. Thomas N. Orchard's *The Astronomy of Paradise Lost* of 1896 was revised in 1913 and 1915. The monumental edition of Arthur W. Verity devoted several appendices to cosmology. And in 1915, William F. Warren, the eccentric religious ethnologist who located biblical Eden at the North Pole, gathered many of these diagrams into *The Universe as Pictured in Milton's Paradise Lost*, probably the best of these early studies. Beginning with Allan H. Gilbert's "Milton and Galileo," *SP*, 19:152–185 (1922), knowledge of the poet's astronomy deepened and broadened. Gilbert's "The Outside Shell of Milton's World," *SP*, 20:444–447 (1923), and "Milton's Textbook of Astronomy," *PMLA*, 38:297–307 (1923), clarified the reference to the cosmological integument and made generally available the substance of Clavius' commentary on the *De Sphaera* of Sacrobosco, which Edward Phillips said Milton used in his teaching. Marjorie Nicolson extended the Milton-Galileo relationship in suggesting the influence of the telescope on Milton's sense of space and distance and contributed enormously to perspective on the poet in her later studies of the new science and literary imagination. Grant McColley, whose series of articles on Milton's astronomy in the late 1930s exploited contemporary sources heavily, differed with Gilbert's conclusion that Milton used Galileo's *Dialogo interno si duo massimi sistemi del mondo tolemaico a Copernicano* and offered somewhat too ambitiously the Ross-Wilkins controversy instead. To say this is not to minimize McColley's "The Astronomy of *Paradise Lost*," which, with Johnson's definitive *Astronomical Thought in Renaissance England*, offers the soundest treatment of the subject. When one adds to this list the work of Curry, Hunter, Whiting, and Robins, the working bibliography is about complete. Whiting's *Milton's Literary Milieu* invokes, for example, a cosmological background composed of Burton's *Anatomy*, Danaeus' *Wonderfull Woorkmanship of the World*, Ralegh's *History*, Mercator's *Atlas*, and Pliny's *Natural History*. Most of the foregoing studies concern only the epic, and most of them, with Whiting's a notable exception, do not employ the popular literature of science, where the bulk of allusion may be explained. The present chapter proposes science in the vernacular for understanding both descriptive and technical astronomy in the whole canon.

5. The golden compasses have created their little eddy in the stream. Harris Fletcher, *Milton's Rabbinical Readings* (Urbana, 1930), pp. 100–109, found the source in Ben Gerson; George W. Whiting, "The Golden Compasses in *Paradise Lost*," *N&Q*, 172:294–295 (1937), suggested that Milton saw or heard of the St. Edmund's church Salisbury stained-glass window, which showed God marking out the world with compasses; Grant McColley, "Milton's Golden Compasses," *N&Q*, 176:

97–98 (1939), noted the conventional nature of the figure and of the Deity as architect. Aside from the fact that Milton owned a pair of compasses himself (see Gunther, *Early Science in Oxford*, I, 134), the chief objection to the suggestions of Whiting and Fletcher is that the figure was, after the Aldine press mark, perhaps the best known printer's device in the Renaissance; see Max Rooses, *Le Musée Plantin Moretus* (Anvers, 1914), p. 26. Milton almost certainly owned Plantin's 1558 printing of Olaus Magnus, *Historia de Gentibus Septentrionalibus*, which bore it. The compasses are central to M. M. Mahood's sensitive analysis of the cosmological symbolism of *PL* in her *Poetry and Humanism*. Appropriately enough, it is Cleanth Brooks, "Milton and the New Criticism," *Sewanee Review*, 59:1–21 (1951), who unites the Donne and Milton figures. See also Marjorie Nicolson, *The Breaking of the Circle* (Evanston, Ill., 1950), pp. xix–xx.

6. See, in addition to Hunter's articles and Peter F. Fisher, "Milton's Theodicy," *JHI*, 27:28–53 (1956), the older list of sources for Milton's attitude toward matter in Taylor, *Milton's Use of DuBartas*, pp. 19–20. The Milton quotations are *PL* V, 181–183, 414–418. *Areopagitica, Works* IV, 298. P. Ansell Robin, *The Old Physiology in English Literature* (1911), p. 25, remarked the antiquity of the theory of elemental interchange and Milton's employment of it.

7. *Il Penseroso* 93–96; *PR* II, 121–126; IV, 201. Johnson, *Astronomical Thought*, p. 56, notes that this habitation of the spheres by spirits was a welcome Neo-platonism in Christian theology. The most popular Renaissance expression was Marcellus Palingenius Stellatus' *Zodiacus Vitae* (c. 1531), translated by Barnaby Googe in 1560. See also Kocher, pp. 119 ff.

8. Bartholomew, f. cxvv; Batman, ff. 118v–119r; Swan, pp. 43–44, 115; Caxton, pp. 51, 49; Vaughan, pp. 39–40. Curry, "The Genesis of Milton's World," *Anglia*, 70:135 (1951), points out that the ethereal quintessence is pretty definitely a sublimation of the four elements.

9. Kocher, pp. 39–40, makes the controversy an example of the way in which the conflict of religion and science ended in victory for both.

10. Johnson, *Astronomical Thought*, pp. 54–55.

11. Bartholomew, ch. ii, Bk. VIII; Swan, pp. 77 ff.

12. *PL* IV, 604–605; III, 574; VIII, 18–19; XI, 205–206; III, 729; IX, 103; *Christian Doctrine, Works* XV, 29. On the "chrystal Firmament" of the Chariot of Paternal Diety, see Thomas Keightley, *An Account of the Life, Opinions, and Writings of John Milton, with an Introduction to Paradise Lost* (1855), pp. 474–479, and Svendsen, *N&Q*, 193:339 (1948). Ants Oras, "Miltonic Elements in Shelley," *Seventeenth Century News*, 13:22 (1955), describes the recurrence of the Chariot in *Prometheus Unbound*, IV.

13. Apian's diagram is reproduced in Johnson, *Astronomical Thought*, p. 46. Caxton, pp. 180, 128–129; Bartholomew, ff. cxviir–cxviiiv; Batman, ff. 121v–122r; La Primaudaye, pp. 746–747, 679; Swan,

pp. 317–318. Batman's "burning Heaven" may be remarked in the frontispiece to Fage's *Description of the Whole World*, p. 49 above.

14. Lodge, pp. 84, 87–88; Ralegh, pp. 11–12; Petavius, p. 2; Pemble, p. 269; Vaughan, *Brief Natural History*, pp. 15–16, *Man-Mouse*, pp. 51–52; Burnet, *The [Sacred] Theory of the Earth* (2nd ed., 1691), p. 17; T. C., p. 43; Comenius, pp. 87–89. Mercator, *Historia Mundi*, pp. 26–27, believed that the firmament separating the waters was made of air, and that the angels were created from the supercelestial waters, which were real waters, not clouds. Kocher, p. 40, notes that the reactionary Alexander Ross had abandoned the supernaturalistic view as early as 1626. For the general question of Comenius-Milton relationships, the latest and best brief treatment is Don M. Wolfe, "Comenius and the Mass Mind," *Yale Prose*, I, 159–166.

15. Swan, pp. 54–71; La Primaudaye, pp. 746–748. Fletcher, pp. 134–135, thinks Ben Gerson Milton's source. George W. Whiting, "Milton's Crystalline Sphere and Ben Gerson's Heavens," *RES*, 8:450–453 (1932), disagrees: Milton's "liquid" is an adjective, not a noun as Fletcher supposed, and the "plain sense of the various passages is that the Firmament is an expanse not of water but of air, and that it is bounded by the Crystalline Sphere. On the other hand, the Crystalline Sphere is composed of water, and it is this sphere on the circumfluous waters of which the world is built, and which protects the Universe from Chaos." Whiting, *Milton's Literary Milieu*, pp. 11, 28–30, equates Ralegh's explanation with Milton's. Additional information is supplied by Geoffrey Carnall, *N&Q*, 197:315–316 (1952), from Sacrobosco. Compare the objections raised by Robins, note 1 above.

16. John Donne, *The Courtier's Library, or Catalogus Librorum Aulicorum incomparabilium et non vendibilium* (ed. Evelyn Simpson, 1930), p. 49; "On the Navigableness of the Waters above Heaven; and whether a ship in the firmament will in the Day of Judgment land there or in our own harbours, by John Dee."

17. Sigmund Spaeth, *Milton's Knowledge of Music: Its Sources and Its Significance in his Works* (Princeton, 1913), pp. 100–123, gathers together all the allusions to, and, pp. 144–148, the sources of, the idea of sphere music. Cleanth Brooks and John Edward Hardy, eds., *Poems of Mr. John Milton with Essays in Analysis* (New York, 1951), discuss the music of the spheres as a dominant image of order in the minor poems. That Masson, *Life*, I, 280, could believe *Merchant of Venice* the source of the fancy that human ears are too feeble to perceive this music shows how much we have learned since his time about the history of ideas and literary genetics. Bartholomew, for example, f. cviiir [for cxviir] explains the theory and cites Macrobius.

18. *Il Penseroso* 170–171; *Works* III, Pt. 1, 314; IV, 190. T. S. K. Scott-Craig has suggested to me the interesting possibility that scientific material which Milton read in the *Syntagma* of Polanus but did not

use in *Christian Doctrine* nevertheless may have contributed elsewhere to his prose and poetry. Yet the poetry so transforms the commonplaces of natural science that they tend to lose their identity; and the residue of Polanus or indeed of Purchas, the undoubted source of Milton's *Brief History of Moscovia*, compares with that of a hundred other repositories. The confidence with which specific sources are still being asserted by scholars may be observed in W. J. Costello's mention of "Keckermann, from whose book, *Systema Physicum*, both Milton and Fuller gathered their natural philosophy," *Renaissance News*, 8:183 (1955).

19. *Eikonoklastes, Works* V, 135; Nicolson, *ELH*, 2:11–12 (1935); Bartholomew, f. cxxv; Batman, f. 124r.

20. Milton always writes of light with special intensity, as he does of music, truth, and nature. See, for example, the "hymne in prose" in *Animadversions* (*Works* III, 146), where Christ is the sun, the "ever begotten light and perfect Image of the Father"; and the comment in E. H. Visiak's review, "Milton's Prose," *Nineteenth Century*, 123:505–506 (1938), on the elevation of style there. On the supposed originals in DuBartas and Rashi of Milton's theory of light, see G. C. Taylor, p. 93, and Fletcher, p. 149. Whiting, *Milton's Literary Milieu*, p. 27, counterclaims that the interpretation was a commonplace in Ralegh, Purchas, and Mercator. Hunter, *JEGP*, 45:68–76 (1946), locates the theory in the Hermetic tradition. Denis Saurat, *Milton Man and Thinker* (New York, 1925), and lately Edgar H. Duncan, "The Natural History of Metals and Minerals in the Universe of Milton's *Paradise Lost*," *Osiris*, 11:386–421 (1954), stress Robert Fludd's concepts. See also Swan, "The Creation of Light," pp. 47–51; and D. C. Allen, "Description as Cosmos," *The Harmonious Vision: Studies in Milton's Poetry* (Baltimore, 1954), pp. 95–109. Brooks and Hardy, pp. 187–234, convincingly explicate the ambivalent light symbolism of *Comus*. Their treatment of it in *L'Allegro–Il Penseroso* is less successful; see Svendsen, *Explicator*, 8:49 (1950). Brooks, *Sewanee Rev.*, 59:10–11 (1951), finds the sun imagery tightly integrated with the narrative, and the simile of Satan darkened like an eclipsing sun "a microcosm for the whole poem." In view of the ambivalence and ambiguities I am concerned with throughout, something should be said here of Jungian studies like Maud Bodkin, *Archetypal Patterns in Poetry* (1934) and R. J. Zwi Werblowsky, *Lucifer and Prometheus: a Study of Milton's Satan* (1952). A century which inherited the mythological tradition of Natale Conti and a passion for hieroglyphs, emblems, and similitudes invites archetypal and psychological analysis. But the clear and present danger of this approach is disregard or neglect of literary identity. Under it *Paradise Lost* softens into the poorly concealed discharge of Milton's unconscious into what is only incidentally or accidentally an epic. However valuable to understanding the writer — and this kind of post-mortem is highly specula-

tive — the method tends to slight the capital facts of formative literary forces and the crucial narrative assumptions of God as good and Satan as evil. The ambivalence of Satan's character is not Milton's unguarded self-revelation but a theologically and practically realistic literary strategy. Whatever Milton may have felt as a man, we must grant the poet his postulates, we must believe that he means what he says, or literary criticism is impossible. Winston Weathers' *"Paradise Lost* as Archetypal Myth," *CE,* 14:261–264 (1953), is acceptable and unpretentious; M. M. Mahood's *Poetry and Humanism* is extraordinarily perceptive; Bodkin's *Archetypal Patterns* is at least defensible where it is not useful. But Werblowsky's *Lucifer and Prometheus* is in effect irrelevant, a book-length misreading, despite occasional literary insights. It depends heavily upon A. J. A. Waldock's anti-Miltonic *Paradise Lost and Its Modern Critics* (1947). Even Tillyard has known the infection; see the exchange of letters between him and C. S. Lewis in *Essays and Studies by Members of the English Association,* 19:7–28 (1934); 21:153–168 (1936). My own assumption is that expressed by Mahood in another connection, "that Milton knew what he wanted to do and did it."

21. Hughes, p. 163, cites Batman; Whiting, pp. 75–76, gives Pliny. La Primaudaye, p. 697; Adelard of Bath, *Dodi-Ve-Nechdi,* p. 157; Bartholomew, f. cxxixr; Swan, pp. 314–315; Margaret Cavendish, Duchess of Newcastle, *Poems* (3rd ed., 1668), p. 40.

22. *Works* III, Pt. 1, 162; Batman, f. 138v.

23. La Primaudaye, pp. 719–720; Bartholomew, ff. cxxviiv–cxxviiir; Swan, pp. 322–323.

24. *Works* V, 172. B. A. Wright, "Milton's Treason in *Paradise Lost,"* *TLS,* June 20, 1929, p. 494, detects in the lines on Satan an allusion to the eclipse of May 29, 1630, birthday of Charles II, and perhaps the reason for objection to them by the Licenser for the Press. Verity, II, 393, had supposed merely that it was too soon after the Restoration for much talk of change. On Satan's negative creativity, see the extensive and persuasive analysis in the second chapter, "Creation," of W. B. C. Watkins' admirable examination of sensuous elements in Milton's language and images, *An Anatomy of Milton's Verse* (Baton Rouge, 1955). His discussion supports the view I develop here and elsewhere; indeed it anticipates mine in several respects.

25. *Works* III, Pt. 2, 270; Bartholomew, f. cxxxvir. The purity of sunlight was a common paradox; see V. deSola Pinto, *Peter Sterry Platonist and Puritan* (Cambridge, 1934), p. 150, where Sterry makes the expected identification of light with the Deity: "Yet as the Sun-Beams fall on a Dunghill, and are not polluted; so God is still himself to himself, high and glorious in the lowest Things." And Peter Charron, *Of Wisdome* (1606), p. 83: "The Sunne shines on the dunghill, and is neither infected nor annoyed therewith." On the cosmic swing of guilt, see M. M. Mahood, *Poetry and Humanism,* and my article,

"Adam's Soliloquy in Book X of *Paradise Lost*," *CE*, 10:366–370 (1949). So strong has been the visual impression of many passages relating to the cosmos that pictorial sources have been sought for these as well as other figures. Todd and Dunster thought Milton's cone-of-night image originated from the frontispiece of DuBartas' *Triumph of Faith* (Todd, VII, 16). Whiting, *Milton's Literary Milieu*, pp. 94–128, deals with Milton's use of maps. Allan H. Gilbert, " 'A Double Janus' (*Paradise Lost* XI, 129)," *PMLA*, 54:1026–1030 (1939), found a picture of one in Joannes Rosinus, *Romanorum Antiquitatum Libri Decem* (Basil, 1583); but Alexander Ross, *Mystagogus Poeticus* (1648), p. 196, describes the same phenomenon. Mario Praz, "Milton and Poussin," *Seventeenth Century Studies Presented to Sir Herbert Grierson* (Oxford, 1938), pp. 192–210, attempts an analogy between Milton's stylistic development and French painting of his time. The solemn sliding board of Uriel (*PL* IV, 555–556, 589–592), which depends for its effect on a visualization of the cosmos and which Addison thought a prettiness beneath Milton, was attributed by Todd, II, 85–86, to Sandys' *Travels*, by Farmer to Shirley's *The Brothers*, by Warton to Drayton's *Legend of Robert Duke of Normandy*, and by Newton, I, 301–302, to a picture by Annibal Caracci. Milton's use of pictures, maps, statuary, and architecture is presently the study of Amy Lee Turner.

26. Bartholomew, f. cxxixr; Batman, f. 133r; Caxton, pp. 124–125; La Primaudaye, p. 721; Swan, p. 323.

27. The controversy over the moon-world and Milton's relation to it were exhaustively studied in the 1930's by Marjorie Nicolson, *A World in the Moon* (Northampton, Mass., 1936); Grant McColley, "The Ross-Wilkins Controversy," *Annals of Science*, 3:153–189 (1938), and his edition of Francis Godwin's *The Man in the Moone*; and Francis Johnson–Sanford Larkey, "Thomas Digges, the Copernican System, and the Idea of the Infinity of the Universe in 1576," *HLB*, 5:69–117 (1934). Some idea of the fervor with which the seventeenth century debated the question appears from Peter Heylyn's having to take serious notice of the moon-world in his *Cosmographie* (3rd ed., 1666), p. 1095, a passage which Nicolson quotes but which apparently neither she nor McColley recognizes as alluding to the Ross-Wilkins quarrel. On the Tuscan artist passage, *PL* I, 286–291, see Nicolson's contrary opinion, *ELH*, 2:1–32 (1935); Neckam, p. 53; Caxton, p. 125 and note, where Prior regards Neckam as Gossouin's source; Swan, pp. 324–325. Rajan, *Paradise Lost and the Seventeenth Century Reader* (1947), pp. 122–123, explicates the figure as characteristic of the distinction between the metaphysical and the heroic style; Brooks, *Sewanee Review*. 59:1–21 (1951), reads it as the extension of the metaphysical into the heroic.

28. *Malleus Maleficarum*, trans. by Montague Summers (1928), pp. 147 ff.; *Compendium Maleficarum*, trans. by E. A. Ashwin (1929), p. 19; *Discoverie of Witchcraft*, ed. by Montague Summers (1930), pp. 12, 34–

35; Jonston, p. 25. John Wilkins, *The Discovery of a World in the Moone* (1638), p. 12, speaks of "the supposed labour of the Moone in her eclipses" as one of the "grosse absurdities . . . entertained by generall consent."

29. *Apology for Smectymnuus, Works* III, Pt. 1, 352; *PL* XI, 486. Jonston, p. 26; Bartholomew, f. cxxxiir, f. cxxxvr, where he cites Albumasar and "Hypocras" that "but if lyght of sterres tempred the thyknesse of ayre by night, al bodyes with soules shud be dystroyed"; Caxton, pp. 144–148. Eve's question had occurred to Milton in somewhat different form and tone in Prolusion VII, *Works* XII, 257: "Will you believe, my auditors, that the great spaces of the enormous firmament, illuminated and adorned by the everlasting fires, sustain so many tremendously rapid motions, travel over such great paths of revolution, for this one reason: that they may furnish light for ignorant and stupid man?"

30. Person, p. 196. McColley, "Milton's Dialogue on Astronomy," pp. 759–760, calls the passage from Book VIII Milton's effort to combat the growing curiosity of an intellectual movement of which he did not approve. It should be noted that "to save appearances" was itself a cliché; see Karl Hammerle, "To Save Appearances (*Par. L.*, VIII. 82), ein Problem der Scholastick," *Anglia*, 62:368–372 (1938), for its history in Aquinas, Buridan, Nicholas d'Oresme, and Bacon. Vaughan, p. 27, commenting on the jargon of astronomers, mentions "Retrogradations, Trepidations, Librations, and I know not what harde words which the Astronomers have devised to reconcile the diversity of the observations." The Milton prose passages are at *Works* III, Pt. 2, 389; VII, 67; V, 271. Howard Schultz's *Milton and Forbidden Knowledge* (New York, 1955), a brilliant and definitive disposition of the charge of anti-intellectualism, appeared too late for me to indicate in detail his confirmation or modification of the views expressed here and elsewhere. In dealing with the "bifurcated sin of dubious speculation (curiosity) on the one hand and corrupted learning (vain philosophy) on the other," Schultz surveys the work of Milton and the whole range of seventeenth-century thought to establish the milieu in which he wrote and the true features of his Christian humanist position.

31. The best study of Renaissance astrology for literary scholars is Don Cameron Allen's *The Star-Crossed Renaissance* (Durham, 1941). Carroll Camden's "Astrology of Shakespeare's Day," *Isis*, 19:26–73 (1933), Hugh De Lacy's "Astrology in the Poetry of Edmund Spenser," *JEGP*, 33:520–543 (1934), and S. V. Larkey's "Astrology and Politics in the First Years of Elizabeth's Reign," *Bulletin of the History of Medicine*, 3:171–186 (1935), are useful. An excellent summary of the conflict of religion and astrology is Kocher's, pp. 201–224. Milton's horoscope, Bodleian MS Ashmole 436, part 1, f. 119, with a facsimile in B. M. Add. MS 24501, f. 8, is reprinted in *Works* XVIII, 348; it was cast by John Gadbury, the almanac maker. Perhaps it should be added here that

Milton's nephew John Phillips wrote some satires against Gadbury's more famous contemporary William Lilly; see William Godwin, *Lives of Edward and John Phillips Nephews and Pupils of Milton* (1815).

32. *Works* III, Pt. 1, 217, 138, 341–342, 293; IV, 190. The heaping up of technical terms in *Animadversions* is of course common satirical practice; for another example, see Joseph T. Curtiss, "The Horoscope in Chaucer's Man of Laws Tale," *JEGP*, 26:24–32 (1927). As Rudolph Kirk and W. P. Baker note in *Yale Prose*, I, 698, Milton is here predicting the decline of the Episcopal cause by winter. In the *Tetrachordon* passage Milton is "saving the phenomena" in a fashion he derided later, not an uncommon practice for one who was quite sure he was right all the time. There he is saying that the apparent aberrations in planetary movement disturb no one; and differences in human nature are likewise reasonable and understandably incompatible. For a contemporary definition of *crasis*, see Thomas Newton's translation, *The Touchstone of Complexions . . . by Levine Lemnie* (1633), p. 50.

33. *PL* VIII, 511–513; IX, 106–110. *Kalender of Shepherdes*, ed. H. O. Sommer (1892), III, 142; La Primaudaye, pp. 708–710, 703–712; Bartholomew, ff. ccxxir–ccxxiir; Batman, ff. 125r–v; Swan, pp. 334–335.

34. Some kind of correspondence or antithesis between the positive creativity of God and the negative creativity of Satan may be found in nearly every incident in *Paradise Lost*. One remarkable coincidence is that between Satan's corruption of Eve through her ear (an addition by Milton to the hexameral story) and the medieval notion that Mary was impregnated by the Holy Ghost through her ear. For discussion of the embarrassed attempts to account for Christ's conception and birth through other than natural channels, see G. Zilboorg and G. W. Henry, *A History of Medical Psychology* (New York, 1941), p. 124, and G. R. Taylor, *Sex in History* (New York, 1954), pp. 61–62.

35. Bush, *Science and English Poetry*, p. 46.

CHAPTER III — THIS VAST SUBLUNAR VAULT

1. For Donne's rejection of the element of fire, see Charles M. Coffin, *John Donne and the New Philosophy* (New York, 1937); and for the impact on literature of the elimination of this sphere, Marjorie Nicolson, "The New Astronomy and English Literary Imagination," *SP*, 32:428–462 (1935). Fage's frontispiece diagram to *A Description of the Whole World* (1658) retained the element of fire.

2. *PL* I, 711; III, 562–565; VII, 14–16, 89–90; *Death of a Fair Infant* 16; *Nativity Ode* 103. Caxton, pp. 122, 49–50; Cuningham, p. 45; Person, pp. 12–14; Swan, p. 78. With reference to celestial air, the allusion to the builders of Babel, who in the upper regions would famish themselves of breath if not of bread (*PL* XII, 78), reflects an interest like that in Michael Scott's *The Philosophers Banquet* (2nd ed. 1614), pp.

156–157, which discusses seriously "Whether ayre be more necessarie to life than meate."

3. *Comus* 80; *PR* IV, 619–620; *PL* I, 745; I, 537; *Works* III, Pt. 1, 314. Swan, pp. 80, 86. *Antiperistasis* was a favored term of meteorologians; Cowley risked it in *Elegy upon Anacreon* and drew Samuel Johnson's censure. Milton's vocabulary is rich in scientific language, but even in his prose it is seldom jargon. Caxton, *loc. cit.*; Bartholomew, Bk. ii: De Aere et eius Impressionibus; Lodge, p. 763; DuPlesis, p. 365.

4. *Works* III, Pt. 1, 50. Fulke, ff. 2r–v; La Primaudaye, p. 740; Swan, pp. 84–85. For the Gilbert-Whiting disagreement, see the former's "Milton and Galileo," *SP*, 19:155–156 (1922), and the reply "Milton and Comets," *ELH*, 4:41–42 (1937).

5. Hill, f. 2v; Lodge, p. 70; Nausea, ff. E5v, D1v–D3v. Person, p. 64, notes that comets move from south to north; perhaps this kind of idea influenced Milton's displacement of Ophiucus. Bartholomew, f. cxxxiv; Howard, ff. 73r–81v; Bainbridge, *passim*, especially pp. 27–42; Jonston, p. 75; Gadbury, *De Cometis*, f. A3v, p. 19; Lilly, p. 4; Comenius, p. 304; Phillips, f. L3v; Swan, p. 99. Even broadside ballads warned of comet-swords; see "A lamentable list of hideous signs," No. 4 in *The Pack of Autolycus*, ed. Hyder Rollins (Cambridge, Mass., 1927), p. 23. The two *PL* passages have attracted many sources. Newton and Todd cited Virgil, Tasso, Spenser, and DuBartas; Verity, II, 421, gave Batman's rendering of the Bartholomew quotation; Nicolson, *ELH*, 2:14 (1935), thought the second passage due to the optic tube but agreed that it might have come from books. Whiting, "Milton and Comets," is probably right in concluding "that for Milton the choice of this simile was almost inevitable."

6. La Primaudaye, p. 746; Swan, pp. 97–98. D. C. Allen, *The Legend of Noah* (Urbana, 1949), Kocher, *Science and Religion*, and Margaret Wiley, *The Subtle Knot* (Cambridge, Mass., 1952) are the current accounts of Renaissance rationalism mentioned.

7. *On the Death of a Fair Infant* 16; *PR* II, 117; *L'Allegro* 74; *The Passion* 56; *PL* II, 931–938. Bartholomew, ff. cliiir, clvir; Swan, p. 137; Caxton, pp. 117–118; La Primaudaye, p. 747. There is no stable stratification of atmosphere in Chaos, but the cloud principle may be assumed like that of the world's regions. Edgar H. Duncan, "Satan-Lucifer: Lightning and Thunderbolt," *PQ*, 30:441–443 (1951), suggests that Satan was sent aloft by a bolt of lightning from the cloud; he quotes Comenius, pp. 207–208.

8. *Works* IX, 49; *PR* IV, 31; *PL* XI, 841–843 — on which see Bartholomew, f. clivr; Swan, p. 176; La Primaudaye, p. 737. Kenelm Digby, *Of Bodies and of Mans Soul* (1669; 1644 in dedication), p. 430, anticipated Milton's fine image: "you shall perceive the Sea begin to wrinkle his smooth face that way the wind will come." On the names of winds, see Whiting, pp. 121–122; Bartholomew, ff. clivv–clvv; La Primaudaye,

p. 756; Swan, pp. 172–173. Mercator, *Historia Mundi*, gave separate charts to Latin, English, and Italian names; Levante, Ponent, and Sirocco are at p. 58.

9. *PL* II, 488–491; Bartholomew, ff. clviiv–clviiir; Caxton's chapter "How the clowdes and rayn come comynly," pp. 117–118, gives the same explanation; La Primaudaye, p. 751; Batman, f. 167v; Person, pp. 69–72; Jonston, pp. 85–86; Godfridus, p. 99.

10. Bartholomew, f. clviv; La Primaudaye, p. 750; Swan, p. 129; Lodge, *DuBartas*, pp. 76–77; Seneca, p. 768; Jonston, p. 88; *An Account of the Late Terrible Earthquake in Sicily*, p. 7.

11. *Works* IX, 171; *PL* XII, 193–194. Caxton, p. 119; Bartholomew, f. clviiiv; La Primaudaye, pp. 743, 742; Swan, pp. 156–157; Fulke, f. 55v; *Mirabilis Annus*, pp. 51–52. On tempests raised by demons, see Kocher, ch. 6; on the storm scene in *PR*, E. M. Pope, *Paradise Regained: the Tradition and the Poem* (Baltimore, 1947), pp. 93, 96–97.

12. *SA* 1695–1696, *Arcades* 115; *Works* III, Pt. 1, 266; VII, 19–21; Milles, p. 661; Hill, f. 53v. We have observed Milton's satisfaction at catching Salmasius in error; John Evelyn also corrected him in *Sylva, or a Discourse of Forest Trees* (1664), p. 17.

13. Bartholomew, ff. clxr–v; Caxton, p. 120; La Primaudaye, pp. 738–753; Swan, pp. 116–122; Hill, ff. 54r–v; Jonston, pp. 78–79. Lodge, *Seneca's Natural Questions*, pp. 781–808 — most of the 59 chapters of Book Two treat lightning and thunder. Harward, pp. 6–15, 4; Fulke, f. 28v; Widdowes, p. 17; Lodge, *DuBartas*, p. 76; *Seneca*, p. 795; Duplesis, p. 207; Renaudot, p. 433; Olaus Magnus, p. 25. Chapman used the figure in *Bussy d'Ambois* IV. ii. 191–192: "A politician must, like lightning, melt the very marrow, and not taint the skin."

14. *Works* III, Pt. 1, 214; 91; V, 221–222; *PL* V, 746–747; XI, 135; *Comus* 351, 639; *PR* I, 303–307. Swan, pp. 80, 152–153; La Primaudaye, pp. 751–752, 852; Maplet, p. 31; Batman, f. 161v. For Aubrey, see *The Early Lives of Milton*, ed. Helen Darbishire (1932), p. 5. Widdowes describes this manna, p. 19; and Blount, *A Natural History*, pp. 61–65, "Observations concerning Manna," says that in physic it is taken for a kind of dew and "choicely kept, as a gentle purger of Choler."

15. *Nativity Ode* 160–162; *Comus* 797–799; *Works* III, Pt. 1, 110. La Primaudaye, pp. 766–777; Person, pp. 81, 50; Jonston, p. 82; Lodge, *DuBartas*, p. 123; *Seneca*, p. 868. The ancient notion of the earth as a living animal survives in these allusions, and appears in the groans uttered at the inception and completing of the fall of Adam and Eve. The debate between vitalists and mechanists had been concluded for new scientists long before *PL* was published. but the endurance of the old vocabulary in popular science and poetry mirrors the long-lasting conviction of man's unity with even a postlapsarian universe.

16. Widdowes, p. 19; Person, p. 27; Bartholomew, f. clxxxviiir; Caxton, pp. 114–115; Agrippa, *Of the Vanity of All the Arts and*

Sciences, p. 132; Swan, pp. 224–226. For the *PL* VI figure, Todd, II, 187, quoted Thyer's belief that Milton was indebted to Spenser.

17. A. O. Lovejoy, "Milton and the Paradox of the Fortunate Fall," *ELH*, 4:161–179 (1937).

18. A good summary of older opinion about the final lines of the epic is C. A. Moore, "The Conclusion of *Paradise Lost*," *PMLA*, 36: 1–34 (1921). W. B. Hunter, "Two Milton Notes," *MLR*, 44:89–91 (1949), quotes John Pettus, *Volatiles from the History of Adam and Eve* (1674): "by this flaming sword & c. is meant an order of evil Angels, appointed also to guard the way to the tree of life." And to the metaphorizing of Satan as comet one may add D. C. Allen, "Two Notes on Paradise Lost," *MLN*, 68:360–361 (1953), an analysis of the passage between Centaur and Scorpio to show Satan subtle and treacherous: "Satan, the baleful, wandering star is returning in his deceit and flushed with triumph, but all that he has done is negated by the resurrection of the God incarnate" — the sun is here rising in Aries as it does on Easter. James Whaler's "The Miltonic Simile," *PMLA*, 46:1034–1074 (1931), is the standard account. L. D. Lerner's article of the same title in *Essays in Criticism*, 4:297–308 (1954), deals intensively with levels of meaning in several of the extended figures, including that on the *ignis fatuus* in PL IX.

19. *Works* III, Pt. 2, 434. Person, pp. 17–18; Renaudot, p. 573; Jonston, p. 76; Swan, pp. 87–89. The title of William Guild's attack on Bellarmine shows that the phrase had passed into general use: *Ignis Fatuus. Or, The Elf-Fire of Purgatorie* (1625). Todd's ascription, II, 363, of Fletcher, *The Faithful Shepherdess*, and Wierus, *De Praestigiis Deorum*, as sources exemplifies early editorial over-rating of verbal resemblances — as the passage from *Speculum Mundi* should make clear.

20. *PL* IV, 321, 488–490, 689, 739; V, 17, 394–395; IX, 385–386, 780, 892, 997, 1037; X, 140. Camerarius's chapter, pp. 121–122, "The right hand is a signe either of peace or enmitie," collects much of the stock symbolism.

CHAPTER IV — THE SECRET POWERS OF STONES AND PLANTS

1. Mercator, pp. 34–35, 32; Maplet, pp. 48–49; Hale, p. 17.

2. Grew, *Musaeum Regalis*, f. A4r; *PL* V, 483, 509–512; IX, 112. The gradual differentiation of species was generally stressed; a late example is Goldsmith's *History of Earth and Animated Nature*, III, 222. Danaeus, ff. 11r, 6v; La Primaudaye, "Epistle Dedicatory," [f. 2r].

3. *Works* IV, 283. Bartholomew, f. ccxxxiv; Batman, ff. 261v, 172v–r. Maplet, as we have seen, judges plants more important than stones, the orthodox opinion. G. C. Taylor, "Milton on Mining," *MLN*, 45:24–27 (1930). Sir John Pettus, *Fodinae Regales, or the History, Laws and Places of the Chief Mines and Mineral Works in England, Wales, and*

the English Pale in Ireland (1670), ff. B2v–C1r. For *Comus*, see Brooks and Hardy, pp. 216–218, and Harry F. Robins, "The Key to a Problem in Milton's *Comus*," *MLQ*, 12:422–428 (1951). Robins explains the problem of excess fertility persuasively; his conclusions, taken with the independent analysis of Brooks and Hardy and the suggestions of D. C. Allen, *MLN*, 64:179–180 (1949), are surely the last word on the lines. I must enter a demurrer, however, against Robins' citing my "Milton and the Encyclopedias of Science," *SP*, 39:303 ff. (1942), as evidence that Milton read Maplet. That is not what I said or meant at all. On Pliny, see Whiting, pp. 92–93. For the Tubal-Cain passage, G. C. Taylor, pp. 114–115, suggested DuBartas. Duncan, *Osiris*, 11:408–409 (1954), relates it to Lucretius, *De Rerum Natura*, Agricola, *De Re Metallica*, and lines 568–571 particularly to Alonso Barba, *Art of Metalls*.

4. Lodge, pp. 856–857; Acosta, pp. 227–228; Agrippa, p. 81. The repetition of *found out* and *searched out* in many of these accounts recalls the controversy over "Found out the Massie Ore," *PL* I, 703. See B. A. Wright's defense of it as Milton's own emendation for *founded* in the first edition, *TLS*, August 9, 1934, p. 553; Svendsen, *N&Q*, 177: 331 (1939); and Pettus, *Fodinae*, ff. C1v, Hh1v: "Discoverer, is any person who doth finde out a Metal or Mineral which was covered, and discovers or reveals it to the Proprietor of the Ground." Duncan, p. 387, begins his account of Milton's mineralogy with Satan's "lesson," *PL*, VI, 472–483, which Peter F. Fisher, "Milton's Theodicy," *JHI*, 27:39 (1956), might have used as additional support to his conclusion that matter, "having originated in God, was in essence free from even the potentiality of evil; inasmuch as it was passive or receptive by nature, its formal potentialities but not its essential incorruptibility could be perverted."

5. Swan, pp. 299–301, 278; Caxton, p. 108; Acosta, p. 197; Maplet, p. 4; *The Works of the Famous Antiquary Polidore Vergil Compendiously Englisht by John Langley* (1663), p. 309. See also Bacon, *Sylva Sylvarum*, p. 459, and Fulke, *Meteors*, f. 65r: "they all agree, that all metalles are generated of sulphur, that is brymstone, which because it is whot, they call the father, and Mercury that is quicksilver, which because it is moyst, they call the mother." See above, Chapter III, note 7, for Duncan's suggestion that the cloud instinct with fire and nitre lifted Satan by a lightning stroke or thunderbolt. Henry Guerlac, "The Poets' Nitre: Studies in the Chemistry of John Mayow," *Isis*, 45:243–255 (1954), supports Duncan; in his view the theory of aerial nitre had by Milton's time become a commonplace. But the alternative friction theory of Seneca and Lucretius is, as he recognizes, the basis of the lightning described in *PL* X, 1069–1075; and, as he also reveals, literary renderings of the sulphur-nitre hypothesis of lightning and thunder derived from "another scientific tradition, besides the alchemical or iatro-chemical one," namely, the medieval accounts of gun-

powder. There is a good deal in common between Milton's incident of the fallen angels' discovery of "Sulphurous and Nitrous Foame" and the incident of the "strong rebuff of some tumultuous cloud" in Chaos. These considerations, plus the fact that (as Milton indicates in *First Defence*) lightning strikes things down instead of lifts them up, suggest to me that Milton was thinking of the rebuff as just that, a pushing upward by an exploding or expanding cloud, and not a stroke of lightning.

6. *PL* II, 168, 434–437, 516–518; IV, 604–605; *Nativity Ode* 195. Virgil had used sweating marble to mark Caesar's death, *Georgics* I, 480. Milton says "seems to sweat," perhaps having in mind some such rational explanation as Bacon's, *Sylva Sylvarum*, pp. 373, 609, though without sacrificing the ominous implication. Jonston, p. 121; Langley, *Vergil*, p. 305; Heydon, p. 47. Here also Duncan's "Donne's Alchemical Figures," *ELH*, 9:257–285 (1942); "The Alchemy in Jonson's *Mercury Vindicated*," *SP*, 39:625–637 (1942); "The Canon Yeoman's Silver Citrinacioun," *MP*, 37:241–262 (1940); and "Thomas Lodge's Use of Agrippa's Chapter on Alchemy," *Vanderbilt Studies in the Humanities*, 1:96–105 (1951), are extremely useful. On the metal called *Alchymy*, see Duncan, *Osiris*, pp. 403–404.

7. *Works* III, Pt. 1, 56, 298; IV, 306. Person, p. 42; Heydon, *Hammegulah Hampaaneah*, p. 47; *The Wise-Mans Crown*, pp. 6–7; Ripley, t. p.; Gesner, p. 180; Jonston, p. 118; Sir Kenelm Digby, *Choice and Experimented Receipts in Physick and Chirurgery* (1668), pp. 194–205; Wanley, p. 225.

8. E. S. LeComte, "New Light on the 'Haemony' Passage in *Comus*," *PQ*, 21:283–298 (1942); Wayne Shumaker, "Flowerets and Sounding Seas: a Study in the Affective Structure of *Lycidas*," *PMLA*, 66:485–494 (1951). Blount, *A Natural History*, f. A4r; Franck, pp. 3–5. McColley, *Paradise Lost*, pp. 168, 174, quotes from *Speculum Mundi*, p. 496, an analogue not so close as Franck to *PL* IX, 790–792. The phrase is hardly one for which a single source may be determined. Compare also with *PL* XII, 585–587, Franck, p. 96: "Now doe I think that the same also happened in the true Paradise of Adams heart. . . . and these two Trees [of Knowledge and of Life] are as God and Satan, so contrary one to another that one brings Life unto us, and the other death."

9. *On the Death of the Vice-Chancellor* 23–24; *Works* XVIII, 132; VIII, 81; VI, 151; *Comus* 626, 254. On Mede (or Meade), see Masson, *Life of Milton*, I, 124–126. Rembert Dodoens, *A New Herball, or Historie of Plants*, tr. Henrie Lyte (1595), pp. 402–409; Lodge, *DuBartas*, p. 130; Maplet, p. 72; Bartholomew, ff. cclvv–cclvir, cclxxir, cclxxivr; Batman, ff. 286v–287r, 303v–304r, 277r, 317r. For one example in book titles, see Wing, *A Short Title Catalogue*, entries A3491–3500, a column of "antidotes" against poisonous propaganda.

10. *Works* III, Pt. 1, 323. Bartholomew, ff. cclxxxvr, cclxiiir; Batman,

ff. 317v–318r, 294r; Swan, p. 243; La Primaudaye, p. 809; Maplet, p. 77; Lupton, p. 42; Dodoens, pp. 46–47; *Regimen Sanitatis Salerni*, p. 154; Topsell, p. 293. Laurie Bowman Zwicky suggested to me the Spenserian quality of the Well of Life.

11. *PL* V, 292–293; cf. *Comus* 991: "*Nard*, and *Cassias* balmy smels"; *Works* III, Pt. 1, 40; IX, 281. Topsell, *Serpents*, p. 105; Maplet, p. 62; La Primaudaye, p. 795; Bartholomew, f. cclxxvr; Dodoens, pp. 659–660. Perhaps Milton would have been equally pleased to think with John Parkinson, *Theatrum Botanicum: The Theater of Plants. Or an Herball of a Large Extent* (1640), pp. 812–813, of the purgative powers of lettuce, especially in choler. Bacon, *Sylva Sylvarum*, p. 513.

12. *Lycidas* 139–140; *Works* III, Pt. 1, 22–23. See Le Comte, "New Light"; Brooks and Hardy, p. 151. For a charge of over-reading against both studies, see Robert M. Adams, "Reading *Comus*," *MP*, 51:18–32 (1953). This piece reappears in *Ikon: John Milton and the Modern Critics* (Ithaca, 1955), where Adams conducts a wholehearted, commonsensical, and occasionally high-handed attack on Milton simulacra and allied errors created by, among others, Woodhouse, Bush, Bodkin, and Allen. My admiration for Adams' essay on Milton's text and for his disposition of Werblowsky and Empson is somewhat embarrassed, because of the complaint, on p. 170, of my "failure to distinguish even approximately between a more or less 'scientific' science and traditional moralizing on the book of creatures" and of my yoking of Bartholomew, Galileo, and Copernicus as scientific sources. Since from the earliest of the articles cited by Adams I have asserted the medievalism (i. e., traditional moralizing) of much of what Milton and his generation accepted as science, I am unable to account for his curious conclusion except as the result of hasty reading, ignorance of the history of science, or simply polemic momentum. And in view of my repeated insistence on the folly of source ascription for commonplace ideas in natural philosophy, I am further embarrassed for both of us by Adams' lumping me with the source hunters. On Milton's references to moly, Sara Watson, *N&Q*, 176:243–244 (1939), suggests Drayton's influence. On Greene, see D. C. Allen, "Science and Invention in Greene's Prose," *PMLA*, 52:1007–1018 (1938). Swan, p. 265. Newton, I, 353, gives the classical parallels to the elm and vine passage; see also Bartholomew, f. cclxxxviiiv; Batman, f. 175v; Maplet, p. 51. Lerner, *Essays in Criticism*, 4:305 (1954), regards this one of the most strikingly sexual passages in *Paradise Lost*. James Brown, *PMLA*, 71:16–17 (1956), discovers a similar effect in his analysis of V, 210–215.

13. Ralegh, pp. 67–69; *Regimen Sanitatis Salerni*, p. 167; Golding, f. Eeiir; Mandeville, ff. B1v–B2r. The sycamore was sometimes identified with the fig tree; see above, Chapter I, note 20.

14. Ralegh, p. 69. Some confirmation of my interpretation may be found in Robert A. Durr's "Dramatic Pattern in *Paradise Lost*," *JAAC*,

13:520–526 (1955). He describes a pattern of fall and rise through the poem, most explicitly in the death in Adam and Eve of their sinful lives and subsequent rebirth or regeneration. Certainly Durr is correct in emphasizing the fact that our attention is never restricted by any one immediate scene but is enriched and qualified by complementary and contrasting scenes.

CHAPTER V — ALL THE BEASTS OF THE EARTH

1. Frantze p. 2. E. S. Le Comte, *Yet Once More* (New York, 1953), includes many of the repeated motifs of animal lore in his detailed study of recurrence in Milton. H. W. Janson's monumental *Apes and Ape Lore in the Middle Ages and Renaissance* (1952) is the full-scale investigation.

2. Allen, *Legend of Noah*, pp. 71–72. Robin, p. 14. An interesting attempt to arrive at what the ordinary Elizabethan really believed of marvels in natural history is Madeleine Doran's "The 'Credulity' of the Elizabethans," *JHI*, 1:151–176 (1940). Fenton, f. 148r. Some light is thrown on Milton's curious allusion by Edmund Gayton's *Pleasant [Festivous] Notes upon Don Quixot* (1654), p. 272, where he writes of the stage: "The Spanish scene is much of it Legend, or some fictions upon Hereticks, and as they did render their persons and visages to be most horrid, odious, and inhumane, to the people of their Countrie, so they never bring any of these sects upon the stage, but they have a Hell, furies, and strange torments provided for them." Perhaps the idea of hideous-faced heretics goes back to the kind of thing reported in Caxton's *Charles the Grete* (ed. Sidney Herrtage. EETS e. s. xxxvi. 1880), where by wearing devil-masks and vizards and by ringing bells the heathen Saracens frighten French horses into flight. Familiarity with the cynocephali may be presumed from their presentation on the Elizabethan stage. Audrey Yoder, *Animal Analogy in Shakespeare's Character Portrayal* (New York, 1947), whose work is descriptive and statistical, not interpretive or analytical, reports the "cenofall" a stage property. She thinks Caliban was costumed as a fish-finned cenofall; see pp. 84–98.

3. *PL* VII, 387–499; X, 529–531; *PR* I, 312. *Reason of Church Government, Works* III, Pt. 1, 252; *Eikonoklastes*, V, 222, 185; *Colasterion*, IV, 237; *Second Defence*, VIII, 37; *Of Reformation*, III, 54. Frantze, p. 11; Jonston, pp. 244–245, 85; Bacon, pp. 557–561. Agrippa, *Female Pre-eminence*, tr. Henry Care (1670), p. 26, reports "*Islands*, where the Women are *Conceiv'd to Conceive* by the Wind." Jonston, p. 218, locates the phenomenon in Portugal. Bartholomew, ff. clxiv–clxviir, ccclxxiiiir, cccxviiir, noting at f. clxxiir that worms are created from the dung of locusts, which are themselves gendered of the south wind. Leonard Mascall, *The First Booke of Cattell* (1587), pp. 103–104, quotes

from Virgil's *Georgics* the wind-impregnation of mares, a notion that forms an example in the simple Latin lessons of William Horman's *Vulgaria* (1519), f. 182r. Further examples are in Conway Zirkle, "Animals Impregnated by the Wind," *Isis*, 25:95–130 (1936), and N. Von Hofsten, "Ideas of Creation and Spontaneous Generation Prior to Darwin," *Isis*, 25:80–94 (1936). Lupton, p. 83; Topsell, *Serpents*, pp. 119–124; Batman, f. 410v; *The Philosophers Banquet*, p. 200. F. L. Huntley, "A Justification of Milton's 'Paradise of Fools' (*P.L.*, III, 431–499)," *ELH*, 21:107–113 (1954). Robin, pp. 84–95; he finds Alexander Neckam, *De Naturis Rerum*, first to advance the cock's egg theory. Peter Lum's popularization, *Fabulous Beasts* (New York, 1951), pp. 42, 59–60, reports the monuments. Thomas Browne's demurrer is at *Works*, ed. Simon Wilkin (1906), I, 250–260. Milles, *Treasurie*, pp. 659–660, and *Mirror of Alchimy*, pp. 59–60, are among many repeating the legend of the deadly look; DuPlesis, *The Resolver*, p. 33, thinks it is a venomous vapor that kills.

4. *Nativity Ode* 172; *Works* III, Pt. 1, 61; Pt. 2, 15; X, 188; *PL* X, 529. Whaler, "Animal Simile in *Paradise Lost*," *PMLA*, 47:534–553 (1932); my account throughout owes a good deal to this unjustly neglected article. Agrippa, *Of the Vanity of All the Arts and Sciences*, p. 28; he is seconded by John Wilkins, *An Essay Towards a Real character and a Philosophical Language* (1668), p. 121, who refuses to offer symbols for gryphon and phoenix because they are "fictitious Animals . . . being but bare names and no more." Editors cite Lucan and Pliny (Newton), Aeschylus (Todd), Herodotus (Verity and Hughes) as sources for the lines on the gryphon. Bartholomew, ff. cccxxxiiiv–cccxxxivr; Batman, f. 368r; Maplet, pp. 148–149; Swan, p. 386; Olaus Magnus, p. 671. Lum, pp. 46–56, 145–158, has chapters on gryphon and hippogrif.

5. *Works* III, Pt. 1, 244; IX, 201–203. Bartholomew, f. clxixv; Batman, f. 183r; Caxton, pp. 82–83; Maplet, p. 165; La Primaudaye, p. 758; Swan, pp. 384–385. Newton, I, 358–359, cites Tasso, Pliny, Ovid, Claudian; Todd, II, 136, adds Marino; Verity, II, 486, Spenser and Lyly; Hughes, p. 158, prefers Tasso; Kathleen Hartwell, *Lactantius and Milton* (Cambridge, Mass., 1929), pp. 124–132, *De Ave Phoenice*; Allan H. Gilbert, *A Geographical Dictionary of Milton* (New Haven, 1919), p. 294, Herodotus. Albert S. Cook, ed., *The Old English Elene, Phoenix, and Physiologus* (New Haven, 1919), pp. xxxix–li, summarizes the classical texts and gives a history of Heliopolis, indissolubly linked with the sun and the phoenix. Whiting, p. 85, thinks Pliny "may have influenced Milton's description of Raphael." Rudolf Gottfried, "Milton, Lactantius, Claudian, and Tasso," *SP*, 30:497–503 (1933), made the point about Thebes; he too prefers Tasso. Michele De Filippis, "Milton and Manso: Cups or Books?" *PMLA*, 51:745–756 (1936), believes the phoenix described in *Damon's Epitaph* as decoration of a cup actually refers to a copy of Tasso's *Le Sette Giornate del Mondo Creato*. Robin, pp. 36–43,

who favors Pliny for Milton, quotes from Chaucer, Skelton, Lyly, Shakespeare, Massinger, Drayton, and Herrick. For Milton's annotation of Browne, see the lines in Gordon Goodwin, ed., *The Poems of William Browne of Tavistock* (1892), I, 110, and "Milton's Marginalia," *Works* XVIII, 338. As a contribution to resolving the confusion of Thebes and Heliopolis, one may offer Batman's account "Of the Province Fenicia," f. 225*v*: "Fenix is a province, and hath that name of Fenice the brother of Cathini. For Fenix was put out of Glebis Thebis in Aegipt, and driven into Siria, and reigned in Sidon, and called the land after his own name Fenicia." The phoenix as a stereotype for singularity and supernatural virtue appears nowhere so frequently as in compliments to Elizabeth; E. C. Wilson, *England's Eliza* (Cambridge, Mass., 1939), pp. 244–245, lists some of these. Lum, p. 239, notes it was the motto or emblem of Elizabeth, Mary Queen of Scots, and Edward VI.

6. *Works* III, Pt. 1, 49, 120; VII, 227; V, 278; IV, 84; *PL* II, 701; *SA* 997–998. Mede, *Works*, p. 286. Bartholomew, f. cccxlvir; Maplet, pp. 168–169. The *Ancren Riwle*, Chaucer, and Chester references are from Robin, pp. 115–116, who quotes also the *Speculum Doctrinale* attributed to Vincent of Beauvais: "Scorpio blandum et quasi virgineum dicitur habere vultum." Sir Thomas Browne, *Works*, I, 375–376, rehearses the controversy over caudal stings in serpents and argues against the probability. I am indebted to Wynema Caswell for some suggestions about the scorpion.

7. *Works* V, 59: III, Pt. 1, 43, 210; VI, 122; XII, 283; *Arcades* 53; *Lycidas* 45. G. B. Harrison, *A Second Elizabethan Journal* (New York, c1931), p. 24, reprints from Anthony Fletcher's *Certain Very Proper and Most Profitable Similes* (1595) a cut of a tree infested with such caterpillars of the commonwealth as Hypocrisy, Blasphemy, and Contempt. Jonston, p. 241; Bartholomew, ff. ccciiir, cccxxxiiv–cccxxxiiiv. Batman, ff. 367r–v, adds that formica, emmet, ampt, and pismire all apply to the same insect. Maplet, pp. 125–126. E. M. Clark, ed., *The Readie and Easie Way to Establish a Free Commonwealth* (New Haven, 1915), pp. 94–95, notes the same figure of the ant in Hobbes, Harrington, and Felltham. Editors and others characteristically disagree over the source of the creation passage. Todd, II, 485, gives Horace and Virgil; Himes, p. 404, cites Proverbs; Verity, II, 546, follows Todd; G. C. Taylor, p. 98, recommends DuBartas; and Whiting, p. 83, Pliny.

8. *Works* V, 253; VII, 87, 279. Bartholomew, ff. cccxiiir–cccxivv; Batman, ff. 345v–347r. Butler, f. a2v; *The Feminine Monarchie* has been revived by Whiting, p. 84, as the probable source of *PL* VII, 489–492. Pearce had advanced it in his reply to Bentley, according to Ants Oras, *Milton's Editors and Commentators* (1931), p. 85. J. A. St. John, ed., *The Prose Works of John Milton* (1868–1883), I, 114, did not understand or approve the extremes to which seventeenth-century controversy extended: "Nothing can be more puerile, than in serious disquisition

in politics, to institute comparisons between the conduct of men and that of the inferior animals." The antipathy of beetles and roses was as old as Pliny; see Robin, p. 113. For other instances of Milton's polemical natural philosophy, see *Apology for Smectymnuus, Works* III, Pt. 1, 348, where he gibes at an antagonist for failing to distinguish between rational and sensible horizons, and VII, 407, where he ridicules Salmasius' confused analogy from the zones of the earth.

9. Bartholomew, ff. clxvr, cccxvr; Maplet, pp. 125–126; La Primaudaye, p. 823; Swan, pp. 413–414. Other allusions in Milton are likewise familiar: wasps (*Works* IX, 69), leeches (III, Pt. 1, 54), lice (XII, 237), flies (IX, 67; *PR* IV, 15–17).

10. *Works* III, Pt. 1, 333, 410; V, 218. *PL* VIII, 347–348, 55; VII, 410, 473. Swan, pp. 375, 362; Holland, *The Historie of the World. Commonly called, The Naturall Historie of C. Plinius Secundus* (1601), p. 249; Bartholomew, f. clxxxvv. Batman, f. 199v, adds confirmation of the remora's powerful properties from travelers to America. Caxton, p. 88; Maplet, p. 143; La Primaudaye, p. 783; Lodge, pp. 225–226; Mede, p. 1061, in a letter to Samuel Hartlib; Jonston, p. 301; Agrippa, *Three Books of Occult Philosophy* (1651), p. 25; Tymme, *A Dialogue Philosophical*, p. 49; Charron, *Of Wisdome*, p. 105; *The Philosophers Banquet*, p. 219; Olaus Magnus, p. 761; Fenton, ff. 50v–51v; Johnson, *Cornucopiae*, ff. A3r–v; George Thomson, *The Pest Anatomized* (1666), p. 180. When one adds to these the examples of the remora collected by Robin, pp. 128–129, it is difficult to accept McColley's suggestion in "Milton's Dialogue on Astronomy," pp. 752–753, of Ross's *The New Planet No Planet* as the source. As even more extensive accumulation might be made on the dolphin, as may be seen from a perusal of Eunice B. Stebbins, *The Dolphin in the Literature and Art of Greece and Rome* (Menasha, Wis., 1929). On the crococile, see Milles, p. 486; Topsell, p. 128.

11. *Works* VII, 343, 345–347, 281; V, 224; XII, 235–237, 283; IX, 201–203. *Comus* 233, 565; *PL* III, 38; IV, 602, 648; V, 40; VIII, 518; *PR* IV, 245; *Nativity Hymn* 68. Maplet, p. 137; Swan, pp. 399, 410; La Primaudaye, p. 760; Bartholomew, f. ccclxxiiv; Batman, f. 409r. Robin, pp. 176–178, finds the halcyon in Varro, Aristophanes, Basil, Lyly, Shakespeare, Drayton, and others. The extravagant horse-doctoring is not mere schoolboy obscenity; see Overbury's "An Arrant Horse Courser," in Gwendolyn Murphy, ed., *A Cabinet of Characters* (Oxford, 1925), p. 106: "For powdring his eares with Quicksilver, and giving him suppositories of live Eeles he's expert."

12. *Works* XII, 283. *Milton's Private Correspondence and Academic Exercises,* tr. P. B. Tillyard, ed. E. M. W. Tillyard (Cambridge, 1932), p. 143, cited with approval by K. A. McEuen, *Yale Prose*, I, 304. Swan, pp. 405–406; Bartholomew, f. clxiiv; Batman, f. 175v; Maplet, pp. 137, 119: "their flight is like a Triangle, sharpe at the ende, and broade

about, and easied therewithal by one another his helping." *Pliny*, tr. Holland, p. 282, says of geese and swans flying "wedge-wise . . . in this their flight they rest their heads upon the former." Robin, pp. 63–64, relates from Basil and Beaumont and Fletcher's *The Spanish Curate* how storks support their feeble parents with their wings. Verity, II, 544, following Keightley, misunderstands the *PL* passage. La Primaudaye, p. 759; Robin, p. 167. Todd, II, 264, and *Yale Prose*, I, 304 accept Cicero, *De Natura Deorum*. G. C. Taylor, pp. 97–98, quotes a DuBartas parallel as convincing as any of these. See Svendsen, "The Prudent Crane: *Paradise Lost* VII, 425–431," *N&Q*, 183:66–67 (1942). T. P. Harrison, who is engaged upon a study of Milton's birds, has suggested to me that the passage from Basil, Migne, *Patrologia Graeca*, XXIX, 175, is closer to Milton than anything else proposed.

13. *Works* IV, 344. Bartholomew, ff. clxiiir–v; Batman, ff. 176v–177r. Caxton, p. 102, includes sun and moon in an abbreviated version. Robin, pp. 159–161: although the idea of renewal is Scriptural the method is not, nor is it classical; it does occur in *Physiologus*, Eustathius' *Hexameron*, Vincent's *Speculum Naturale*, Bartholomew, and Spenser.

14. *Works* IV, 88; XII, 283. The neglectful ostrich is in Job. See also Bartholomew, f. clxxiiiir; La Primaudaye, p. 762; Neckam, p. 101: "Struthio ova sua in sabulo aut arena linquens, diligentiam maternae sollicitudinis ignorare videtur." Swan, p. 387, extracts a moral from the ostrich not unlike Milton's; and asserts, p. 392: "from the Stork Ibis, men first learned to purge by clyster." Maplet, p. 152, and Milles, p. 547, repeat this. On raven and vulture, see Bartholomew, ff. clxviiiv, clxxiiiiv; Maplet, p. 178; Swan, p. 338. Newton, II, 243, gives Lucan's *Pharsalia* as source; Todd, II, 410, Beaumont and Fletcher's *Beggars Bush*. Keightley, II, 117, who disparaged the attainments in science of earlier editors, lacks a little himself here: "We have not met anywhere with an account of birds of prey thus scenting the carnage *before* the battle." The skeptical Digby, *Of Bodies*, pp. 415–431, allows only natural causes for the prescience. The lore of the vulture was varied and widespread. See, in addition to Huntley's article, Loren MacKinney's monograph, "The Vulture in Medical Lore," *Ciba Symposia*, 4:1258–1292 (1942). For a recent treatment of Sin and Death's foreknowledge as one more manifestation of the ambivalence between good and evil, see Durr's suggestion, *JAAC*, 13:521 (1955), that from a similar collaboration of God and Satan evolves a progressive cycle of good and evil, creation and ruin.

15. *Works* III, Pt. 2, 397. Milles, pp. 546, 439; Frantze, p. 12; Torquemada, ff. 96r–98v; Charles Blount, *Anima Mundi: or an Historical Narration of the Opinions of the Ancients concerning Mans Soul After this Life: According to unenlightened Nature* (1679), p. 30; Lupton, p. 30; Golding, ff. Rir Qiiiiv; Vergil, p. 59; Swan, pp. 459, 401, 406, 149,

161; Caxton, pp. 88, 102; Maplet, pp. 150, 122; Ling, f. 264*v*; Bartholomew, f. clix*v*; Batman, f. 163*v*. W. B. Hunter, "A Note on *Lycidas*," *MLN*, 65:544 (1950), recommends Aristotle. Other supporters of the conventional attitude toward reasoning in animals are Nemesius in George Wither's translation *The Nature of Man* (1636), pp. 170–178; Person, pp. 30–31; Kenelm Digby, *Two Treatises* (Paris, 1644), p. 312; DuPlesis, pp. 37–38; J. Shafte, *The Great Law of Nature* (1673), pp. 23–24. For the opposite view see Plutarch, *The Morals*, trans. Philemon Holland (1603), pp. 561–570, 949–980; Camerarius, pp. 87–90; Charron, *Of Wisdom* (1606), pp. 105–107; Christian Huygens, *The Celestial Worlds Discover'd* (1698), p. 6; Renaudot, pp. 318–319. My interpretation of this problem was challenged when it appeared as "The Power to Reason: a Milton Paradox," *N&Q*, 184:368–370 (1943). See H. W. Crundell's objections, *N&Q*, 185:113 (1943).

16. *Works* XII, 333, 341, 237; IX, 147, 117, 199, 125. *PR* I, 339–340. Harris Fletcher, "A Note on Two Words in Milton's *History of Moscovia*," *Renaissance Studies in Honor of Hardin Craig* (Stanford, 1941), pp. 309–319. Jonston, p. 221; Torquemada, ff. 146*v*–147*r*. Olaus Magnus, p. 605; on p. 757 a woodcut accompanying the chapter "De Rosmaro sive Morso Norvagico" shows the morse climbing rocks. As Fletcher notes, the gulon or wolverine is in *Speculum Mundi*. Bartholomew, ff. cccvii*v*–cccviii*r*, cccxxxiiii*v*–cccxxxv*r*; Batman, ff. 340*v*–341*r*, 368*v*–369*r*; Golding, f. S1*r*; Topsell, pp. 435–445. The *Volpone* parallel about the hyena, mentioned in Robin, pp. 49–50, was thought Milton's source by Todd, III, 270–271. For the ape, see Bartholomew, f. cccxliiii*r*, and Topsell, pp. 2–5; the lion, La Primaudaye, p. 829, and Swan, p. 431; the camel, Maplet, p. 130, and Johnson, *Cornucopiae*, f. D2*v*. To these might be added as conventional ornamentation from the classics the speechless Seriphian frogs of the first prolusion and the Caspian tigress of the fifth of November poem.

17. *PL* IV, 196, 397–408, 800; *SA* 936–937; *Works* IV, 252, 98, IX, 5; VII, 401; III, Pt. 1, 320, 117, 77, 275; Pt. 2, 225. Topsell, *Serpents*, pp. 193, 41–42, 51, 53, 57, 5; Bartholomew, ff. cccxxxviii*r*, cxi*v*. Howard Schultz, "Satan's Serenade," *PQ*, 27:17–26 (1948). Fletcher, *Milton's Semitic Studies* (Chicago, 1926), pp. 131–132. Mede, *Works*, p. 281; Milles, p. 28; Lewis de Mayerne Turquet, *The Generall Historie of Spaine*, tr. Edward Grimeston (1612), p. 51. Camerarius, p. 249. Kirkconnell's analogues to *PL* in *The Celestial Cycle* include several, ancient and modern, which involve a sexual component to Satan's temptation. To these should be added Karl Shapiro's "Adam and Eve" suite, admirably explicated by Frederick Eckman, *Texas Studies in English*, 35 (1956).

18. *PL* X, 216–218. Mercator, *Historia Mundi*, p. 45. J. B. Broadbent, "Milton's Paradise," *MP*, 51:160–176 (1954). Milton himself points out one feature of the symbolism:

Nor hee thir outward onely with Skins
Of Beasts, but inward nakedness, much more
Opprobrious, with his Robe of righteousness,
Arraying cover'd from his Father's sight.   X, 220–223

Arnold Williams, "Milton and the Renaissance Commentaries on Genesis," *MP*, 37:276–277 (1940), quotes an extended parallel from Musculus to show how common the motif was. It should be added that covering them from the Father's sight is of course a ritual gesture; even the deep tract of Hell hides nothing from his view. The real cover or protection comes only with the Atonement, of which this is a prefiguring. Pettus, *Volatiles*, p. 150, reports the interesting alternative from "the Targum of Uz" that God covered the sinners with the skin of the serpent that tempted them.

19. William Diaper and John Jones, tr., *Oppian's Halieuticks* (Oxford, 1722), pp. 6–13, quoted in *The Complete Works of William Diaper*, ed. Dorothy Broughton (Muses' Library, Cambridge, Mass., 1952), pp. lx–lxi.

CHAPTER VI — THE STRUCTURE AND SURGERY OF THE HUMAN BODY

1. James H. Hanford, "John Milton Forswears Physic," *Bulletin of the Medical Library Association*, 32:23–34 (1944), though not addressed to Miltonists, is an excellent survey of the poet's trials. Somewhat older studies of interest if not always of value are Eleanor G. Brown's *Milton's Blindness* (New York, 1934); Arnold Sorsby, "On the Nature of Milton's Blindness," *The British Journal of Ophthalmology*, 14: 339–354 (1930); W. H. Wilmer, "The Blindness of Milton," *Bulletin of the Institute for the History of Medicine*, 1:85–106 (1933). Denis Saurat, *Milton Man and Thinker* (New York, 1925), pp. 329–341, fluttered the dove-cotes with the hypothesis that congenital syphilis was probably the cause of Milton's glaucoma, as well as the many miscarriages and high infant mortality in his family. Heinrich Mutschman, *The Secret of John Milton* (Dorpat, 1925), based his argument for Milton's albinism in part on Aubrey's note that Milton had *abrown* hair, which Mutschman takes as equivalent to Latin *alburnus* or whitish. Eleanor Brown disposed of this notion. As to the Renaissance medical background, the studies alluded to are Ruth L. Anderson, *Elizabethan Psychology and Shakespeare's Plays* (Iowa City, 1927), Lily B. Campbell, *Shakespeare's Tragic Heroes Slaves of Passion* (Cambridge, 1930), P. Ansell Robin, *The Old Physiology in English Literature* (1911), John W. Draper, *The Humors and Shakespeare's Characters* (Durham, 1945), Lawrence Babb, *The Elizabethan Malady: a Study of Melancholia in English Literature from 1580 to 1640* (East Lansing, Mich., 1951). This last is a model for relating a particular science to literature, and Babb's "The Background of 'Il Penseroso,'" *SP*, 37:257–273 (1940), a notable exception to general

neglect of medical lore in the poetry. The discovery of Renaissance psychology in the 1920's and 1930's encouraged so heavy a reliance upon Timothy Bright's *A Treatise of Melancholie* (1586) and similar books that one might have thought all dramatis personae Jonsonian. Louise C. Turner Forest, "A Caveat for Critics Against Invoking Elizabethan Psychology," *PMLA*, 61:651–672 (1946), gave a purge to this modern vulgar error of accounting for dramatic motivation and characterization too literally from medical texts. Francis R. Johnson's rejoinder appeared in *English Studies Today*, ed. Wrenn and Bullough.

2. *Works* VII, 67; XII, 265; IV, 283, 174; VI, 80–81, 151–152; III, Pt. 1, 117, 182, 189, 257, 298; IX, 11. Medical education was a standard humanistic recommendation. Robin, pp. 93–94, notes Herbert of Cherbury's emphasis on it for all gentlemen; and Herbert Silvette, "Medicine in Utopia," *Bulletin of the Institute of the History of Medicine*, 6:1013–1036 (1939), reveals the ideal commonwealths of Plato, More, Campanella, Bacon, and others in the same tradition. On the relation of medicine to other sciences, see Joan Evans and Mary S. Serjeantson, eds., *English Medieval Lapidaries* (EETS, o. s., 190. 1933); Thomas O. Cockayne, *Leechdoms, Wortcunning, and Starcraft of Early England* (Rolls Series No. 35. 3 vols. 1864–1866); Eleanour S. Rohde, *The Old English Herbals* (1922); Walter Clyde Curry, *Chaucer and the Medieval Sciences* (New York, 1926); Carroll Camden, "Elizabethan Astrological Medicine," *Annals of Medical History*, n. s. 2:217–226 (1930); the more recent work of Babb; and Kocher, *Science and Religion in Elizabethan England*. The undeserved scandalous reputation of the profession and the whole problem of theological medicine are admirably treated by Kocher, pp. 239–283, in "The Physician as Atheist" and "God in Medicine."

3. *Works* III, Pt. 1, 313, 63, 260, 351; IV, 250, 98, *PL* II, 274–277. Bartholomew, f. cxiii*v*; La Primaudaye, p. 547. The cosmic identities have been thoroughly explored; see George P. Conger, *Theories of Macrocosms and Microcosms in the History of Philosophy* (New York, 1922), Appendix II, Chapter III: "Use of the Term Microcosm to Denote Man, in English Literature from 1400 to 1650"; Campbell, pp. 51–62; Allen, *SAB*, 14:182–189 (1939); Milton A. Rugoff, *Donne's Imagery; a Study in Creative Sources* (New York, 1939), pp. 43–46. Jonston, *A History of the Wonderful Things of Nature*, p. 309, carried out even an analogy to the quarters of the earth: "He hath the East in his mouth, the West in his Fundament; the South in his Navel, the North in his Back." Nicolson's *The Breaking of the Circle*, pp. 1–33, is the best recent summation of the cosmic correlatives.

4. *Works* III, Pt. 1, 110, 117, 254, 182; Pt. 2, 484; V, 201. *Comus* 668–670, 808–809. *PL* XI, 542–546, 482. Bartholomew, ff. lviv–lviiir; La Primaudaye, pp. 358, 524, 534; Batman, Bk. VII, ch. 41. DuPlesis, f. A8*v*, exemplifies the proverb in asking who among the physicians can give a "cleare and true Reason of the coming and going of the

Ague." Robin's chapter "On the Blood and Its Distribution," pp. 107–138, is a useful general introduction here; Babb's "The Physiology and Psychology of the Renaissance," pp. 1–20, is the best brief summary in print; see his account of radical heat and moisture and the melancholic character of old age. Whiting, *Milton's Literary Milieu*, pp. 129–176, makes an extended case for Milton's regarding his own personality as the melancholic type.

5. *Works* XII, 199–201; XV, 25. *PL* VII, 388; IV, 804–806. *SA* 606–616. Person, *Varieties*, p. 181, defined as futile the exercise of questions which (like Milton's fifth prolusion) merely perplex: "Such as this, is that of the multiplicity of forms in one selfe same subject." La Primaudaye, p. 403; Bartholomew, ff. xiiiir, xiir. Vaughan, *A Brief Natural History*, p. 76, rejects the theory of three ventricles; but Richard Bentley's sermon, *Matter and Motion Cannot Think* (1692), p. 20, still approves it. The comprehensive study of the faculty of the third cell is Carroll Camden's "Memory, the Warder of the Brain," *PQ*, 18:52–72 (1939). For Robin's erroneous analysis, see his pp. 139–175.

6. *Works* III, Pt. 1, 49, 168–169; IV, 261; XVIII, 205. *PR* IV, 407–409; I, 393–396. *PL* XII, 610–614; V, 3–5; IX, 1046–1052. The definitive articles by William B. Hunter, noted under Chapter I above, extend further the relation of Milton's dreams and visions to current scientific and patristic theory. For contributory information from *Malleus Maleficarum* and *Compendium Maleficarum* on demonic instigation of dreams and corruption of the faculty of fancy, see Svendsen, "Milton and Medical Lore," *Bulletin of the History of Medicine*, 13:170–172 (1943). Tillyard's subscription to the now popular view that Adam and Eve began to fall early in the story appears as "The Crisis of *Paradise Lost*," *Studies in Milton* (1951). This is a circumstance, if there are any such in the poem, where language and art were simply unequal to the demand; for Adam and Eve must remain historical (unfallen until Satan's success) yet not static (the fall must be made probable as narrative). Millicent Bell, "The Fallacy of the Fall in *Paradise Lost*," *PMLA*, 68:863–883 (1953), extends Tillyard's argument into what seems to me an insupportable construction of Milton's intention. In an exchange of notes, *PMLA*, 70:1185–1203 (1955), Wayne Shumaker defends the traditional view that Adam and Eve are unfallen until Book IX.

7. *PL* VIII, 465–466. Verity, II, 612. Institor and Sprenger, p. 44; Bacon, *Sylva Sylvarum*, II, 631; Bartholomew, f. lir; Swetnam, f. B1r; Sowernam, p. 3. Pettus, *Volatiles*, p. 64, distinguishes (from "the more general Anatomists") between the five perfect and seven imperfect ribs of Adam and debates inconclusively from which Eve was made. Adam's speech reflects Milton's awareness of the issue. See also my "Milton and *Malleus Maleficarum*," *MLN*, 60:118–119 (1945).

8. *Works* XII, 145; IV, 192, 309; IX, 124–125; III, Pt. 1, 19, 11–13, 298; V, 96, 86; VIII, 81; *SA* 176–177; *PL* XI, 311–313. Topsell, pp. 452–454; his use of "exemptile" instead of the Columbia edition "remov-

able" identifies it as the technically exact translation, as indeed "of a Lamia" would have been preferable to the Columbia "of a witch" in this context. Arnold Williams, "A Note on *Samson Agonistes* ll. 90–94," *MLN*, 63:537 (1948), shows the query to be a familiar complaint. Robert West, "Milton's Angelological Heresies," *JHI*, 14:116–123 (1953), reveals one to be this very matter of Raphael's human hunger and digestion. The counterpoise of "Wisdom to Folly" in Raphael's advice on moderation in knowledge echoes in Adam's intemperate and hybristic praise of Eve as one in whose presence wisdom "Looses discoun'nanc't, and like folly shewes."

9. *Works* III, Pt. 1, 211; Pt. 2, 370; V, 110, 217, 101; *PL* XI, 685–689. Bartholomew, f. lxxiiiir; Batman, f. 63r.

10. *Works* V, 186; IV, 76; VII, 281, 349; VIII, 15, 39, 37. Torquemada, ff. 7r–v; Mandeville, ff. O3r–v; Allott, f. 158v. Fletcher, *Milton's Rabbinical Readings*, pp. 176–177, finds the fabling in Rashi; Arnold Williams, *MP*, 37:271–272 (1940), modifies this view with parallels from Pareus, Grotius, and Zanchius. Pettus, *Volatiles*, p. 79, like Milton denies that "male and female created he them" means hermaphroditism.

11. La Primaudaye, p. 539. Browne's remark in *Religio Medici* drew a humorless reply from Alexander Ross which reverted to Adam and Eve. Browne had said, Pt. II, Sec. 9: "I could be content that we might procreate like Trees without conjunction, or that there were any way to perpetuate the world without this trivial and vulgar way of coition; it is the foolishest act a wise man commits in all his life, nor is there any thing that will more deject his cool'd imagination, when he shall consider what an odd and unworthy piece of folly he hath committed." Ross, *Medicus Medicatus* (1645), p. 77, argues precedent: "and surely, there had been no other way in Paradise to propagate man, but this *foolish way*." The 1686 edition of Browne locates the idea in Aulus Gellius, Paracelsus, Campanella, and Montaigne. The best guides to Renaissance angelology are Robert West's *The Invisible World* (Athens, Ga. 1939) and his articles on Milton. The sensible suggestion that the war in Heaven may be justified on its own merits as an epic battle is made by John Edward Hardy, *Sewanee Review*, 62 (1954).

12. *Works* V, 214; III, Pt. 1, 21, 3, 13, 310, 329; VI, 68; *Nativity Ode* 138. Bartholomew, ff. lxviiiv, cviiiv. Tillyard, *Milton*, p. 126, compares the imagery of the passage on crusting of the skin to *Comus* 463–469.

13. *Works* IX, 11, 187; III, Pt. 2, 472, 367–368; Pt. 1, 47, 137, 264, 62, 117; VI, 101; IV, 234–235; *Comus* 8. Banister, pp. 3–62 ff.

14. *Works* VIII, 185; III, Pt. 1, 47–49. Batman, f. 94v; Le Loyer, ff. 95r–v; Banister, p. 82; La Primaudaye, p. 528. On *Lingua* see H. K. Russell, "Tudor and Stuart Dramatizations of the Doctrines of Natural and Moral Philosophy," *SP*, 31:1–27 (1934).

15. *Works* III, Pt. 2. 371, 426; VII, 551; VIII, 189. *SA* 183–186, 605.

La Primaudaye, p. 530; Le Loyer, ff. 110r–v; Bartholomew, ff. lxxxviiv–lxxxviiir; Batman, f. 88v; Milles, p. 594; Plutarch, *Morals*, pp. 312–315.

16. Lodge, p. 44; Batman, f. 91v. Verity, II, 630. Masson, *Works*, III, 539, read his DuBartas in quarto. Hughes, p. 372, urges here the influence of DuBartas first suggested by Walter Raleigh, *Milton* (New York, 1900), p. 237. On the inductive pattern of Michael's instruction, see Svendsen, *CE*, 10:366–370 (1949).

17. *Works* III, Pt. 1, 298, 123, 255–257, 313, 276, 230–231, 33, 189; V, 279; IV, 250. *PL* III, 25. *Kitchin-physick* was, as Milton implies, a familiar expression; Thomas Cook used it as the title of his compendium of 1676. Renaudot, *Discourses*, p. 319: "if the Eye being sound and clear, yet some obstruction hinders the afflux of the spirits to it, (as in *Gutta Serena*) there is no vision made." See also Andreas Laurentius, *A Discourse of the Preservation of the Sight*, trans. Richard Surphlet (1599), p. 57.

18. *Works* III, Pt. 2, 386; Pt. 1, 254–257, 264–267. Horman, f. 43r; Bartholomew, ff. lxxxviir–v; La Primaudaye, p. 546. Compare also the figure in *Animadversions*, *Works* III, Pt. 1, 145: "[God] sent first to us a healing messenger to touch softly our sores, and carry a gentle hand over our wounds: he knockt once and twice, and came againe, opening our drousie eyelids leasurely by that glimmering light which *Wicklef*, and his followers dispers't, and still taking off by degrees the inveterat scales from our nigh perisht sight, purg'd also our deaf eares, and prepar'd them to attend his second warning trumpet in our Grand-sires days." This sounds a good deal like Michael's preparation of Adam for the vision of the future.

19. *Works* IV, 174, 93. Bartholomew, f. cviiiv; Cawdrey, pp. 35–36.

CHAPTER VII — PRECEPTS OF BENEFICENCE IN PROSE

1. The critical history of Milton's prose will soon be a subject in itself. After Masson, Pattison, and Raleigh, one of the earliest assessments was E. N. S. Thompson's "Milton's Prose Style," *PQ*, 14:1–15 (1925), which quite properly asserted its place in an over-all estimate of Milton as an artist. Later critics, like William Gilman, *Milton's Rhetoric: Studies in his Defense of Liberty* (Columbia, Missouri, 1939), and E. H. Visiak, "Milton's Prose," *Nineteenth Century*, 133:499–508 (1938), find a stronger general organization to the prose than Thompson allowed. Tillyard's suggestion about the date of *L'Allegro–Il Penseroso* occurs in *The Miltonic Setting, Past and Present* (Cambridge, 1938), pp. 1–28; E. S. Le Comte's demurrer, *Yet Once More*, p. 60, remarks a similar disapproval by A. S. P. Woodhouse, "Notes on Milton's Early Development," *UTQ*, 13:85 (1943). For factual autobiography in the prose, see John S. Diekhoff, *Milton on Himself* (New York, 1939), and the notes in M. C. Jochums, ed., *John Milton's An Apology* (Urbana, 1950) and *Yale Prose*, I.

2. B. Rajan, *Paradise Lost and the Seventeenth Century Reader*, pp. 22-38, is the first to deal at length with "the dangers of using Milton's systematic prose in order to elucidate his poetry." George F. Sensabaugh's *That Grand Whig Milton* (Stanford, 1952) exemplifies current interest in defining political influence. The other directions taken by contemporary students of the prose are the investigation of source and milieu (as in *Yale Prose*, I) and the revival and extension of rhetorical and linguistic analysis. The New Critics, "that small infantry/Warr'd on by Cranes," have done little here, but others have not been idle. See F. E. Ekfelt, "The Graphic Diction of Milton's Prose," *PQ*, 25:46-69 (1946); "Latinate Diction in Milton's English Prose," *PQ*, 28:53-71 (1949); and Joshua H. Neumann, "Milton's Prose Vocabulary," *PMLA*, 60:102-120 (1945). Price's "Incidental Imagery in *Areopagitica*," *MP*, 49:217-222 (1952), exploits the dominance of war, health and sickness, fruitfulness and aridity. His conclusion illustrates the kind of insight available from such analysis: "Milton's method, then, is poetic; he universalizes the particular, evoking vividly and accurately the individual state, and at the same time transfiguring it, so that the wider, enduring significance shines through" (222). This new view of the prose should make us sensitive to such announcement of medical-anatomical imagery as occurs on the very first page of *Reason of Church Government, Works* III, 181: "without reason or Preface, like a physicall prescript," i. e., medical prescription. It should also illuminate Eliot's confession of difficulty in reading Milton's prose because of its poetic quality. His remark, characteristic of the discomfort in that most curiously imperceptive of recantations, appears in "Milton," *Sewanee Review*, 56:185-209 (1948).

3. The Renaissance cross-fertilization of rhetoric and logic and poetic has been richly documented in recent years, most notably by Rosemond Tuve, *Elizabethan and Metaphysical Imagery* (Chicago, 1947). A familiar example of Renaissance awareness of the fusion is in *Defence of Poesie*, where Sidney remarks that he should be "pounded for straying from poetry to oratory; but that both have such an affinity in this wordish consideration." See Allan Gilbert's note to the passage, *Literary Criticism, Plato to Dryden* (New York, 1940), p. 455.

4. Merritt Y. Hughes, ed. *John Milton: Prose Selections* (New York, 1947), pp. 206-207, cites passages from Daniel's *Musophilus* and Vaughan's *To his Books* as poetic analogues to Milton's famous definition.

5. *Works* III, Pt. 2, 368, 419, 402. See further allegorizing in the passage, p. 418, on the "twofold Seminary or stock in nature." Poetic implications of the Eros-Anteros myth have been traced from the *Phaedrus* forward by Robert V. Merrill, "Eros and Anteros," *Speculum*, 19:265-284 (1945). See also Hughes, *op. cit.*, p. 190. Evion Owen, "Milton and Selden on Divorce," *SP*, 43:237 (1946), remarks the myth in the

lines contributed by Selden to William Browne's pastorals, but does not urge the parallel.

6. Cf. Thomas Hanley's statement, Pref. to his transl. of H. A. Rommen, *The Natural Law: A Study in Legal and Social History and Philosophy* (St. Louis, 1948), p. viii: "In fact, the church and its theologians have always viewed human nature, man's natural faculties and their objects, the natural law — in a word, the natural order — as indispensable sources for determining the proper lines of human conduct which, with the aid of divine grace and with supernatural equipment, man must follow in his quest of his supernatural goal." Owen, p. 356, shows that Milton's practical conclusions were similar to Selden's but that Milton did not use *De Jure Naturali* in this pamphlet because his views of Christian liberty and of marriage were different from Selden's. Arthur Barker, "Christian Liberty in Milton's Divorce Pamphlet," *MLR*, 35:160 (1940).

7. William Empson, "Emotion in Words Again," *KR*, 10:579–601 (1948), points out that "all," which occurs 612 times in *PL*, appears in nearly every scene of emotional pressure. Josephine Miles, *Major Adjectives in English Poetry from Wyatt to Auden*, Univ. of Calif. Pubs. in Eng., XII, iii (Berkeley, 1946), 317, finds "heaven" the most frequently recurring important word in Milton's poetry (600 times). Her special criteria and methods perhaps account for the discrepancy. She is less interested than Empson in analyzing significant structural functions of words in particular scenes and lines. But both these studies suggest a concern with recurrent words in total effect comparable to the concern of the present chapter. *Works* III, 482, 496, 499, 476, 458. Cf.: "To forbid divorce compulsively, is not only against nature, but against law" (p. 501). *PL* VI, 176.

8. Tuve, pp. 251–280, and especially Appendix R, pp. 422–423.

9. *Works* III, 389, 370, 416, 417, 418, 401, 436. See Chapter II above for the purity of sunlight and the poetic use of this astronomical commonplace about "saving appearances" in *PL* VIII, 82. "Prutenic tables" are the astronomical computations of 1551 based on the *De Revolutionibus Orbium* of Copernicus by Erasmus Reinhold and named for his patron Duke Albrecht of Prussia. See Gilbert, "Milton and Galileo," *SP*, 19:156 (1922), and Johnson, *Astronomical Thought*, pp. 111–112. We have seen that the encyclopedias and other scientific treatises are full of this astronomical and astrological lore. Milton is using *crasis, apogœum,* and *homogeneal* in their technical senses, a practice apparently so common in sermons that Eachard, *Works*, pp. 46, 54, complained specifically of apogaeum and generally of figurative prose. For other astronomical allusions, see in context "fals and dazling fires" (434); "Chaos . . . worlds diameter multiply'd" (442); "load-starre" (493); "firmament" (506).

10. *Works* III, 505, 449, 468, 372, 367, 368, 395, 377, 401, 389, 385.

For other allusions of this type, see in context "blind and Serpentine body" (368); "borrow'd garb," "blind side" (401); "polluted skirt" (446); "remorseles obscurity," "native lustre" (494).

11. *Works* III, 393, 505, 510, 418, 394, 426, 368, 419, 425, 459, 478. Note that *influence* retains its Latin force and thus contributes to the sense of movement here. On the stoppage of nature's current, see *The French Academie*, p. 530, and Chapter VI above. For other allusions of this kind, see in context "[no] man should be shut up incurably under a worse evill" (392); "if it happen that nature hath stopt or extinguisht the veins of sensuality" (393); "veile . . . body impenetrable" (395); "hazardous and accidentall doore of mariage to shut upon us like the gate of death" (461); "chains . . . curb . . . canon bit" (486); "ill-knotted mariage" (492); "*Gordian* difficulties" (494).

12. *Works* III, 410, 500, 509–510. For the remora see Chapter V above. The legend of Ocnus evidently appealed to Milton. He combines here two common illustrations of futility, the rope of sand and the occupation of Ocnus, both of which he uses elsewhere. In *Tetrachordon* (IV, 97) he says that compelling incompatibles into one flesh is as vain as trying "to weav a garment of drie sand." In the *Third Prolusion* (XII, 169) "cunning quibblers," will have "this appropriate punishment inflicted: that they shall twist ropes in hell with the famous Ocnus." In *First Defence* (VII, 475): "This man twists conclusions as Ocnus does ropes in Hell; which are but to be eaten by asses." The rope of sand was well known from legends about the tasks Michael Scot set his devil; see Herbert's "The Collar" and T. O. Mabbot's explanation, *Explicator*, 3:12 (1944); F. T. Palgrave, ed., *The Poetical Works of Sir Walter Scott* (1928), p. 499, n. 19; and J. Wood Brown, *The Life and Legend of Michael Scot* (Edinburgh, 1897), p. 218. Ocnus twisted ropes of straw; Renaissance writers knew the story from the 35th book of Pliny's *Natural History* or the 4th elegy of Propertius; see *Propertius*, ed. H. E. Butler (Cambridge, 1930), p. 283 and note, p. 357.

13. *Works* III, 472, 367–368, 437, 370–371, 386, 429–430, 448. See Chapter VI above for the diffusion in the encyclopedias of the medical and physiological lore here. Hughes, p. 163, notes the bold use of the Minerva myth in *PL* II, 757–758. Several of the scientific figures are mixed. Some are uncomplicated by subtlety; e. g.: "when human frailty surcharg'd, is at such a losse, charity ought to venture much, and use bold physick, lest an over-tost faith endanger to shipwrack" (p. 400). In others the effect, as above, is clearly satiric: e.g.: "But how among the drove of Custom and Prejudice this will be relisht, by such whose capacity, since their youth run ahead into the easie creek of a system or a Medulla, sayls there at will under the blown physiognomy of their unlabour'd rudiments, for them, what their tast will be, I have also surety sufficient, from the entire league that hath bin ever between formal ignorance and grave obstinacie" (377–378). For other anatomical

and medical allusions, see in context "joynt or sinew" (369); "peevish madnesse" (373); "lifegiving remedies of *Moses*" (385); "cure . . . complexion . . . melancholy" (391); "wast away . . . under a secret affliction" (392); "impetuous nerve" (394); "spirituall contagion" (407); "noysomnesse or disfigurement of body" (419); "weak pulse" (431); "rigorous knife" (450); "cordiall and exhilarating cup of solace" (461); "hand of Justice rot off" (474); "hard spleen . . . sanguifie" (484); "*bitter water . . . curse of rottennesse and tympany*" (488); "misbegott'n infants" (505).

14. *Works* III, 420.

CHAPTER VIII — NATURAL PHILOSOPHY AND PARADISE LOST

1. *PL* VII, 210–264. Nicolson, *The Breaking of the Circle*, p. 106. Watson Kirkconnell, *The Celestial Cycle* (Toronto, 1953), p. xii. My identification of Mammon with the architect of Pandaemonium, favored by Masson, *Works* III, 402, is generally questioned (Verity, II, 396). But Mammon seems to lead the whole construction gang, the "numerous Brigad," the "crew," the "second multitude," and the "third" by whose separate labors the structure rises. His proposal to build an empire in Hell sorts well with this view, for the project includes architecture: "Nor want we skill or art, from whence to raise /Magnificence" (II, 273–274). Certainly the group he leads can be called "an industrious crew" (I, 751) like the architects. And certainly Milton presents Mammon as something more than the stereotype of greedy worldliness; note the "also" which introduces gold-mining as an afterthought to Mammon's main business. Agrippa, *Of the Vanity of Arts and Sciences*, links the two occupations in the opening of chapter 29: "To *Architecture* is adjoyn'd Mining and Digging of Metals."

2. The immensity of Milton's universe is recognized even outside literary scholarship; see the recent statement of it in Frederick Nussbaum, *The Triumph of Science and Reason 1660–1685* (New York, 1953), p. 9. The telescope and the new astronomy have been thought responsible for this impression; but as we have seen, the universe was enormous to medieval thinkers too. Their conviction of its order and regularity have given rise to the notion that they thought it a tight *little* cosmos. But Copernicanism disturbed men not merely because it predicated a larger universe but also because dislocation of the earth introduced disorder into that tight cosmos. Kirkconnell lists *De Proprietatibus Rerum, Mirrour of the World*, and *Speculum Mundi* in his Descriptive Catalogue.

3. *PL* I, 670–675; II, 891–1033; III, 418–742; IV, 801–809; V, 100–119, 404–433; VI, 469–520; VII, 210–264; VIII, 1–178; IX, 494–531, 1099–1130; X, 648–714; XI, 466–493; XII, 624–649. Most of the passages

in the present chapter have been discussed earlier as mineralogy, zoology, and the like; and so I do not repeat documentation here.

4. Allen, *Harmonious Vision*, p. 102; Banks, *Milton's Imagery*, p. 172.

5. *Works* III, 142. Maud Bodkin, *Archetypal Patterns in Poetry*, has already been remarked for her exploration of *Paradise Lost*, but one may recall in the present context her discussions of Paradise–Hades, Eve, Satan, and rebirth as types. For the ambivalent features of man's place in the *scala naturae*, see Herschel Baker's summary of the Christian humanist conception of the estate of man, *The Wars of Truth*, pp. 24–42.

6. Mahood, p. 176; Nicolson, *The Breaking of the Circle*, pp. 163–164. Mahood, p. 180, makes the common error of identifying Milton with Adam: "As a natural philosopher, Milton's main objection to the Ptolemaic astronomy seems to have been that it postulated an incredible speed in the revolutions of the outer spheres around this 'punctual spot,' the earth." Bearing in mind Milton's advice about characters speaking in their own persons, not the author's, one hesitates, and recalling the perfectly conventional familiarity of the notion, one is quite sure that it is a piece of stock characterization for Adam.

7. Milton's anti-intellectualism has shared attention lately with the revived controversy over the unity of Satan's character and his place in the poem. See George F. Sensabaugh, "Milton on Learning," *SP*, 43: 258–272 (1946), and Irene Samuel's reply, "Milton on Learning and Wisdom," *PMLA*, 64: 708–723 (1949).

8. E. M. W. Tillyard, *The Renaissance: Fact or Fiction?* (Baltimore, 1952), p. 11. Rajan, p. 58. He quotes the extract from Eachard's *Grounds and Occasions of the Contempt of the Clergy and Religion* (1670). My quotations are from Eachard's *Works*, pp. 22–23.

9. I use *total intention* in its widest sense to mean the purpose or design of the whole poem, not Milton's immediate intention to write an epic on the fall and regeneration of man. See W. K. Wimsatt, Jr., and M. C. Beardsley, "The Intentional Fallacy," *Sewanee Review*, 54:468–488 (1946). A. R. Benham, "Things Unattempted Yet in Prose or Rime," *MLQ*, 14:341–347 (1953), argues that Milton thought his version original because it began in the middle. Kirkconnell, p. xxii, points out that *PL* is unique in combining creation, war in Heaven, fall, and atonement in one poem. As to modern loss of awareness of the epic as a genre, it may be observed that a great cause for the popularity of C. S. Lewis's *A Preface to Paradise Lost* with beginners in Milton is its re-education in that faculty. On Browne, see E. S. Merton, *Science and Imagination in Sir Thomas Browne* (New York, 1949), especially pp. 120–134.

Index